# ELEMENTARY
# NUMERICAL
# ANALYSIS

Prentice-Hall
Series in Applied Mathematics

# ELEMENTARY
# NUMERICAL
# ANALYSIS

**Charles B. Tompkins**

DEPARTMENT OF MATHEMATICS
UNIVERSITY OF CALIFORNIA AT LOS ANGELES

**Walter L. Wilson, Jr.**

DEPARTMENT OF MATHEMATICS
UNIVERSITY OF ALABAMA AT TUSCALOOSA

**Prentice-Hall, Inc. Englewood Cliffs, N.J.**

Current printing (last digit):

10 9 8 7 6 5 4 3 2

13-259424-2
Library of Congress Catalog Card Number: 78-81734
Printed in the United States of America

PRENTICE-HALL INTERNATIONAL, INC., *London*
PRENTICE-HALL OF AUSTRALIA, PTY. LTD., *Sydney*
PRENTICE-HALL OF CANADA LTD., *Toronto*
PRENTICE-HALL OF INDIA PRIVATE LTD., *New Delhi*
PRENTICE-HALL OF JAPAN, INC., *Tokyo*

**To Our Wives**

In Appreciation for Years of Understanding

# PREFACE

The ultimate objective of numerical analysis is to facilitate (or to enable) numerical computation. In order to do this, the numerical analyst uses tools that have been developed in other mathematical studies. These tools include the arithmetic tools, subject to the limited precision that is available in any computing instrument, the analytical tools that are developed in mathematical analysis (calculus and the study of differential equations, for example), algebraic tools (relating to the properties of matrices and determinants, for example), and the mechanical, electromechanical, and electronic tools that have been developed to aid in extensive computation. These last tools include tables, perhaps, and certainly the tools used to compute tables and to carry out other computation: slide rules, desk calculators, and, most important, the electronic calculating instruments that have become available since the late 1940's and which have generated an enhanced interest in numerical analysis. The digital computer is the most popular of these electronic calculators, and the notation and methods presented here are chosen with this in mind.

We introduce a tool, the iterative algorithm, which may not have been seriously considered as a tool in the early training of many people who will read this text. This tool is an essential element used in the programming of automatic digital computers.

The *output* of a digital computer is usually presented to the user on printed pages. This print-out is achieved one line at a time. Most modern computer systems allow the printing of alphanumeric (Hollerith) information. One may print expressions involving decimal digits (0, 1, 2, 3, 4, 5, 6, 7, 8, 9), some mathematical symbols ($=, <, \leq, >, \geq, +, -, *$ for multiplication, $/$ for division, and parentheses), marks of punctuation (period, comma), and the twenty-six capital letters of the alphabet (A, B, C, . . ., Z). Lower case letters are also available on some printers.

Massive compiler systems, like FORTRAN and PL/I, have evolved to a point where laboratory students of elementary numerical analysis can be expected to program the computer during the first week of classes. After a very few weeks of laboratory work, students can write sophisticated programs involving print-out of headings for data and sufficient prose descriptions of the problem to make the pages printed by the computer acceptable for inclusion in a "formal report." As a practicing numerical analyst, scientist, engineer, or man of business, he will probably be asked to produce reports on his work, and many pages of these reports are likely to be printed by a computer. The subscript and superscript notations of classical mathematical analysis are impractical (if not impossible) in the one-line format of computer print-out.

We have chosen a one-line format for displaying mathematical expressions in this text. Three reasons for this choice are: (1) The reader is exposed to a one-line format even if he does not use one in the laboratory section for this course; (2) the notation used here is easily produced on the typewriter without adjusting the carriage for subscripts and superscripts, and it requires a minimum of hand fill-in; (3) the "function" interpretation for subscripted variables is emphasized. We have included a few symbols that are not currently available on some computer printers, notably: $\sum$ for summation, the integral $\int$, $\in$ for "is an element of," and various "levels" of parentheses (to facilitate reading). We modify expressions involving these symbols to fit a one-line notation. Otherwise the symbols we use are now standard. Our notation is discussed in the first section of Chapter 1 (Introduction), and a brief summary is printed in the Appendix for handy reference.

This very important tool, the electronic digital computer, has prompted our adoption of a notation different from the conventional mathematical notation. Its speed in performing arithmetic and logical operations, and its extensive memory banks make possible calculations involving millions of arithmetic operations. This capability leads to concern with problems involving representation and handling of data. These problems suggest studies of number systems used by computers.

In §1.2 we consider some "interpretations" for numbers. In §1.3 we define a typical system of "computing numbers," and list some of its (unfortunate) properties. Then, in §1.4, we define some types of error involved in computing. Finally, in §1.5, we suggest that an answer to "Why Numerical Analysis?" is the *need* for estimates. The remainder of the text contains discussions (using the real-number system) of some classical methods used to compute estimates.

The most important single tool available to the numerical analyst is mathematical analysis. The competent applied mathematician (scientist, engineer, business man, etc.) has a background in mathematical analysis, and understands the *desirability* of being precise and rigorous. But he is frustrated by the need to say something "useful" about a system defined by a set of conditions not all of which are known to him. He could wait (if he lives that long) until a complete set of conditions that characterize the system are available. But the *active* applied mathematician will not wait. He will formulate a "best" set of conditions (using *available* information about the system). For example, the applied mathematician may be asked to study a certain characteristic (like motion) of a part of a complex physical system. Almost certainly the "best" that he can do is (use estimates like Newton's Laws of Motion) to define a *mathematical model* (problem) which corresponds to the physical system in the sense that a solution of the mathematical problem corresponds to the pertinent characteristic of the physical system. If no mathematical method is known that defines the desired solution explicitly, then the applied mathematician must alter his mathematical model in such a way that the new mathematical model (problem) is known to have a solution *and* so that methods are known which can produce *usable estimates* to the desired solution (corresponding to the characteristic of the physical system to be studied). That is, the applied mathematician is required to formulate mathematical models for his problems, where the models *yield* to computer solution.

A course in elementary numerical analysis should be useful to the applied mathematician as an introduction to classical methods of *computing* estimates to solutions of a few basic problems that occur in many contexts. Many of these methods are chosen because there exists a formal representation of the error of the estimate. Later, the practitioner will invent other methods (probably related to these classical ones).

We discuss Taylor Polynomials in Chapter 2 as estimates to F(X) in the neighborhood of a point, and we use them in several contexts when defining other methods to compute estimates.

The *existence* of polynomials that define estimates to F(X) on a specified interval is assured by *Weierstrass' (Uniform) Approximation Theorem:* Let F(X) be continuous on [A, B] and choose any E > 0, then there exists a polynomial P(N, X) (of sufficiently high degree N) for which

$$|F(X) - P(N, X)| \leq E, \text{ for each } X \in [A, B].$$

[See Davis, P. J. (1963): *Interpolation and Approximation.* Blaisdell Publishing Co. New York. (Page 107, and note Theorem 6.2.1, Figure 6.3.1, and Theorems 6.4.1 and 6.5.1, there.).] It is important to note that only *continuity* of F(X) on [A, B] is required in Weierstrass' Theorem, while the existence of certain derivatives of F(X) are required in Taylor's Theorem (§2.2). Weierstrass'

Theorem contributes to our motivation for studying interpolation, least-square, and Chebyshev estimates.

A basic numerical analysis sequence may consist of three semester courses (three units each). At least the first (semester) course should have a laboratory section. A typical (semester) laboratory assignment might include the following problems.

(1) Write a computer program to execute twenty-five steps of the iteration process in Exercise 2 of §1.1.

(2) Consider Example 1 of §2.2. Write computer programs to evaluate $P(5; X, 0)$, $F(X)$, and bounds $B1(X)$, $B2(X)$, and $B3(X)$ at the points $X(K) = .01 * K$ for each $K \in // - 60, 50//$. Use this computed data to sketch $F(X)$, $P(5; X, 0)$, and the "best" choice for $G(X)$, superimposed on one sheet of graph paper. Compare this with Figure 2.2.3. On another sheet of graph paper sketch $R(5; X, 0) \equiv F(X) - P(5; X, 0)$ where one scale is used on the interval $-.2 \leq X \leq .2$, and a larger scale is used for $|X| \geq .3$. Now, sketch (superimpose) the bounds $B1(X)$, $B2(X)$, $B3(X)$, and $B4(X) = $ (constant). Compare your sketch with Figure 2.2.4.

(3) Write a computer program for one of the following:
   (a) Exercise 1 of §2.2. (Compare Example 2.)
   (b) Exercise 3 of §2.2 with $X = 5$.
   (c) Exercise 4 of §3.2.
   (d) The example associated with Figure 3.5.3a, b.

(4) Write a computer program for one of the following:
   (a) Exercise 2 of §3.6.
   (b) Exercise 1 of §3.7.
   (c) Exercise 1 of §3.8.
   (d) Exercises 1, 2, 3 of §3.9.

(5) Write a computer program for one of the following:
   (a) Execute Gauss Elimination or Crout Reduction. Allow read-in of matrices as data, and include $DET(A)$ in the print-out.
   (b) For use in Chapter 7, produce a table of the binomial coefficient function $BINCO(S, N)$. Specifically, use (6.5.4) with (6.5.3a) substituted to compute $BINCO(S, 2)$, $BINCO(S, 3)$, $BINCO(S, 4)$, and $BINCO(S, 5)$ for each $S \in // - 1, .01, 1//$. Look for relations between columns of each table.

The quantity of text material covered in the first (semester) course will depend on the amount of laboratory work required. When only five programs (like those listed above) are required, we have surveyed most of the course material from §1.1 through §4.5, and from §6.1 through §7.4.

The second (semester) course might include a five class-hour review of the first course, and then a survey (with some student presentations) of material in the remainder of this text.

The third (semester) course is more flexible, usually with student presentations of subjects considered here, but expanded with material from more advanced texts and journals. We also assign subjects not included in this text.

Exercises are provided with the early sections of this text, but in later sections the reader is advised (often with "The reader should . . ." statements) to supply the details of analyses and examples. In many cases we have intentionally left out some details so that the student (or the instructor) will want to supply them. We find this to be sufficient exercise. Of course, each instructor has his "pet" exercises, and we assume he will inject them as needed.

We do not supply tables in appendices. But, we assume the reader has available a good handbook of tables. The only tables referenced below are in *Handbook of Mathematical Functions with Formulas, Graphs, and Mathematical Tables*. (1964): National Bureau of Standards Applied Mathematics Series 55. The only tables required in this text that are not easily available are tables of the binomial coefficient function for noninteger arguments (needed in Chapter 7). We usually ask the student to produce these tables as laboratory exercises.

The authors acknowledge indebtedness to many people and sources. A few are listed in Suggested Reading at the end of each chapter. In addition, we wish to thank Professor George E. Forsythe at Stanford University, and Professor Charles L. Seebeck, Jr. at University of Alabama for many helpful suggestions and discussions of the material in the early versions of the manuscript. We are indebted to the students in Professor Wilson's numerical analysis classes where the several versions of the manuscript were classroom tested and improved by their constructive criticism. Frances Wilson (Mrs. W. L., Jr.) typed all versions of the manuscript and assisted in reading proofs. Polly Tompkins (Mrs. C. B.) prepared the Index. Finally, we wish to thank Prentice-Hall, Inc. for their encouragement and patience.

CHARLES B. TOMPKINS
WALTER L. WILSON, JR.

# CONTENTS

# ELEMENTARY
# NUMERICAL
# ANALYSIS

# 1  INTRODUCTION

## 1.1. NOTATION

For the reasons given in the Preface, we have chosen a one-line notation. In particular, we do not use superscripts or subscripts on the symbols involved in this text. Most of the characters involved are now available on printers used with FORTRAN and PL/I compilers, and on many typewriters.

Our choice of notation is explained in this section; for easy reference, a brief summary is printed in the Appendix.

We try to reserve the term "approximation" for special names, notably the Chebyshev Approximation. We prefer the term "estimate."

$X \doteq A$ is read: An *estimate* to X is A, or simply: the estimate $X \doteq A$.
$X < A$ is read: X is less than A.
$X \ll A$ is read: X is much less than A.

The asterisk ($*$) is used to denote the operation multiplication, and when multiplication is meant the $*$ is never omitted. The double asterisk ($**$) is used to indicate exponentiation (i.e., that an exponent or superscript follows $**$); and $+$, $-$, $/$ denote addition, subtraction, division, respectively. Capital sigma ($\Sigma$) is used in a symbol for summation.

| WE USE | FOR |
|--------|-----|
| A $*$ B | $ab$, or $a \cdot b$ |
| A $**$ B | $a^b$ |
| A $*$ B $**$ C | $a \cdot b^c$ |

1

| WE USE | FOR |
|---|---|
| $A * B ** C/D = A/D * B ** C$ | $\dfrac{a \cdot b^c}{d}$ |
| $A * B ** (C/D)$ | $a \cdot b^{c/d}$ |
| $A + B/C$ | $a + \dfrac{b}{c}$ |
| $(A + B)/C$ | $\dfrac{a + b}{c}$ |
| $(A + B)/C + 2 * F$ | $\dfrac{a + b}{c} + 2f$ |
| $(A + B)/(C + 2 * F)$ | $\dfrac{a + b}{c + 2f}$ |
| $ABC * F/G$ | $\dfrac{d \cdot f}{g}$, where $d$ was *named* ABC. |

The only symbol used for *grouping* is parentheses, but we use various levels of boldness of type for the parentheses to reduce the effort involved in the usual "counting" of parentheses, and allow concentration of attention on the expression presented. Brackets [    ] are used to denote closed intervals, used as a "frame" for matrices, and used as part of a name for certain functions like the divided difference operator. Braces {    } are used sparingly to denote certain sets. The much used *sets of integers*

$$P, P + 1, P + 2, \ldots, P + N = R$$
$$P, P + 1, P + 2, \ldots$$
$$P, P + Q, P + 2 * Q, P + 3 * Q, \ldots, P + N * Q = R$$

are written

$$//P, R//, \quad //P, \infty//, \quad //P, Q, R//,$$

respectively, where Q may be a negative integer. (Commas are required as indicated.)

| WE USE | FOR |
|---|---|
| $\sum A(K) * X ** K, K \in //0, N//,$ | $\sum\limits_{k=0}^{n} a_k x^k$ |
| $PROD(X - X(J)), J \in //0, N//,$ | $(x - x_0)(x - x_1) \cdots (x - x_n)$ |

We use

$$\sum \sum A(I, J) * X(I) * X(J), I \in //1, N //, J \in // 1, N //,$$

for

$$\sum_{j=1}^{n} \sum_{i=1}^{n} a_{ij} x_i x_j.$$

PROD(X − X(J)), J ∈ //0, N//, for $(x - x_0)(x - x_1) \cdots (x - x_n)$.

*Note.* This product in equation (7.4.12) is called POLP(X): the polynomial part.

PROD$(X - X(J))$, J ∈ //0, N//, and J ≠ K,

for $(x - x_0) \cdots (x - x_{k-1})(x - x_{k+1}) \cdots (x - x_n)$.

*Names* for functions, coefficients, variables, and indices are combinations of the capital letters A, B, C, ..., Z and the decimal digits. We make a few exceptions for a few special functions (operators) and use their "usual" names.

$\Delta$: Forward difference operator

$\nabla$: Backward difference operator.

$\delta$: Central difference operator.

$[\cdots]F$: Divided difference operator.

$\mu$: Averaging operator.

$\int$ : Integral operator.

The symbol ∈ is used only in its set theoretic context, and means "in" or "is an element of."

Indices, subscripts, and/or variables are listed as arguments in parentheses following a name. We have tried to be consistent in listing *multiple arguments* in the order

(index, subscript, variable, parameter).

The *index* position in a list of arguments may be used to specify a particular element of a family (sequence) of objects. For example, the index position may contain the degree of a polynomial, and thus specify a particular polynomial in a sequence of polynomials. This position is also used for an iteration index. The *subscript* position may be used to specify a particular element of a finite set (like the coefficients of a polynomial). The *variable* position is used for the "usual" argument of the function. The *parameter* position is the "catch all" position, and in one case involves an interval (when we invent a name for definite integral).

A semicolon may be used to separate different "kinds" of arguments, but usually it is used to make one name "stand out" among other names. For example, P(N; X) is the name of *the* Lagrange polynomial of degree N in X for a specified grid; and PF(N; X, C) is *the* Taylor polynomial of degree N in X, where C is the point about which we "expand" the function F(X). Note that F is part of the name of this polynomial. We now list some names of elementary functions.

| WE USE | FOR |
|---|---|
| SIN(X), COS(X), etc. | $\sin x$, $\cos x$, etc. |
| ARCTAN(X) | $\tan^{-1} x$, or $\arctan x$ |
| EXP(X) | $e^x$ |
| LOGN(X), LOGC(X), LOGA(X) | $\ln x$, $\log_{10} x$, $\log_a x$ |
| SQRT(X) $=$ X ** (1/2) | $\sqrt{x}$ |
| X ** (1/K) | $\sqrt[k]{x}$ |
| ABS(F(X)), or \|F(X)\| | $\|f(x)\|$ |
| BINCO(N, K) | $\binom{n}{k}$, binomial coefficient |
| ORDB(H ** 2) | order function: $O(h^2)$. |

The element in the I*th* row and J*th* column of a matrix A is written A(I, J). The corresponding element of the matrix A1 is A1(I, J), and the matrix A1 need not be related to the matrix A. The *dimension* of a matrix with M rows and N columns is written M*by*N. The product of matrices A and B (in that order) is written A ∗ B.

| WE USE | FOR |
|---|---|
| TRAN [X(1)   X(2)   X(3)] | $\begin{bmatrix} x_1 \\ x_2 \\ x_3 \end{bmatrix}$ |
| DET(A) | determinant: $\|A\|$ |
| CHARP(L) $=$ DET(A $-$ L ∗ I) | characteristic polynomial of A |
| MINP(X) | minimal polynomial of A |

Other functions and operators are written as follows: (commas are required as indicated)

| WE USE | FOR |
|---|---|
| MAX (F(X)), over X $\in$ [A, B], | $\max\limits_{[a,b]} f(x)$ |
| MAX\|F(X)\|, over X $\in$ [A, B], | $\max\limits_{[a,b]} \|f(x)\|$ |
| MIN\|F(X)\|, over X $\in$ [A, B], | $\min\limits_{[a,b]} \|f(x)\|$ |
| LIM(F(X)) $=$ B, as X App A, or LIM(F(X)), as X App A, $=$ B | $\lim\limits_{x \to a} f(x) = b$ |
| LIM(F(N, X)) $=$ G(X), as N App $\infty$, | $\lim\limits_{n \to \infty} f_n(x) = g(x)$ |
| $\int$ F(T, X), over T $\in$ (A, B), $=$ G(X) | $\int_a^b f(t, x)\, dt = g(x)$ |

*Note.* $\int F(T)$, over $T \in (A, B)$, $= -\int F(T)$, over $T \in (B, A)$. We write $T \in (A, B)$ whether the integral is proper or improper.

| | |
|---|---|
| DER $(F(A)) = F'(A)$ | $f'(a)$ |
| DER $** (2)F(A) = F''(A)$ | $f''(a)$ |
| DER $** (K)F(A)$ | $f^{(k)}(a)$ |
| PAR $** (1, 0)F(X, Y) \equiv$ PAR $** (1,)F(X, Y)$ | $\dfrac{\partial f}{\partial x}(x, y)$ |
| PAR $** (0, 1)F(X, Y) \equiv$ PAR $** (, 1)F(X, Y)$ | $\dfrac{\partial f}{\partial y}(x, y)$ |
| PAR $** (J, K)F(A, B)$ | $\dfrac{\partial^{j+k} f}{\partial x^j \partial y^k}(a, b).$ |

*Note.* We sometimes invent local abbreviations. See footnote in §3.6. For classroom presentations we soon revert to the usual mathematical notation.

At the end of each chapter we have placed a list of "Suggested Reading." This list is not intended to be encyclopedic, but is the type of material that should be researched. References are cited in the text by numbers in brackets referring to entries in the list of Suggested Reading for the chapter that contains the citation.

**EXERCISES**

**1.** Use the quadratic formula to write in *one-line notation* the solutions of the quadratic equation

$$A * X ** 2 + B * X + C = 0.$$

How would you "compute" the square root?

**2.** In Chapter 3 we define an *iteration process* as any formula of the form

$$X(N + 1) = T(X(N)), \text{ for } N \in // 0, \infty //,$$

which defines a sequence $X(J)$, $J \in //0, \infty//$. The following is an illustration of a process considered in §3.5. Compare the example associated with Figure 3.5.3a, b. We solve $Y ** 2 - 5 * Y + 4 = 0$ for Y in the form $Y = (Y ** 2 + 4)/5$, and define the iteration process

$$Y(N + 1) = (Y(N) ** 2 + 4)/5, N \in //0, \infty//.$$

With *starting-value* $Y(0) = 0$, substitute $Y(0)$ into the right-hand side of the iteration formula and compute $Y(1)$. Use $Y(1)$ to compute $Y(2)$, etc., until you have computed $Y(10)$. Observe that $Y(10) \doteq 1$; indeed, $Y(25) \doteq$ .999999999952. Check by substitution that $Y = 1$ is a solution of the given equation. We say that the iteration process appears to converge to a solution of the equation. With $Y(0) = 2$, compute a few terms of the sequence defined by the above iteration formula to see that the generated sequence appears to converge to the root $Y = 1$. Try $Y(0) = 5$, or any $Y(0) > 4$. Conclude that the iteration process appears to converge to $Y = 1$ for $Y(0) < 4$, and appears to diverge for $Y(0) > 4$.

*Note.* For this exercise, a starting-value is considered a *first guess* at a solution of the quadratic equation.

**3.** Define another iteration process by solving $Y ** 2 - 5 * Y + 4 = 0$ for $Y = \text{SQRT}(5 * Y - 4)$. That is,

$$Y(N + 1) = \text{SQRT}(5 * Y(N) - 4), \, N \in //0, \infty//.$$

Compute a few terms of the sequences corresponding to each of the first guesses $Y(0) = 116/125$, $Y(0) = 2$, and $Y(0) = 5$. When (for what starting-values) does the iteration process appear to converge? When it converges, name the root to which it converges. Conclude that the selection of an iteration process for a problem may amount to selecting a particular solution to be estimated.

### 1.2. WHAT IS A NUMBER?

Number is a *name* used for elements of certain sets. The sets are *models* for mathematical systems. A mathematical system is a "set" S with a relation "equals" and one or more "binary operations" defined on pairs of elements of S.

The mathematical system $(G, =, \oplus)$ is called a *group* if $(=, \text{and} \oplus$ are defined so that) the elements of G satisfy the conditions (postulates):

G1: If A and B are any elements in G, then there is an element C in G such that $C = A \oplus B$. (We say G is *closed* with respect to $\oplus$, and name this property *closure*.)

G2: If A, B, and C are any elements of G, then $(A \oplus B) \oplus C = A \oplus (B \oplus C)$. (G is *associative* with respect to $\oplus$.)

G3: There is exactly one element E in G such that $A \oplus E = A = E \oplus A$ holds for every element A in G. (G has an *identity* element with respect to $\oplus$.)

G4: For each element A in G there is exactly one element B in G such that $A \oplus B = E = B \oplus A$. (Every element of G has a unique *inverse* with respect to $\oplus$.)

We may say simply that G is a group with respect to $\oplus$. The group G is *commutative* if the elements of G satisfy the additional postulate

G5: If A and B are any elements of G, then $A \oplus B = B \oplus A$.

There are many well-known *models* of a group. One model has G the set of translations in the plane and the operation "followed by." In another model, the elements of G are nonsingular matrices of order 2, and the operation is matrix multiplication. The most familiar model of a commutative group is the set I of integers (positive, zero, and negative) with the operation addition. Elements of I are named integers and are sometimes called counting *numbers*.

The mathematical system $(F, =, \oplus, \odot)$ is called a *field* if the following conditions hold.

F1: F is a commutative group with respect to "addition" $\oplus$.

F2: F without the additive identity is a commutative group with respect to "multiplication" $\odot$.

F3: Multiplication $\odot$ is distributive with respect to addition $\oplus$. If A, B, and C are any elements of F, then

$$A \odot (B \oplus C) = A \odot B \oplus A \odot C.$$

We add other postulates and define another mathematical system $(F, =, \oplus, \odot, <)$ called an *ordered field*, which involves an order relation denoted by $<$. When we add the completeness postulate to the postulates for an ordered field we get a characterization for a *complete ordered field*.

*Models* for these mathematical systems are: The *complex-number* system is a field. The system of *rational numbers* is an ordered field. The *real-number* system is *the* model for a complete ordered field.

Again, *certain* models of mathematical systems are called number systems, and *elements* of the sets involved are called *numbers*. In many contexts we find it convenient to think of the set of integers as being embedded in the set of rationals, and we think of the set of rationals as being embedded in the set of real numbers.

A variety of *names* are used for numbers. Elements of the set of integers are usually denoted by the names

$$\ldots, -5, -4, -3, -2, -1, 0, 1, 2, 3, \ldots.$$

When we wish to refer to an integer without specifying one in particular, we usually denote the (abstract) integer by one of the symbols (letters) I, J, K, M, N, P, Q. We often write rational numbers in the from P/Q, a quotient of integers P and Q with $Q \neq 0$. A real number (which may be an integer, a rational number, or an irrational number) may be written in abstract form as one of the letters A, B, C, D, U, V, W, X, Y, Z.

We have a *uniform* set of names for real numbers: the infinite decimal representation. In this representation, integers are written

$$\ldots, -1.0, 0.0, 1.0, 2.0, \ldots,$$

where it is understood that an infinite number of zeros follow the last zero listed. Rational numbers appear in the infinite decimal format with a "block" of digits being repeated indefinitely.

$1/3 = .33333\ldots$ (3 is repeated).
$1/8 = .125000\ldots$ (0 is repeated).
$1/21 = .047619047619047619\ldots$ (the block 047619 is repeated).

Customarily, the three dots (...) are deleted when only 0 is repeated. Thus, $1/8 = .125$. The infinite decimal representation of irrational numbers does not possess this repeating block characteristic.

Certain irrational numbers appear often in applications, so they are given special *names*, and a few digits[1] of their decimal representation have been tabulated.

$$\pi = 3.14159\ 26535\ldots$$
$$SQRT(2) = 1.41421\ 35623\ldots$$
$$EXP(1) = 2.71828\ 18284\ldots.$$

We are able to "define" the infinite decimal representation of certain irrational numbers using the principle of definition by induction and the idea of Dedekind cut. For example, the infinite decimal representation of the irrational number *named* SQRT(2) is the least upper bound of the sequence of rational numbers

---

[1] $\pi$ has been tabulated to 100,000 decimal places. See [3].

$$1.4, 1.41, 1.414, 1.4142, 1.41421, \ldots,$$

where the N*th* element in the sequence involves exactly N decimal digits to the right of the decimal point, and it is the largest such rational number whose square is less than or equal to 2. Of course, in computing we are interested in methods for computing decimal representations of numbers like SQRT (2) which produce more than one new decimal place at each step. See Newton's Method below, where the number of "correct" decimal places is almost doubled at each step. We prefer analytical definitions for irrational numbers whose decimal representation is desired. For example, the irrational number named $\pi$ may be defined as the number that is the circumference of any circle divided by its diameter. This is not a very practical criterion for computing digits of the decimal representation of $\pi$.

In computing, we *use* only a finite number of digits of the infinite decimal representation of real numbers, and we say that the "computing number" is obtained by a *chopping* or *round-off* process. There are two formats for "computing numbers" in common use: the *fixed-point* and the *floating-point* formats.

A calculation is executed in a fixed-point format if all numbers involved in the calculation are represented as decimal numbers with the same number of digits to the right of the decimal point. For example,

$$A = .123400$$
$$\frac{B = .001234}{A + B = .124634}.$$

Also, fixed-point numbers are not allowed to exceed a specified number (say, unity). If a calculation attempts to produce a number exceeding this limit, then we say the calculation produced *overflow* (in the computer, and some sort of ERROR FLAG results).

A corresponding calculation involving numbers in floating format is more complicated. A number written in floating format consists of two parts: a *mantissa* (fractional part), and an *exponent*. For example, with a four-digit normalized mantissa

$$A = .123400 \text{ is written } A = (+.1234) * 10 ** (0).$$
$$B = .001234 \text{ is written } B = (+.1234) * 10 ** (-2).$$

The results of operations involving these numbers are required to have four-digit mantissas, each with the first digit not zero unless the number (result) is zero. A variety of rules for *chopping* a result to a four-digit mantissa are in use. Statistically, the "best" rule for chopping is:

1. if the chopped part is greater than one-half a unit in the last digit retained, then round-up (without regard to sign, add one unit to the last digit retained),
2. if the chopped part is less than one-half a unit in the last digit retained, then round-down, and
3. if the chopped part equals one-half a unit in the last digit retained, then round-up if the last digit retained is odd, otherwise round-down.

The sum of A and B becomes

$$A = (+.1234) * 10 ** (0)$$
$$\frac{B = (+.1234) * 10 ** (-2)}{A \oplus B = (+.1246) * 10 ** (0)},$$

where the chopped part of the sum is .000034, so we round-down.

Most scientific computing is achieved on electronic digital computers using numbers in floating format. A principal reason for this is that many calculations may be executed before an intermediate result is recorded (printed), and an analysis of each problem to insure that the calculation (with fixed-point numbers) will proceed without experiencing an overflow HALT is usually impractical (too expensive). In the following section we discuss some properties of a typical system of "computing numbers" defined in floating format. This system has none of the nice properties that we associate with the real-number system.

We conclude this section with an *interpretation* for "computing numbers." The purpose is to indicate how round-off errors can accumulate. First, we consider fixed-point numbers. Since we only allowed six digits to define $A = .123400$, then A could "represent" *any* real number X in the interval

$$.123399500 \ldots \leq X \leq .123400500 \ldots,$$

where the above "best" rule for round-off is used. This interval (of length .000001) is called the *interval of doubt* for A. Similarly, $B = .001234$ could be a rounded representation for *any* real number Y in the interval (of length .000001)

$$.001233500 \ldots \leq Y \leq .001234500 \ldots.$$

A natural "sum of intervals" would be

$$.12463300\ldots \leq Z \leq .12463500\ldots$$

so that the sum A + B could correspond to any real number Z in the interval of length .000002. Thus, we see the interval of doubt *grows* with each addition. If two digits of a number format in an electronic computer are used to store the exponent of a floating number, a corresponding interval of doubt for floating numbers will be even larger.

The floating number A = (+.1234) * 10 ** (0) might represent any real number X in the interval of doubt (of length .0001)

$$.1233500\ldots \leq X \leq .1234500\ldots.$$

The interval of doubt for B = (+.1234) * 10 ** (−2) is

$$.001233500\ldots \leq Y \leq .001234500\ldots,$$

which has length .000001. The "sum of intervals" is

$$.124583500\ldots \leq Z \leq .124684500\ldots,$$

which has length .000101. This interval does not include (nor is it included in) the interval of doubt for the tabulated number A ⊕ B which has length .0001. It is about fifty times as large as the interval of doubt for the sum in fixed-point format. Some really depressing properties of floating numbers are indicated in §1.3.

### EXERCISES

1. We are all familiar with the "power series in 10" interpretation for the infinite decimal representation of real numbers. The integer 10 is called the *base* of this power series representation. For example, A = 1234.5 is a list of *coefficients* in the form

$$A = 1 * 10 ** 3 + 2 * 10 ** 2 + 3 * 10 ** 1$$
$$+ 4 * 10 ** 0 + 5 * 10 ** (−1),$$

where the decimal point is placed between the coefficients of $10 ** 0$ and $10 ** (-1)$. Also, $B = 1.333\ldots$ is written

$$B = 1 * 10 ** 0 + 3 * 10 ** (-1) + 3 * 10 ** (-2)$$
$$+ 3 * 10 ** (-3) + \cdots,$$

where $+ \cdots$ means that each of the remaining *coefficients* in this power series is equal to 3. When we add two numbers in this "power series in 10" format, if some coefficient of the *sum* "power series in 10" is greater than 10, then we "carry the one," etc. Similarly, in subtraction we "borrow." When writing a product of numbers in this format we may have to "carry" as many as eight of some power of 10. In this context, explain *in detail* how we compute $X + Y$, $X - Y$, and $X * Y$ for $X = 7898.76$ and $Y = 567.8912$.

2. A "power series in 2" interpretation for real numbers (similar to the interpretation given in Exercise 1 for the decimal representation of real numbers) defines the *binary* representation of real numbers. Of course, the binary representation is defined in terms of the (presumed known and understood) decimal representation. The "binary form"

$$A = A2 * 2 ** 2 + A1 * 2 ** 1 + A0 * 2 ** 0$$
$$+ AM1 * 2 ** (-1) + AM2 * 2 ** (-2)$$

has each *binary coefficient* one of the integers 0 or 1.

*Note.* The name AM1 suggests "A minus one."

For example (the comma is the binary point),

$$A = (A2 \ A1 \ A0, AM1 \ AM2) = (1 \ 0 \ 1, 1 \ 1)$$

*means*

$$A = 1 * 2 ** 2 + 0 * 2 ** 1 + 1 * 2 ** 0$$
$$+ 1 * 2 ** (-1) + 1 * 2 ** (-2)$$
$$= 4 + 1 + .5 + .25 = 5.75 \text{ (in decimal format)}.$$

That is, (deleting the extra spaces)

$$A = (101, 11) \text{ BASE } (2)$$
$$= (5.75) \text{ BASE } (10).$$

Show that

   (12345.) BASE (10) = (11000000111001,) BASE (2).
    (37.25) BASE (10) = (100101, 01) BASE (2).
    (12.2) BASE (10) = (1100, 001100110011 . . .) BASE (2),

where 0011 repeats indefinitely.

   (12345.) BASE (10) = ((01)(23)(45),) BASE (100).
      (6.) BASE (10) = (110,) BASE (2) = (6,) BASE (8).
    (37.25) BASE (10) = (45, 2) BASE (8).
    (12.2) BASE (10) = (14, 146314631463. . .) BASE (8).

3. State an algorithm to compute the BASE (K) representation of the decimal
   number (A1 A2 $\cdots$ AN. B1 B2 $\cdots$ BM).

   *Hint.* Divide the integer part (A1 A2 $\cdots$ AN.) by K, and record the
   quotient Q1 and the remainder R1. Then, divide Q1 by K to get Q2 and
   R2, etc. The integer part equals R1 + R2 * K + R3 * K ** 2 + $\cdots$. For
   the fractional part, *multiply* by K, etc.

4. The problem of finding a solution X of the equation

$$F(X) = 7 - A * X = 0$$

   may be interpreted as the problem of computing zero. Use numbers in
   normalized four-digit floating format and the "best" rule for round-off to
   find the interval of doubt for X for each of the values:

   A = +.1000 * 10 ** (−4),    A = +.1000 * 10 ** (1),
   A = +.1000 * 10 ** (4).

   Conclude that the *sensitivity* of F(X) to variations in X depends on the
   value of A. That is, a fixed "small" change in X produces various changes
   in F(X), depending on the value of A. One of the most difficult problems
   in numerical analysis is that of determining when we have computed zero,
   and which corresponding value of the unknown to accept as "the" solution
   that produced zero.

5. Find the interval of doubt of the multiplicative inverse X of +.2000 * 10
   ** (0).

*Hint.* $X = +.5000 * 10 ** (1)$, $X = +.5001 * 10 ** (1)$, and $X = +.5002 * 10 ** (1)$ are solutions of

$$G(X) = +.1000 * 10 ** (1) - .2000 * 10 ** (0) * X = 0.$$

What is the length of the interval of doubt for the solutions X of $G(X) = 0$?

*Answer.* $+4.9995 \leq X \leq 5.0025$. Length $= .003$.

### 1.3. A SYSTEM OF COMPUTING NUMBERS

In this section we define a system of numbers much like those utilized by many electronic digital computers. The principal difference is that we always round-down instead of using the "best" rule for round-off given in §1.2. The system considered here is decimal [BASE(10)], but similar systems with other bases [say, BASE(2): binary] have the "unfortunate" properties of this system; also, we get a new system if we vary the number of digits in the mantissa, change the placement of the decimal point in the mantissa, or vary the range of the exponent.

Our purpose is to help the reader understand *why* we consider a variety of methods to solve one problem. In particular, he should see that we are *not* privileged to use the real-number system in computing. Consequently, if we execute in our system of computing numbers a sequence of operations that correspond to operations in the real-number system, then we do not expect to compute the corresponding real number. If the real operations define a *solution* to a particular problem, we say that the set of operations define an *algorithm* for the problem. We should not expect to *compute* this solution exactly, but we may be able to *select* from a set of algorithms that define this solution *one* algorithm that can be used as a guide when defining a *method* (a set of operations on computing numbers) for computing a *usable estimate* to the solution. We usually refer to a set of real operations as a "method" or a "process," anticipating its application using computing numbers.

We define a system $(T, =, \oplus, \odot, <)$ of normalized eight-digit floating numbers; we define this number system in terms of the system of real numbers. Every element of T will represent a real number, but not every real number has a representative in T. (We do not consider here the intervals of doubt discussed in §1.2.) A typical *element* of T has the form

$$A = (\pm\ .A1\ A2\ A3\ A4\ A5\ A6\ A7\ A8) * 10 ** K,$$

where each of the digits A1, A2, ..., A8 is one of the integers 0, 1, 2,..., 9, and K is an integer satisfying $-50 \leq K \leq 49$. We assume A1 $\neq$ 0 and say A is *normalized* (unless A = 0, in which case A1 = A2 = $\cdots$ = A8 = 0 and K is any integer satisfying $-50 \leq K \leq 49$). The signed eight-dight number $(\pm .A1 \ A2 \ A3 \cdots A8)$ is called the *mantissa* of A, and K is the *exponent* of A. The mantissa of A $(\neq 0)$ is in absolute value less than unity and greater than or equal to .1. Numbers with these properties are said to be in *normalized eight-digit floating* format. For example,

$$-1.0 = (-.10000000) * 10 ** 1$$
$$+123.45 = (+.12345000) * 10 ** 3$$
$$+.000123 = (+.12300000) * 10 ** (-3).$$

Two nonzero elements of T are *equal* if they are identical. That is, they have the same mantissa and exponent.

There is only a finite number of elements in T. How many? An indication of the distribution of elements of T on the real line is given in Figure 1.3.1.

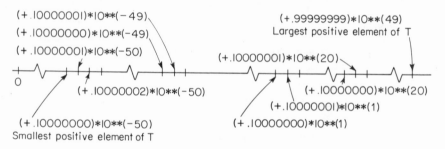

**Figure 1.3.1**

We define the operations $\oplus$ and $\odot$ with the rule for round-off: always round-down. Corresponding operations when built into a modern electronic computer usually involve the "best" rule for round-off given in §1.2.

## ADDITION

$\oplus$ in $(T, =, \oplus, \odot, <)$ is defined for certain pairs of elements of T

$$A = (\pm.A1 \ A2 \ A3 \cdots A8) * 10 ** K1$$
$$B = (\pm.B1 \ B2 \ B3 \cdots B8) * 10 ** K2.$$

The *sum*

$$A \oplus B = (\pm .C1 \ C2 \ C3 \cdots C8) * 10 ** K3 \equiv C$$

is obtained as follows:

1. If $K1 = K2$, then proceed to step (2). If the exponents are not equal, say $K1 > K2$, then shift the digits of the mantissa of B to the right $K1 - K2$ places, zeros are introduced in the positions vacated by B1 as it is shifted, and B8, B7, etc., are *lost* (and not retrievable). Thus we get a new eight-digit mantissa and exponent $(=K1)$ which we associate with B.
2. A and B now have the same exponent. The current representations for the mantissas of A and B are added as real numbers giving at most nine digits. They are then shifted with appropriate alteration of the exponent defining K3, and chopped to eight digits[1] to define the normalized eight-digit floating sum C.

*Note.* If $K3 \geq 50$, or $K3 \leq -51$ with $C1 \neq 0$, the sum is not defined in T and we say *overflow* or *underflow*,[2] respectively, has occurred.

**Example**

$$(+.12345000) * 10 ** 3 \oplus (+.12300000) * 10 ** (-3)$$
$$= (+.12345012) * 10 ** 3$$

for we actually compute

$$(+.12345000) * 10 ** 3 + (+.00000012) * 10 ** 3.$$

In the reals, the sum $+123.45 + .000123 = +123.450123$ has nine digits and cannot be represented exactly by an element of T.

**Example**

$$(+.98700000) * 10 ** 1 \oplus (+.12300000) * 10 ** 1$$
$$= (+.11100000) * 10 ** 2.$$

---

[1]The first nonzero digit of the sum (or later: difference, product, quotient) with the following seven digits is retained—extra digits, if there are any, are simply dropped without considering the possibility of round-up, and if eight digits are not available then zeros are adjoined on the right to complete the eight-digit format.

[2]In most computers, provision is made for the user to elect to replace the result of an operation giving underflow with *zero* and to ignore any signal by the computer that underflow has occurred.

Here the exponents agree, so the mantissas are added to give 1.11000000 which is shifted right one place and $+1$ is added to the common exponent of the summands. There results the normalized sum indicated.

### Example

$(+.90000000) * 10 ** 49 \oplus (+.10000000) * 10 ** 49$ is not defined in T, for, according to our definition of $\oplus$, we would get $(+.10000000) * 10 ** 50$, and $K = 50$ is not permitted for elements of T. Thus, T is *not closed* with respect to $\oplus$.

### SUBTRACTION

$\ominus$ in T is defined by: add the minuend and the additive inverse of the subtrahend to get the difference; also, T is *not closed* with respect to $\ominus$.

### MULTIPLICATION

$\odot$ in T is defined by

$$A \odot B = (\pm.A1 \ A2 \cdots A8) * 10 ** K1 \odot (\pm.B1 \ B2 \cdots B8) * 10 ** K2$$
$$= (\pm.C1 \ C2 \cdots C8) * 10 ** K3 \equiv C,$$

where the real product of mantissas is taken, giving a real number with a sixteen-digit mantissa and with exponent equal $K1 + K2$. After normalization with appropriate adjustment of the exponent defining $K3$, and chopping the mantissa to eight-digits, we get the normalized eight-digit floating product C. As with the definition of $\oplus$, care must be exercised to detect possible overflow or underflow. Construct an example to show that T is *not closed* with respect to $\odot$.

### DIVISION

$\oslash$ in T is defined similarly, where $A \oslash B$ for $B = 0$ is not defined (since division by zero is not defined in the real-number system). T is *not closed* with respect to $\oslash$.

T is *not associative* relative to $\oplus$ because T is not closed relative to $\oplus$. But also, $A \oplus (B \oplus C) \neq (A \oplus B) \oplus C$ when

$$A = (+.11111111) * 10 ** (-4), \qquad B = (+.10000000) * 10 ** 1,$$

and

$$C = (-.10000000) * 10 ** 1,$$

For, $A \oplus (B \oplus C) = A$ while $(A \oplus B) \oplus C = (+.11100000) * 10 ** (-4)$.

T is *not associative* relative to $\odot$ because T is not closed relative to $\odot$. Also, $A \odot (B \odot C) \neq (A \odot B) \odot C$ when

$$A = (+.11111111) * 10 ** 0, \qquad B = (+.11111111) * 10 ** 0,$$

and

$$C = (+.50000000) * 10 ** 1.$$

For, $A \odot (B \odot C) = (+.61728393) * 10 ** (-1)$ while $(A \odot B) \odot C = (+.61728390) * 10 ** (-1)$.

An *additive identity* in T is any element with zero mantissa. The *additive inverse* of any A in T is the element of T with mantissa consisting of the digits in the mantissa of A but with opposite sign and with exponent the same as that of A. Clearly, T *is commutative* relative to $\oplus$.

The *multiplicative identity* is $(+.10000000) * 10 ** 1$. The element $(+.10000000) * 10 ** (-49)$, and each element of T with exponent $K = -50$, has no multiplicative inverse in T. A *multiplicative inverse* (if it exists) of an element of T may not be unique. For example, $A = (+.33333333) * 10 ** 0$ has three multiplicative inverses $1/A = (+.30000001) * 10 ** 1$, $1/A = (+.30000002) * 10 ** 1$, and $1/A = (+.30000003)$, while the natural guess $(+.30000000) * 10 ** 1$ is not an inverse of A. The reader should find the multiplicative inverses for $A = (+.20000000) * 10 ** 0$, using the "best" rule for round-off; also, T *is commutative* relative to $\odot$.

In T the *distributive law* does *not* hold. For, with $A = (+.33333333) * 10 ** 0$, $B = (+.10000002) * 10 ** 0$, and $C = B$, we get $A \odot (B \oplus C) = (+.66666679) * 10 ** (-1)$, and $(A \odot B) \oplus (A \odot C) = (+.66666678) * 10 ** (-1)$.

The relation less than $(<)$ in our system $(T, =, \oplus, \odot, <)$ is the *same* as the order relation for the reals. That is, elements of T are ordered according to the ordering of corresponding real numbers. In an ordered field, $A < B$ and $C > 0$ implies $A * C < B * C$. Our number system does *not* have this property, for, if

$$A = (+.30000001) * 10 ** 1, B = (+.30000002) * 10 ** 1, \text{ and}$$
$$C = (+.33333333) * 10 ** 0,$$

then

$$A < B \text{ and } C > 0,$$

but

$$A \odot C = B \odot C = (+.10000000) * 10 ** 1.$$

Care must be exercised when we consider functions defined on T. In particular, the limit of a sequence exists only if all but a finite number of elements of the sequence are the same element of T. This is because we have only a finite number of elements in T.

In computing we attempt to *apply* concepts, methods, and theorems defined in the real-number system *in* number systems like $(T, =, \oplus, \odot, <)$, where sometimes the concepts are not even defined. Recognition of these facts may help the beginning student to understand the occasional use by numerical analysts of phrases like: "sometimes the . . . method leads to a useable solution"; "if that doesn't work, we might try . . ."; "under certain nice (undefined) circumstances . . ."; "your bound on the error for that method is smaller than my bound for this method, but . . . !?! . . . this method gives me better results"; etc.

### EXERCISES

1. Supply the details of the arithmetic in the text of this section. Remember, our rule for round-off was "always round down."

2. The smallest positive element of T is $A = (+.10000000) * 10 ** (-50)$. Let B denote the next larger element of T. Compute $B - A$ in the reals. Can we compute $B \ominus A$ in T?

   *Answer.* $B - A = (+.10000000) * 10 ** (-57)$, so $B \ominus A$ results in underflow.

3. How many elements of T are in the interval $[(+.10000000) * 10 ** (-50), (+.10000000) * 10 ** (-49)]$? What is the length of this interval?

**4.** The largest element of T is A $= (+.99999999) * 10 ** 49$, and the second largest element is B $= (+.99999998) * 10 ** 49$. What is the length of the interval [B, A]?

**5.** The real positive root of $X ** 2 - 2 = 0$ is written $X = SQRT(2)$. Since $SQRT(2)$ is irrational, then $SQRT(2)$ is not an element of T. Is there an element A in T such that $A \odot A = (+.20000000) * 10 ** 1$?

*Note.* $SQRT(2) = 1.41421356237\ldots$.

**6.** Construct an example to show that $A \oplus (B \ominus (A \oplus B)) \neq 0$ can happen.

**7.** Construct an example to show that $A \odot X = B$ may have *no* solution in T, where A and B are in T. Also, show that the linear equation may have *two* solutions in T.

**8.** Suppose T is a set of numbers in normalized one-digit floating format. The graph of $Y = F(X) = X$ for the elements $X(J) = .1 * J$ for $J \in //0, 10//$, is a set of eleven points in the X, Y-plane, namely, the eleven equally spaced points on the line $Y = X$

$$(0.0, 0.0), \qquad (.1, .1), \qquad (.2, .2), \qquad \ldots, \qquad (1.0, 1.0).$$

Plot the graph of $Y = .5 * X$ for the elements $X(J) = .1 * J, J \in //0, 10//$, and use the "best" rule for round-off when computing $Y(J) = .5 * X(J)$, $J \in //0, 10//$. That is, plot the points

$$(0.0, 0.0), \qquad (.1, .0), \qquad (.2, .1), \qquad (.3, .2), \qquad \ldots, \qquad (1.0, .5).$$

## 1.4. SOME TYPES OF ERROR

Suppose it is required to *estimate* the result Y of executing a specified set of operations (or instructions) defined on a given set of data. Specifically, suppose we are asked to *compute*

(1.4.1)                               $Y = F(X).$

The data X might be a real number, or a finite set of numbers, or a function, or even a set of functions.

The set of operations F defined on X might be:

1. *Display* X in decimal format (Y = X);
2. *Execute certain algebraic operations* on X [e.g., $Y = 2 * X ** 2 + 1$, or $Y = SQRT(X)$]; or
3. *Solve a matrix equation* where X is the set of coefficient matrices and Y is a solution matrix.

More generally, the instructions in F might be: find Y (a number, or function, etc.) which is a root of an equation, say $G(X, Y) = 0$, where X is given. In the latter case, the equation might be a differential equation with solution Y (a function).

**Example 1.** We are already familiar with some of the problems involved in *displaying* a real number. Suppose in $Y = F(X)$ we have $X = \pi$ and define

F: display X in decimal format.

Then, in practice we would *change the problem* and define a new F, say

FF: display X in P-digit decimal format (using some rule for round-off).

In this case we define

$$YY = FF(X)$$

as an *estimate* to the Y in the original problem $Y = F(X)$, and write

$$\Delta Y \equiv Y - YY = F(X) - FF(X).$$

When F is *display* we call $\Delta Y$ the *round-off error in YY*, where YY is considered an estimate to Y.

**Example 2.** Suppose that the data X cannot be utilized in its original form by the device that is to execute the operations defined by F; suppose also that the operations in F are executed exactly on data that are acceptable to the computing device. If we denote an acceptable estimate to X by XX and define

(1.4.2a) $$YY = F(XX)$$

as an *estimate* to Y in $Y = F(X)$, then

(1.4.2b) $$\Delta Y \equiv Y - YY = F(X) - F(XX)$$

is called the *propagated error in YY*, where YY is considered an estimate to Y. Of course, $\Delta X \equiv X - XX$ could represent round-off error experienced when displaying the given data. Or, $\Delta X$ could represent any errors experienced in obtaining the data, say by experiment.

*Note.* In computing we are seldom able to execute exactly the operations in an F associated with a practical problem (not a classroom example). However, we are very much interested in determining the sensitivity of Y to variations in the data X, and we are often willing to pay for experimental evidence when an analysis of this sensitivity is not available.

**Example 3.** If a computing device is not available to execute the operations defined by F, then we usually *change the problem* by defining a new sequence of operations (denoted by FF) and define the *estimate*

$$(1.4.3a) \qquad YY = FF(X).$$

For example, F might be "compute a definite integral of X (a function)," and FF might be compute a Riemann Sum involving X. If no errors are experienced when displaying the data X for the computing device, and if no errors are committed by the computing device[1] when executing with X the operations which define FF, then

$$(1.4.3b) \qquad \Delta Y \equiv Y - YY = F(X) - FF(X)$$

is the *truncation error in YY*, where YY is considered an estimate to Y. Compare Example 1, where that important special case (F: display) was distinguished by the name *round-off error*.

When *combinations* of errors are involved in an estimate $YY = FF(XX)$, we sometimes use the form

$$(1.4.3c) \qquad \Delta Y \equiv Y - YY = F(X) - FF(XX)$$

and call $\Delta Y$ *total error*.

The remaining chapters of this text are presented as an outline of certain classical problems

$$(1.4.4a) \qquad Y = F(X)$$

with a brief discussion of a few classical elementary *methods*

$$(1.4.4b) \qquad YY = FF(X)$$

for obtaining *estimates* YY to solutions Y of these problems. Generally, *the only error we will consider is truncation error in the sense of Example 3*

$$(1.4.4c) \qquad \Delta Y \equiv Y - YY = F(X) - FF(X) = E(X, F, FF).$$

---

[1]No gross errors are experienced, and in particular all arithmetic operations are performed without round-off errors.

In particular, we do not further consider the important problem of round-off error (Example 1). The reader is referred to [1] and [2]. Propagated error (Example 2) is considered in Chapter 4 in an analysis of inherent error, and only briefly in various discussions concerning stability and convergence of iteration processes. We assume that *no gross errors* are experienced and that we work in the real-number system with the classical analysis of elementary calculus available to us.

For one problem (F) we may consider several methods (FF), and investigate some merits of these methods with certain classes of data (X). Our motivation for looking at several methods for one problem is the existence of round-off error in computing.

We often examine a representation of the truncation error (1.4.4c), and list some of its properties in an attempt to describe the "quality" of the associated estimate. See Remark 9 at the end of §1.5. Sometimes we use the order symbol ORDB, defined as follows [read: E(T) is at most of the order G(T)]:

$$E(T) = ORDB(G(T)) \text{ if } E(T)/G(T) \text{ remains } \textit{bounded}$$

as T tends to its limit (usually 0 or $+\infty$).

For example, $E(T) = ORDB(1)$ says $E(T)$ is bounded as T tends to its limit. The limit for T is usually not made a part of the order symbol, but is understood from context. If $E(T)$ is a vector, then boundedness in the definition of ORDB refers to the components of the vector.

### EXERCISES

1. Consider the problem FF of displaying the real numbers $X \in [0, 1]$ in normalized one-digit floating format, using the "best" rule for round-off. Sketch the graph of $YY = FF(X)$ with $X \in [0, 1]$ in the X, Y-plane. Get a set of line segments [e.g., $FF(X) = .1$ for each $X \in (.05, .15)$] parallel to the X-axis. Discuss (see Example 1) the *round-off error* in YY, where YY is considered an estimate to $Y = F(X) \equiv X$. Compare the above graph with the line $Y = X$.

2. Suppose we are using a computing device that requires operands to be represented in normalized one-digit floating format. For YY, a normalized one-digit floating number, "use the computer" to obtain $ZZ = G(YY) \equiv 5 * YY$. Suppose no round-off errors are experienced when we compute

ZZ using YY. With YY = FF(X) defined in Exercise 1, and ZZ = G(YY) defined here, discuss the *propagated error* (see Example 2) in

$$ZZ = G\,(FF(X)), \qquad X \in [0, 1],$$

where ZZ is considered an estimate to $Z = G(X) \equiv 5 * X$ for $X \in [0, 1]$. Make a sketch in X, Y, Z-space, and get line segments lying above the line segments in the X, Y-plane of Exercise 1. Compare this graph with the line segment $(X, Y, Z) = (X, X, 5 * X)$, $X \in [0, 1]$. Discuss corresponding graphs for corresponding problems where we are using numbers in normalized P-digit floating format. First use $P = 2$, then use $P = 8$, finally, use P "large".

3. The Taylor Series Expansion of G(X) about X = A at X = A + H is

$$G(A + H) = G(A) + G'(A) * H + G''(A) * H ** 2/2! + \cdots.$$

We solve this form for G'(A) to obtain

$$G'(A) = (G(A + H) - G(A))/H - H * G''(A)/2!$$
$$- H ** 2 * G'''(A)/3! - \cdots.$$

If it is known that the second and higher derivatives of G(X) at X = A are bounded [G(X) = SIN(X) has this property] and if H is small, then we may write

$$G'(A) = (G(A + H) - G(A))/H + E(H),$$

where E(H) is the *truncation error* of the estimate

$$G'(A) \doteq (G(A + H) - G(A))/H,$$

and E(H) has the property

$$E(H) = ORDB(H).$$

That is, E(H) approaches zero as H approaches zero. Discuss this estimate using the terminology of Example 3.

*Hint.* Use $Y = G'(A) = F(H) \equiv (G(A + H) - G(A))/H - H * G''(A)/2! - \cdots$, and $YY = FF(H) \equiv (G(A + H) - G(A))/H$.

### 1.5. WHY NUMERICAL ANALYSIS?

We have said that the objective of numerical analysis is to facilitate computing. The *need* for computed estimates to solutions of problems is the reason for the development of the discipline in applied mathematics called numerical analysis. There is room (and a need) for the practitioner and the theorist in numerical analysis.

The practitioner may be asked to *recommend a method* which will produce "usable" estimates to solutions of a specified class of problems. Suppose that the problems involve a set of parameters, and a set of ranges for the parameters is specified, also suppose that the method is needed for inclusion in a production program to begin operation on a specific date, so that the recommendation is required on an earlier date (e.g., ten days after the request is made). Since most of his time on the job is used studying the literature, the practitioner is probably familiar with a variety of methods for solving a classical problem "something like" the problems at hand; but he may never have attempted to solve a problem in the proposed set. Indeed, he may not know that a solution exists, but he cannot wait for someone to prove that it does exist. He hopes to demonstrate that solutions exist by "finding" them. A program for finding a method that he can recommend might include the following steps: (i) Select a few sample problems from the specified class of problems; (ii) Apply classical methods (for similar problems) to the sample problems and "determine" if the computed estimates are usable. It may happen that one classical method is "usable" for a subset of the specified set of parameter values, while another classical method is "usable" for another subset of parameter values, etc. The "recommended method" could then be a set of classical methods, each to be used with an associated set of parameter values; (iii) If none of the classical methods in the practitioner's "file of methods" defines usable estimates to solutions for a subset of the specified set of problems, he may invent a method (often a combination of classical methods) and try it. Occasionally he invents a method, finds that it produces usable results, and is not sure "why" it works.

The practitioner's happier adventures in computing are published in reports circulated in a company or throughout an industry, and in certain national and international journals.

The theoretical numerical analyst is usually two things: an expert in his particular field (engineering, physics, mathematics, business, etc.), with an understanding of elementary classical mathematics (e.g., through advanced calculus), and he is also a person with a genuine interest in computing estimates to solutions of problems. He attempts to explain "why" a method does or does not give usable estimates to solutions of a problem, and "why" this method is better or worse than another method. He supports his explanation with a list of properties of the method. Entries in this list might include: (i) The number of multiplications involved in its execution; (ii) The expense of obtaining "initial data" before the method can be applied; (iii) An indication of how an error is propagated during execution; and (iv) A relation between the estimate and a corresponding solution of the problem.

The theorist's results are published in advanced textbooks, reports, and journals which are available to the practitioner. The practitioner provides him with evidence that supports (and sometimes suggests) his theoretical method of attack on a problem, but the theorist must be able and willing to grind out additional computed evidence. The electronic digital computer is playing an increasingly important role in basic research in many fields.

We conclude this section with some *remarks* and associated questions to indicate a *need* for an analysis of computed estimates. The reader is not expected to have very satisfying answers to the questions. We only ask that he state what he now feels constitutes an answer, and indicate where estimates are involved. Note particularly any reference made to sum of an infinite series, definite or indefinite integral, limit of a sequence, maximum of a function, or any concept that you may not be able to *compute*. Include remarks on plotting accuracy.

CONCLUDING REMARKS

1. A *relation* defined by an equation $F(X, Y) = 0$ is a collection of ordered pairs $(X, Y)$ that satisfy the equation.

$$\{(X, Y)|F(X, Y) = 0\}.$$

The *graph* of this relation is the set of points in the X, Y-plane that have coordinates exactly the elements of the relation. For example, the relation with exactly the two elements $(0, 0)$ and $(1, 1)$ has for its graph the two points in the plane with these number pairs as coordinates (in particular, the two points are not connected by a line segment). List those classes of equations $F(X, Y) = 0$ for which you can produce an "accurate" graph. (What do you mean by accurate?) How would you sketch the graph of the relation defined by

$$Y - 2 = 0?$$

$$Y - 2 * X + 3 = 0?$$

$$Y ** 2 + X ** 2 - 1 = 0?$$

$$4 * Y ** 2 + 9 * X ** 2 - 36 = 0?$$

$$Y - SIN(X) = 0?$$

$$Y - SIN(X + EXP(X)) = 0?$$

$$F(X, Y) = 0?$$

How accurate is your sketch of each relation?

2. For what classes of functions F(T) are you able to *execute* the integration in

$$\int F(T), \text{ over } T \in (A, X), = G(X)?$$

3. The linear differential equation problem

$$Y'(X) + P(X) * Y(X) = Q(X), \qquad Y(A) = B$$

*has* a solution Y(X) if P(X) and Q(X) are continuous on an interval containing A. For what classes of functions P(X) and Q(X) can you *compute* the exact solution of this differential equation problem?

4. How many infinite series (besides geometric series) can you sum exactly? Remember, SIN(X) is just a *name* for the sum

$$X - X ** 3/3! + X ** 5/5! - \cdots .$$

The sum SIN(X) is known to exist for each real number X, but can you find the decimal representation for SIN(X) when X = .15 radian? How would you compute a decimal representation for $\pi$?

5. We would use Cramer's Rule to solve two linear equations in two unknowns, but we would use a method like Gauss Elimination to solve a system of 50 linear equations in 50 unknowns. Why not use Cramer's Rule for large systems?

6. Suppose that a property of a physical system is examined under a variety of conditions, and suppose that the observations (say, measurements) are *tabulated* to form a finite set of ordered pairs (X(K), Y(K)), $K \in //1, N//$.

| K | 1 | 2 | 3 | ... | N |
|------|---|---|---|-----|---|
| X(K) |   |   |   |     |   |
| Y(K) |   |   |   |     |   |

Suppose that the measurements X(K) and Y(K) were made using a steel tape graduated in tenths of an inch, and that the tabulated numbers are in doubt by ±.05 inch. If the property measured has the form Y = P(X), then we can only expect the graph of Y = P(X) to pass through the boxes indicated in Figure 1.5.1.

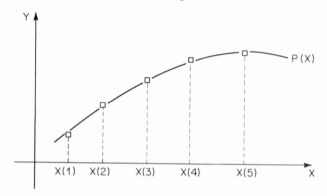

**Figure 1.5.1**

The scientist will plot the tabulated points and use his "best judgement" to sketch a curve "close" to the plotted points. Suppose he has tabulated five points, and "knows" that the graph of P(X) is supposed to be a straight line, even though the tabulated points are not colinear. How would he decide where to draw the line? Compare this problem to your sketch problems in Remark 1.

7. In the classroom we say the solution of the differential equation problem

$$Y'(X) = F(X, Y(X)), \qquad Y(X0) = Y0, \qquad X \in [A, B]$$

is a *function* (single-valued relation)

$$G: \{(X, Y)|X \in [A, B], Y = G(X), \text{ and } G'(X) = F(X, G(X)) \\ \text{for each } X \in [A, B]\},$$

where the number pair (X0, Y0) is in the set G. This is a marvelously complicated set of ordered pairs. Each element $(T, G(T))$ in G is related to its "neighbors" by

$$LIM((G(T + H) - G(T))/H), \text{ as } H \text{ App } 0, = F(T, G(T)).$$

Even when we know that a unique solution exists, it is not likely that we can *find* all the elements of G in a finite number of steps (computations.) The best that we can hope for is to *produce*

$$GG: \{(X(K), Y(K)) | K \in //0, M//, (X(K), Y(K)) \in G\}.$$

This is a finite set of elements of the solution G. Almost certainly, the best that we can do is to *produce*

$$GGG: \{(X(K), Y(K)) | K \in //0, M//, X(K) \in [A, B],$$
$$Y(K) \doteq G(X(K))\},$$

where each Y(K) is only an *estimate* to $G(X(K))$. One obvious formula for defining an estimate is $Y(K) = Y0$ for *each* K. (We can usually do better than this.) This might be a pretty good estimate for X(K) near X = X0, but probably is not a very good estimate elsewhere in the interval [A, B]. We will consider some classical methods for defining estimates Y(K) to $G(X(K))$. The finite collection GGG of estimates to elements of G is called a *numerical solution* of the differential equation problem. Relate this discussion to Remark 3 above.

8. Generally, we can only expect to compute estimates to solutions of simple problems like "find the zeros of a quadratic polynomial," so we are not surprised at the popularity of iteration processes which define sequences of estimates to solutions of problems. A method which defines only "one estimate" has a serious disadvantage when compared to a corresponding iteration algorithm: if the "one estimate" is not usable, then the obvious alternative is to repeat the method using computing numbers with more digits in the mantissa, while in an iteration process we can get a new estimate by simply executing another step in the iteration. Conceivably, a usable estimate could be obtained with a few steps of an iteration process at less cost (in programming and computing time) than one execution of a corresponding noniteration algorithm for the problem.

9. We will discuss "quality" of methods using the classical representations of truncation error. However, we ask the reader to remember that a very important (and difficult to measure) criterion for choosing a method is the *sensitivity* of the computed solution of a "big" problem to the computed solution of a smaller "atomic" problem. In Figure 1.5.2 the "big" problem is represented as a chain of boxes, and each box represents an "atomic" problem. We must select a *method* for

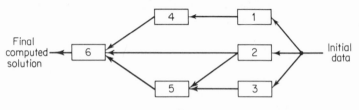

**Figure 1.5.2**

each atomic problem which (1) can use as input the initial data and/or computed output from boxes appearing "upstream" in the chain, and (2) can produce usable input for boxes "downstream." For example, suppose box number 3 is an interpolation problem, and suppose the final computed solution is so insensitive to the output of box number 3 that linear interpolation is adequate to give a usable output from box number 6. In this case it would be wasteful to use computer time to execute a "more accurate" interpolation method. As another example, suppose the atomic problem in box number 2 requires solution of a linear system, and suppose Gauss Elimination using single precision arithmetic produces a computed solution which is usable as input for box number 5, but suppose this output from box number 2 is not accurate enough for use as input into box number 6. Then we might decide for box number 2 to use Gauss Elimination with an estimate-improving process, or to use Gauss Elimination with multiple-precision arithmetic, or to use another method, maybe an iteration process. A formal analysis of this type of sensitivity is usually impractical, but estimates to it are often obtained by experiment (execution of a few test cases with selected methods for "key" atomic problems). When the "big" problem is not a production problem (production problems are usually solved using a computer program which allows variation of parameters by input data, and the program is run many times) we might choose the best method we know (and can afford to execute) for each atomic problem. Of course, for a program to be run one time, this may well be the "best" (cheapest) choice of methods.

## SUGGESTED READING

1. Henrici, P. (1963): *Error Propagation for Difference Methods.* John Wiley & Sons, Inc., New York.

2. Wilkinson, J. H. (1963): *Rounding Errors in Algebraic Processes.* Prentice-Hall, Inc., Englewood Cliffs, N. J.

3. Shanks, D. and J. W. Wrench, Jr. (1962): "Calculation of $\pi$ to 100,000 Decimals." *Mathematics of Computation,* Vol. 16. No. 77. (Page 76).

4. Hamming, R. W. (1962): *Numerical Methods for Scientists and Engineers.* McGraw-Hill Book Company, New York. Note particularly: Chapter $N + 1$, the last chapter, and Chapter 2.

# 2 TAYLOR'S FORMULA: TRUNCATION ERROR

## 2.1. MOTIVATION

The remainder of this text is presented as an outline of certain classical problems

$$(2.1.1a) \qquad Y = F(X)$$

with a brief discussion of a few classical elementary *methods*

$$(2.1.1b) \qquad YY = FF(X)$$

for obtaining *estimates* YY to solutions Y of these problems. Generally, the only error we will consider is *truncation error* in the sense of Example 3 in §1.4

$$(2.1.1c) \qquad \Delta Y \equiv Y - YY = F(X) - FF(X) = E(X, F, FF).$$

In particular, we do not further consider the important problem of round-off error (Example 1 of §1.4). Propagated error (Example 2 of §1.4) is considered in Chapter 4 in an analysis of inherent error, and only briefly in various discussions concerning stability, and convergence of iteration processes. We assume that *no gross errors* are experienced, and assume that we work in the real-number system with the classical analysis of elementary calculus available to us.

For one problem (F) we may consider several methods (FF), and investigate some merits of these methods with certain classes of data (X). Our motivation for looking at several methods for one problem is the existence of round-off error in computing.

Every modern sequence in differential and integral calculus includes a study of estimates (FF) to functions (F) in the neighborhood of a point by polynomials (FF). Two theorems applied in this connection are Taylor's Theorem with Remainder (also called the *extended theorem of the mean*) for functions of one and two independent variables. These theorems represent in various forms the truncation error E(X, F, FF) for the estimation of F by Taylor Polynomials FF. Because they are fundamental to advanced as well as to elementary studies in numerical analysis, we devote this chapter to a discussion of these theorems with particular emphasis on estimates to, and interpretations for, the error terms.

We hope that this discussion of bounds on the truncation error for this method, *local* estimation of functions by Taylor Polynomials, will leave the beginning student with enough confidence to attempt an interpretation and seek bounds for various representations of truncation error for other methods. (Recall remarks in Preface about Weierstrass' Theorem.)

Bounds on the truncation error obtained by the methods of this chapter are frequently too conservative. That is, the actual error is often much less than the bound guarantees. Sometimes we prefer more realistic (but less reliable) *statistical bounds* on the truncation and/or round-off error. That is, we can make statements like: The probability is P that the error does not exceed D. A discussion of statistical bounds would take us too far afield.

## 2.2. TAYLOR'S FORMULA IN ONE VARIABLE

**Taylor's Theorem in One Variable.**

H1: N is a nonnegative integer.

H2: F(X), F'(X), F''(X), ..., DER ** (N)F(X) are continuous, and DER ** (N + 1)F(X) exists on [A, B].

H3: A ≤ C ≤ B.

H4: The *Taylor Polynomial*[1] of degree N of F(X) at C is

---

[1]The notation PF(N; X, C) will sometimes be used when we want to distinguish Taylor Polynomials of different functions. Notice that the independent variable X is listed immediately after the semicolon, and derivatives are taken with respect to this variable. P(N; X, C) is read: P sub N of X and C.

(2.2.1)      P(N; X, C)

$$= \sum \text{DER} ** (M)F(C) * (X - C) ** M/M!, \; M \in //0, N//,$$

where DER ** (0)F(C) $\equiv$ F(C) and, for M > 0, DER ** (M)F(C)
is the M*th* derivative of F(X) evaluated at X = C.

C: For each X in [A, B], there exists a number Z = Z(X) between X
and C (X $\leq$ Z $\leq$ C or C $\leq$ Z $\leq$ X) such that

(2.2.2a)          F(X) = P(N; X, C) + R(N; X, C),

where the truncation error (*Lagrange Form* for the remainder)

(2.2.2b)      R(N; X, C) = F(X) − P(N; X, C)

$$= \text{DER} ** (N + 1)F(Z) * (X - C) ** (N + 1)/(N + 1)!.$$

The equation (2.2.2a) with (2.2.2b) substituted is called *Taylor's formula
in one variable* with the Lagrange Form for the remainder. The Taylor
Polynomial P(N; X, C) corresponds to the estimate FF(X), and R(N; X, C)
is $\Delta$Y or E(X, F, FF) in (2.1.1c).

Another important form for the truncation error (which does not involve the mysterious point Z) is the following *integral* form for the remainder

(2.2.2c)   R(N; X, C) = F(X) − P(N; X, C)

$$= (1/N!) * \int \text{DER} ** (N + 1)F(T) * (X - T) ** N, \text{ over } T \in (C, X).$$

Proofs of Taylor's Theorem with (2.2.2b) and (2.2.2c) are not presented
here. We prefer to require the student to produce as a homework assignment
*detailed* proofs of this most important theorem. The student is referred to
[1] and [2].

Since we are not yet prepared to estimate integrals, we will restrict our
attention to the Lagrange Form for the remainder.

The *characterizing properties* of the Taylor Polynomial are

DER ** (M)P(N; C, C) = DER ** (M)F(C), for each M $\in$ //0, N//,

where DER ** (M)P(N; C, C) is the M*th* derivative of P(N; X, C) with respect to X evaluated at X = C. That is, the N + 1 coefficients of P(N; X, C)
are determined so that the graph of the polynomial passes through the point
(C, F(C)), with the same slope as F(X) at X = C (if N $\geq$ 1), and the first N
derivatives of P(N; X, C) agree with those of F(X) at X = C. See Figure

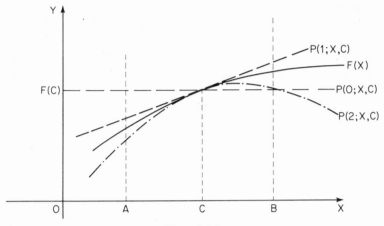

**Figure 2.2.1**

2.2.1. Clearly, if $F(X)$ is a polynomial of degree K then $P(N; X, C) = F(X)$ whenever $N \geq K$.

The truncation error (Lagrange Form)

$$R(N; X, C) = F(X) - P(N; X, C)$$
$$= \text{DER} ** (N + 1)F(Z) * (X - C) ** (N + 1)/(N + 1)!$$

is explicitly a function of $Z = Z(X)$ and $X$, where $Z(X)$ is usually not known— Taylor's Theorem only guarantees its *existence*.

If $Z(X)$ or $F(X)$ can be evaluated we are able to sketch the error curve as indicated in Figure 2.2.2. If $F(X)$ is a polynomial of degree $K \leq N$, then $\text{DER} ** (N + 1)F(X) \equiv 0$ and $R(N; X, C) \equiv 0$.

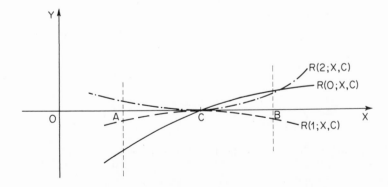

**Figure 2.2.2**

In practice, we know R(N; X, C) only at X = C where R(N; C, C) = 0. Hence, we shall be interested in various estimates for R(N; X, C). For example, we might seek a replacement for the factor DER ∗∗ (N + 1)F(Z) involving the mysterious argument Z, say by a function of X or a constant. We may also be able to use information about the sign of R(N; X, C). Clearly,

$$
\text{SIGN } [R(N; X, C)] =
\begin{cases}
\text{SIGN } [\text{DER} \ast\ast (N + 1)F(Z)] \text{ for N-odd, or for} \\
\qquad\qquad\qquad\qquad\qquad\qquad X > C \text{ and N-even} \\
\text{SIGN } [- \text{DER} \ast\ast (N + 1)F(Z)] \text{ for } X < C \\
\qquad\qquad\qquad\qquad\qquad\qquad \text{and N-even.}
\end{cases}
$$

Specifically, if we want to estimate F(X) on an interval [A, B] with the Taylor Polynomial P(N; X, C), A ≤ C ≤ B, we might write

(2.2.3)   |R(N; X, C)| = |DER ∗∗(N + 1)F(Z) ∗ (X − C) ∗∗ (N + 1)/(N + 1)!|

$\qquad\qquad$ ≤ |M2 ∗ (X − C) ∗∗ (N + 1)/(N + 1)!|

$\qquad\qquad$ ≤ |M1 ∗ (X − C) ∗∗ (N + 1)/(N + 1)!|

$\qquad\qquad$ ≤ M1 ∗ M3/(N + 1)!,

where

(2.2.4)     M1 = MAX|DER ∗∗ (N + 1)F(Z)|, over Z ∈ [A, B],

$\qquad\qquad$ = constant;

if we can find such a G(X),

(2.2.5)     M2 = G(X) ≥ MAX|DER ∗∗ (N + 1)F(Z)|,

$\qquad\qquad\qquad\qquad\qquad$ over Z ∈ [X, C] or Z ∈ [C, X],

G(X) ≤ M1 on [A, B]; and

(2.2.6)     M3 = MAX|(X − C) ∗∗ (N + 1)|, over X ∈ [A, B],

$\qquad\qquad$ = constant.

**Example 1.** Discuss the estimate P(5; X, 0) of F(X) = EXP(X) on [−.6, .5]. P(5; X, 0) = 1 + X + X ∗∗ 2/2! + X ∗∗ 3/3! + X ∗∗ 4/4! + X ∗∗ 5/5!. R(5; X, 0) = EXP(Z) ∗ (X − 0) ∗∗ (5 + 1)/(5 + 1)! = EXP(Z) ∗ X ∗∗ 6/6! ≥ 0, so P(5; X, 0) lies *below* EXP(X) for X ≠ 0. Since EXP(X) is an increasing function, the *best* choice for G(X) gives

$$|R(5; X, 0)| \le |M2 * X ** 6/6!|$$

$$= \begin{cases} \text{EXP(X)} * X ** 6/6! \text{ for } X \ge 0 \\ 1 * X ** 6/6! \text{ for } X < 0 \end{cases} \qquad \text{Bound B1.}$$

A more *useful* choice for G(X) is the line through $(-.6, 1)$ and $(.5, \text{EXP}(.5))$.

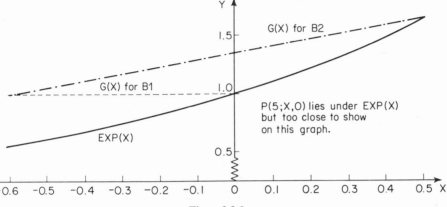

**Figure 2.2.3**

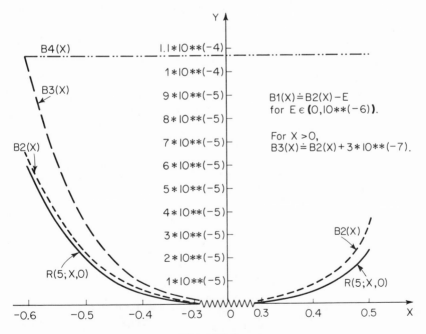

**Figure 2.2.4**

$$|R(5; X, 0)| \le |M2 * X ** 6/6!|$$
$$= ((EXP(.5) - 1) * (X - .5)/(.5 + .6) + EXP(.5))$$
$$* X ** 6/6! \qquad \text{Bound B2.}$$
$$|R(5; X, 0)| \le |M1 * X ** 6/6!|$$
$$= EXP(.5) * X ** 6/6! \qquad \text{Bound B3.}$$

Also,

$$|R(5; X, 0)| \le M1 * M3/6! = EXP(.5) * (-.6) ** 6/6! \qquad \text{Bound B4.}$$

We now list *three basic problems* associated with estimates using Taylor's Formula.

**Problem 1.** Given $F(X)$, $C$, $N$, and $I = [A, B]$. Find the least upper bound, $D$, of the error of estimation of $F(X)$ by $P(N; X, C)$ on $I$ [i.e., find the "smallest" $D$ so that $|R(N; X, C)| \le D$ for each $X \in I$].

**Problem 2.** Given $F(X)$, $C$, $N$, and $D$. Find the "largest" interval $I = [A, B]$ containing $C$ in which $P(N; X, C)$ estimates $F(X)$ with error not exceeding $D$.

**Problem 3.** Given $F(X)$, $C$, $I = [A, B]$, and $D$. Find the "smallest" integer $N$ so that $P(N; X, C)$ estimates $F(X)$ within $I$ with error not exceeding $D$.

The words "smallest" and "largest" are in quotations to indicate that in practice we usually cannot determine the relation $Z = Z(X)$ involved in $R(N; X, C)$, thus we use a bound on $R(N; X, C)$ [see (2.2.3)] to determine a "smallest" $D$, etc. Specifically, in Problem 1 we seek $D = M1 * M3/(N + 1)!$, and suggest for Problems 2 and 3 that we use[2] $|M1 * (X - C) ** (N + 1)/(N + 1)!| \le D$ as the measure of the quality of estimation of $F(X)$ by $P(N; X, C)$. In Problem 3 the "smallest" $N$ is usually found by trial and error after making an appropriate choice for $X$.

**Example 2.** Discuss basic Problems 1, 2, and 3 for $F(X) = EXP(X)$, $C = 0$, and appropriate pairs from $I = [-.6, .5]$, $D = 10 ** (-5)$, and $N = 5$.

**a. Problem 1.** Find the "smallest" real number $D$ such that

$$|R(5; X, 0)| = |EXP(X) - P(5; X, 0)| \le D \text{ for all } -.6 \le X \le .5.$$

SOLUTION. We use Bound B4 of Example 1,

$$|R(5; X, 0)| = |EXP(Z) * (X - 0) ** (5 + 1)/(5 + 1)!|$$
$$\le EXP(.5) * (-.6) ** 6/6! \doteq .0001068 = D.$$

[2]Unless we can find a useful (say a polynomial) form for $G(X)$, see (2.2.5).

**b. Problem 2.** Find the "largest" interval $I = [A, B]$ containing C in which $P(5; X, 0)$ estimates $EXP(X)$ with error not exceeding $D = 10 ** (- 5)$.

SOLUTION. We use Bound B3 of Example 1 to find the largest (in absolute value) numbers $B \geq 0$ so that

$$|Bound\ B3| = |EXP(.5) * B ** 6/6!| \leq 10 ** (- 5),$$

and $A \leq 0$ so that

$$|EXP(.5) * A ** 6/6!| \leq 10 ** (-5).$$

Here, $A = - B$. And

$$B = \big(10 ** (- 5) * 6! * EXP(-. 5)\big) ** (1/6) \doteq (.004367) ** (1/6) \doteq .404$$

so that the desired "largest" interval is $I = [-.404, .404]$.

*Note.* If we had used Bound B2, then the interval $I = [A, B]$ would not have been symmetric about $C = 0$. Here, Problem 2 could be solved by *reading* the coordinates of the intersection of $Y = 10 ** (- 5)$ and the appropriate bound in Figure 2.2.4.

**c. Problem 3.** Find the "smallest" integer N so that $P(N; X, 0)$ estimates $EXP(X)$ within $I = [-.6, .5]$ with error not exceeding $D = 10 ** (-5)$.

SOLUTION. We use Bound B3 of Example 1

$$|Bound\ B3| = |EXP(.5) * X ** (N + 1)/(N + 1)!|,$$

and note for any positive integer K

$$MAX|X ** K| = |(-.6) ** K|, \text{ over } -.6 \leq X \leq .5.$$

The problem is to find the smallest positive integer N such that

$$|EXP(.5) * (-.6) ** (N + 1)/(N + 1)!| \leq 10 ** (- 5).$$

We *try* $N = 5$:

$$|EXP(.5) * (-.6) ** 6/6!| \doteq 1.068 * 10 ** (- 4) > 10 ** (- 5).$$

That is, $N = 5$ is too small. *Try* $N = 6$:

$$|EXP(.5) * (-.6) ** 7/7!| \doteq .9157 * 10 ** (-5) < 10 ** (-5)$$

so that with $N = 6$, $|Bound\ B3| < 10 ** (- 5)$, and $N = 6$ is the smallest integer with this property.

One special case deserves mention. If F(X) is *representable* in I = [A, B] by its Taylor Series Expansion about X = C, [i.e., for every X in I, LIM (R(N; X, C)) = 0, as N App ∞,], and if for each X in I the terms of the series alternate in sign,[3] then the truncation error of the estimation of F(X) by the Taylor Polynomial P(N; X, C) in I does not exceed the absolute value of the next term in the series,

$$|R(N; X, C)| \leq |DER ** (N + 1)F(C) * (X - C) ** (N + 1)/(N + 1)!|$$

(2.2.7)                          [and, if DER ** (N + 1)F(C) = 0]

$$\leq |DER ** (N + 2)F(C) * (X - C) ** (N + 2)/(N + 2)!|, \text{etc.}$$

If X < 0, then the Taylor Series Expansion for EXP(X) about C = 0 is an alternating series, so |R(N; X, 0)| ≤ |X ** (N + 1)/(N + 1)!|. This is the *same* as Bound B1 (in Example 1) for X < 0. However, if F(X) = COS(X), then the Taylor Series for COS(X) expanded about C = 0 is an alternating series involving only even powers of X. Thus, if N is even, (2.2.7) gives |R(N; X, 0)| ≤ |X ** (N + 2)/(N + 2)!|, while a bound obtained like Bound B1 of Example 1 would involve X ** (N + 1) and (N + 1)!.

Finally, we present an example to *discourage* the reader from assuming that

$$LIM (R(N; T, C)) = 0, \text{as N App } \infty,$$

is *sufficient* grounds for using a Taylor Polynomial P(N; T, C) to *compute* an estimate to F(T). We usually try to keep |T − C| ≤ .5.

**Example 3.** Given F(X) = ARCTAN(X), C = 0. The Taylor Series Expansion for ARCTAN(X) about C = 0 is

$$ARCTAN(X) = X - X ** 3/3 + X ** 5/5$$
$$- \cdots + (-1) ** (N - 1) * X ** (2 * N - 1)/(2 * N - 1)$$
$$+ \cdots, \text{for } |X| \leq 1.$$

In particular[4]

$$ARCTAN(1) = \pi/4 = 1 - 1/3 + 1/5 - 1/7 + \cdots.$$

This alternating series converges, but it converges too slowly to be used as a practical vehicle for computing π/4. [The Nth term is (− 1) ** (N − 1)/(2 * N− 1), and

---

[3]In this case, for each X in I the alternating series *represents* F(X) if the sequence of magnitudes of the terms is monotone decreasing and converges to zero.
[4]A similar discussion can be made for .5 < X ≤ 1.

to be sure that the error is less than $10 ** (-5)$ one would need to sum 50,000 terms.] In this case we are able to use the identity

$$\text{ARCTAN}(X) \pm \text{ARCTAN}(Y) = \text{ARCTAN}\big((X \pm Y)/(1 \mp X * Y)\big).$$

With

$$(X \pm Y)/(1 \mp X * Y) = 1,$$

if we *pick* $X = .5$ and solve for $Y(= 1/3)$, then we may easily compute

$$\text{ARCTAN}(.5) + \text{ARCTAN}(1/3) = \text{ARCTAN}(1) = \pi/4.$$

For

$$\text{ARCTAN}(.5) = .5 - (.5) ** 3/3 + (.5) ** 5/5 - (.5) ** 7/7 + \cdots$$
$$\text{ARCTAN}(1/3) = 1/3 - (1/3) ** 3/3 + (1/3) ** 5/5 - (1/3) ** 7/7 + \cdots$$

and to compute ARCTAN (.5) with error not exceeding $10 ** (-5)$ we need only sum M terms where M $(= 6)$ is the smallest integer satisfying $10 ** 5 < (2 * M + 1) * 2 ** (2 * M + 1)$. To compute ARCTAN(1/3) with error not exceeding $10 ** (-5)$ we need only sum K terms where K $(= 4)$ is the smallest integer satisfying $10 ** 5 < (2 * K + 1) * 3 ** (2 * K + 1)$.

## EXERCISES

1. Discuss basic problems 1, 2, and 3 for $F(X) = SIN(X)$, $C = 0$, and appropriate pairs from $I = [-.6, .5]$, $D = 10 ** (-5)$, and $N = 5$.

2. State the three basic problems and include a condition that $F(X)$ and $P(N; X, C)$ lie inside the strip

$$S: \{(X, Y) | A < X < B, F(X) - D < Y < F(X) + D\}.$$

For example:
Problem 1: Given $F(X)$, C, N, and $I = [A, B]$. Find the "smallest" positive number D so that $P(N; X, C)$ lies inside S. Give an appropriate sketch.

3.[5] Given $1 \leq X < 10$ and

[5]This exercise has nothing to do with Taylor's Formula but is included to indicate a simple algorithm to compute $LOG(X)$, and to give the reader some practice operating with binary numbers. See Exercise 2 of §1.2. We write $LOGN(X)$, $LOGC(X)$, and $LOGA(X)$ for $\ln X$, $\log_{10} X$, and $\log_a X$, respectively.

$$X = 10 ** LOGC(X) = 10** (A(-1)*2**(-1) + A(-2)*2**(-2)$$
$$+ A(-3) * 2 ** (-3) + \cdots).$$

(a) Compute 27 bits of the binary representation of LOGC(X).

*Hint.* With $X1 = X ** 2 = 10** (A(-1)*2**0 + A(-2)*2**(-1)$ $+A(-3) * 2 ** (-2)+ \cdots )$, $X1 < 10$ implies $A(-1) = 0$, while $X1 \geq 10$ implies $A(-1) = 1$. If $A(-1) = 0$, then look at $X1 ** 2$ to determine $A(-2)$, etc. If $A(-1) = 1$, then look at $(X1/10) ** 2$ to determine $A(-2)$, etc.

(b) Write a flow chart for the method suggested in the above hint.

**4.** Write $P(N; X, 0)$ and the Lagrange Form for $R(N; X, 0)$ for $F(X)=$ LOGN(1 + X).

**5.** Write $P(N; X, 0)$ and the Lagrange Form for $R(N; X, 0)$ for $F(X)=$ LOGN(1 − X).

**6.** Write $P(2 * N; X, 0)$ and the Lagrange Form for $R(2 * N; X, 0)$ for $F(X)$ $= LOGN((1 − X)/(1 + X)) = LOGN(1 − X) − LOGN(1 + X)$.

*Note.* $LOGN(Y) = LOGN((1 − X)/(1 + X))$ is defined for $|X| < 1$, where $0 < Y \leq 1$ for $0 \leq X < 1$, and $Y > 1$ for $-1 < X < 0$.

**7.** Find another representation for $R(2 * N; X, 0)$ in Exercise 6 using

$$LOGN(Y) = \int -2/(1 − T ** 2), \text{ over } T \in (0, X),$$
$$= P(2 * N; X, 0)$$
$$-2 * \int (T ** (2 * N) + T ** (2 * N + 2) + \cdots), \text{ over } T \in (0, X),$$
$$= P(2 * N; X, 0)$$
$$-2 * \int T ** (2 * N)/(1 − T ** 2), \text{ over } T \in (0, X),$$

and the mean value theorem for the last integral.

**8.** (a) For $K = 1, 2, 3,$ and 4 find the *smallest* integer NK so that $P(NK; X, K)$ estimates $LOGN(X)$ on $IK = [K − .5, K + .5]$ with error not exceeding $D = 10 ** (−5)$.

(b) Find the *smallest* integer M so that $P(M; X, 1)$ estimates $LOGN(X)$ on $I = [.5, 4.5]$ with error not exceeding $D = 10 ** (−5)$.

## 2.3. TAYLOR'S FORMULA IN TWO VARIABLES

**Taylor's Theorem in Two Variables.**

H1: N is a nonnegative integer.

H2: $F(X, Y)$ and all partial derivatives up to and including $(N + 1)$-order are continuous in a region

R: $\{(X, Y) | SQRT((X - A) ** 2 + (Y - B) ** 2) < D1\}$,
where $D1 > 0$.

H3: $P(N; (X, Y), (A, B)) = F(A, B)$
$+ ((X - A) * PAR ** (1, )F(A, B)$
$+ (Y - B) * PAR ** (, 1)F(A, B))$
$+ (1/2!) * ((X - A) ** 2 * PAR ** (2, )F(A, B)$
$+ 2 * (X - A) * (Y - B) * PAR ** (1, 1)F(A, B)$
$+ (Y - B) ** 2 * PAR ** (, 2)F(A, B))$
$+ \cdots$
$+ (1/N!) * ((X - A) ** N * PAR ** (N, )F(A, B) + BINCO(N, 1)$
$* (X - A) ** (N - 1) * (Y - B) * PAR ** (N - 1, 1)F(A, B)$
$+ BINCO(N, 2) * (X - A) ** (N - 2) * (Y - B) ** 2$
$* PAR ** (N - 2, 2)F(A, B)$
$+ \cdots + (Y - B) ** N * PAR ** (, N)F(A, B))$

is the Taylor Polynomial[1] in two variables of degree N of $F(X, Y)$ at $(A, B)$.

C: For each $(X, Y)$ in R, there exists a point $(X1, Y1)$ on the line segment joining $(A, B)$ and $(X, Y)$ such that

(2.3.1a)        $F(X, Y) = P(N; (X, Y), (A, B)) + R(N; (X, Y), (A, B))$,

where

[1] The notation $PF(N; (X, Y), (A, B))$ is also used. The independent variable is $(X, Y)$, and partial derivatives are taken with respect to positions of this argument. As usual, the notation $PAR ** (1, )F(A, B)$ means $\frac{\partial}{\partial x} f(x, y)$ evaluated at $(x, y) = (a, b)$, and we assume that the order of taking partial derivatives is immaterial. $BINCO(N, K)$ means

$$\binom{n}{k} = \frac{n(n - 1) \cdots (n - k + 1)}{k!} = \frac{n!}{k!(n - k)!},$$

the binomial coefficients.

(2.3.1b)   $R(N; (X, Y), (A, B)) = (1/(N + 1)!) * \{((X - A) * PAR ** (1, )$
$+ (Y - B) * PAR ** (, 1)) ** (N + 1)\}F(X1, Y1)$

$\equiv (1/(N + 1)!) * ((X - A) ** (N + 1)$

$* PAR ** (N + 1,)F(X1, Y1)$

$+ BINCO(N + 1, 1) * (X - A) ** N * (Y - B)$

$* PAR ** (N, 1)F(X1, Y1)$

$+ BINCO(N + 1, 2) * (X - A) ** (N - 1) * (Y - B) ** 2$

$* PAR ** (N - 1, 2)F(X1, Y1)$

$+ \cdots + (Y - B) ** (N + 1) * PAR ** (, N + 1)F(X1, Y1)).$

This theorem is proved in most texts of Advanced Calculus. For example see [3].

The characterizing properties of $P(N; (X, Y), (A, B))$ are: $P(N; (A, B), (A, B)) = F(A, B)$, and for each $K \leq N$ *all* K*th* partial derivatives of $P(N; (X, Y), (A, B))$ at $(X, Y) = (A, B)$ agree with the corresponding partial derivatives of $F(X, Y)$ at $(X, Y) = (A, B)$.

For a geometric interpretation of *Taylor's Formula in two variables*, equation (2.3.1a) with (2.3.1b) substituted, we consider the surface $Z = F(X, Y)$, and the estimates: the plane $Z = P(0; (X, Y), (A, B)) \equiv F(A, B)$; the plane tangent to $Z = F(X, Y)$ at $(A, B, F(A, B))$, $Z = P(1; (X, Y), (A, B))$; a surface $Z = P(2; (X, Y), (A, B))$ which intersects the plane $Z = Z1(=\text{constant})$ in the conic $Z1 = P(2; (X, Y), (A, B))$. See §3.7 where these polynomials are discussed in some detail.

Remarks entirely analogous to those concerning $R(N; X, C)$ are applicable to $R(N; (X, Y), (A, B))$. For example, $Z = |R(N; (X, Y), (A, B))|$ is a surface passing through the point $(A, B, 0)$. Bounds on $|R(N; (X, Y), (A, B))|$ are obtained by replacing the several partial derivatives which involve the usually unknown point $(X1, Y1)$ by functions of $(X, Y)$ or by constants. The *three basic problems* of §2.2 have obvious analogs here.

## EXERCISES

**1.** Write the Taylor Polynomial in two variables of degree 2 of $F(X, Y) = (X + Y) ** (-1)$ at $(A, B) = (1, 2)$. Check the characterizing properties of this polynomial.

The function T0 might be something like "choose $Y(0)$ to be a specified estimate to a solution." Conceivably, T1 through T5 are one "rule" and T6, T7, etc. are another "rule" for combining X and $Y(N - 1)$ to define $Y(N)$. In practice, when our problem is new to us and is moderately complicated, we often find that a first choice for the "rule" is not a best choice, so we change the "rule" until usable estimates are obtained. Of course, we would not pass the method on to someone else and ask him to use all the "rules" that we tried before finding "the rule" that gave the usable results. Instead, we would suggest some rule that defined a usable first estimate and suggest that he use "the rule" for all the remaining T1, T2, T3, . . . .

Several important questions present themselves. We pause here to mention only two of them. *Does the sequence of estimates defined by* (3.1.2a, b) *converge?* That is, is there a B such that

$$\text{LIM}\,(Y(N)) = B, \text{ as N App } \infty \,?$$

And, if the sequence of estimates converges, *does it converge to a solution of the original equation* (3.1.1a)? That is,

$$\text{LIM}\,(Y(N)) = B, \text{ as N App } \infty, \text{ and } G(X, B) = 0?$$

An answer to the first question is often difficult to obtain. Since the limit B is needed for substitution into (3.1.1a), the second question frequently goes unanswered.

In what follows, the T0 in (3.1.2a) will usually be something equivalant to "make an educated guess . . . ," and in (3.1.2b) the T1, T2, T3, . . . will all be the *same function* of two variables. In that case, we generally use one name for the function and delete the given data symbol X. For example, let the given data (X) in (3.1.1a) be the coefficients in a polynomial equation in the variable Y. Then, (3.1.1a) becomes $G(Y) = 0$. The F in (3.1.1b) will read "is a root of the polynomial equation with cofficients X." and T0 in (3.1.2a) might read "take $Y(0) = 1$ as a first guess at Y," while (3.1.2b) becomes $Y(N + 1) = T\,(Y(N)), N \in //0, \infty//$.

Now we agree to use the customary $X(N)$ instead of $Y(N)$. Any formula such as

(3.1.3)     $$X(M + 1) = T\,(X(M)), \qquad M \in //0, \infty//,$$

that is used to define a sequence of numbers, N-tuples, functions, etc. is called an *iteration process*. $X(0)$ is given and is called the *starting-value*. In some contexts $X(0)$ is called a *first guess*.

Most iteration processes are used to define *sequences* which (it is hoped) converge to zeros of functions or solutions of equations. The functions are usually *not linear*. Since a highly developed theory of linear systems is available to us and since only rational operations ($+$, $-$, $*$, and $/$ are the operations usually built into most modern computers) are required to solve linear systems, then *we favor* a formula (3.1.3) for an iteration process that is equivalent to a system of *linear estimates* to the functions involved in the equations whose simultaneous solution is being sought. Note that if XX is a solution of $F(X) = 0$, then $(X, Y) = (XX, 0)$ is a simultaneous solution of $Y = F(X)$ *and* $Y = 0$. See (3.2.2), (3.5.5), (3.6.2) below.

Of course, we can compute only a *finite* number of elements of a sequence defined by an iteration process, so we must use various *test* schemes to determine *when to stop the iteration*. All such tests that we have used in practice would fail to show that the harmonic series diverges, so probably some independent check (such as substitution of an estimate to a solution into the original equation) should be attempted.

The *Absolute Error Test* is

$$(3.1.4) \qquad |EA| = |X(N + 1) - X(N)| < D?$$

Consider the sequence $X(0), X(1), \ldots, X(N), \ldots$ such that $X(N)$ is the largest N-digit decimal number less than SQRT(2), i.e., 1, 1. 4, 1.41, 1.414, .... Choose $D = 10 ** (-N)$. From the fact that the elements of this particular sequence pass the *test* (3.1.4) with $D = 10 ** (-N)$ we can conclude that the first N digits of $X(N + 1)$ agree with the first N digits of $X(N)$. This test is often used when computing with fixed-point numbers (numbers with a fixed number of digits to the right of the decimal point). The sequence defined by multiplying elements of the above sequence by $10 ** (-10)$ is such that $|X(1) - X(0)| < 10 ** (-10)$ while $X(1)$ and $X(0)$ agree to only one digit. Thus when computing with floating numbers the test (3.1.4) is unsatisfactory unless we can be certain of the magnitudes of the numbers involved.

A more reliable test for "digits of agreement" is the *Relative Error Test*, $|ER| < D?$ Here, when the test

$$(3.1.5) \qquad |ER| = |(X(N + 1) - X(N))/X(N + 1)| < 10 ** (-K)?$$

passes, then we may expect *approximately* K digits of agreement in $X(N)$ and $X(N + 1)$.

In this chapter we discuss several iteration processes for finding real zeros of real functions, and one method for finding complex zeros of real polynomials.

In later chapters we discuss iterative procedures that define estimates to N-tuples that are solutions of matrix equations, and estimates to functions that are solutions to differential equations.

### EXERCISE

1. Discuss the relative error test as a measure of convergence of a sequence X(N), N $\in$ //1, $\infty$ //, when LIM(X(N)) = A, as N App $\infty$, and A is very small or zero, and the X(N) are numbers represented in normalized eight-digit floating format. If an iterant, X(K), can be zero in an electronic computer program, then some provision should be made in the program to avoid an automatic HALT or EXIT due to an attempt to divide by zero. If X(N + 1) = 0, one might ask if X = 0 is the solution being sought by iteration (recall Exercise 4 of §1.2); if X = 0 is not the desired solution, then one might set X(N + 2) = .5 * X(N) and attempt another step in the iteration. If X(N + 3) = 0, then PRINT X(N + 2) (and some data which may be useful in determining which of other alternatives to use) and EXIT the program.

### 3.2 NEWTON'S METHOD

The iteration formula most often associated with Newton's Method is defined for F(X) a real function of a single real variable with continuous first derivative on an interval [A, B]. The sequence of estimates to a zero of F(X) is defined by

$$(3.2.1) \qquad X(N + 1) = X(N) - F(X(N))/F'(X(N)), \qquad [=T(X(N))].$$

Compare (3.1.3). This method is known (see [1]) to define a sequence X(1), X(2), X(3), . . . which converges to a zero of F(X) if: (i) F(X) has a single zero in an interval [A, B], (ii) F'(X) and F''(X) are continuous, not zero, and do not change sign in [A, B], and (iii) the first guess X(0) is in [A, B]. Under these conditions, Newton's Method is an algorithm for the problem F(X) = 0. In practice we may not be willing or able to check these conditions for a specific function, so the method becomes just another that we might try.

The formula (3.2.1) may be derived from the Taylor Polynomial equation

(3.2.2)      $PF(1; X(N + 1), X(N))$

$$= F(X(N)) + F'(X(N)) * (X(N + 1) - X(N)) = 0,$$

which is equivalent to the linear system $Y = PF(1; X, X(N))$ *and* $Y = 0$. Thus, $X(N + 1)$ is the X-intercept of the tangent line to $F(X)$ at $(X(N), F(X(N)))$. See Figure 3.2.1.

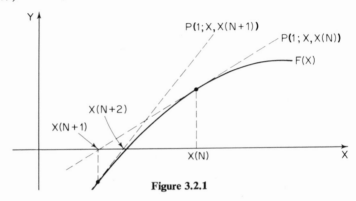

**Figure 3.2.1**

A first guess $X(0)$ might be obtained as follows. Use any information at hand to pick an interval that contains a zero of $F(X)$; evaluate $F(X)$ at various points in the interval to determine two points $X1$ and $X2$ so that $F(X1)$ and $F(X2)$ are opposite in sign; take $X(0)$ to be the average of $X1$ and $X2$. The reader can devise more and better methods for finding an $X(0)$. Graeffe's Root-Squaring Process, see § 3.5 below, is often used to find an $X(0)$.

## EXERCISES

1. Derive the Newton-Raphson Formula to compute $A ** (1 / K)$. Use $F(X) = X ** K - A$ in Newton's Method.

2. Write the formula derived in Exercise 1 in a form so that the number of additions and multiplications required for evaluation is minimized. Count them.

3. Show that $F(X(K))$ and $F'(X(K))$, where $F(X) = A0 * X ** 4 + A1 * X ** 3 + A2 * X ** 2 + A3 * X + A4$, can be obtained by two successive synthetic divisions.

| $X(K)$ | A0 | A1 | A2 | A3 | A4 |
|---|---|---|---|---|---|
| (add) | | B0 * X(K) | B1 * X(K) | B2 * X(K) | B3 * X(K) |
| | B0 | B1 | B2 | B3 | B4 = F(X(K)) |
| (add) | | C0 * X(K) | C1 * X(K) | C2 * X(K) | |
| | C0 | C1 | C2 | C3 = F'(X(K)). | |

*Hint.* If B4 = 0, then F(X) = (X − X(K)) * (B0 * X**3 + B1 * X ** 2 + B2 * X + B3). In any event F(X) = (X − X(K)) * (B0 * X ** 3 + B1 * X ** 2 + B2 * X + B3) + F(X(K)) so that F'(X(K)) = B0 * X(K) ** 3 + B1 * X(K) ** 2 + B2 * X(K) + B3.

**4.** Complete five lines in the following *form* to estimate SQRT(2). Use synthetic division to compute F(X(K)) and F'(X(K)).

| K | X(K) | F(X(K)) | F'(X(K)) | F(X(K))/F'(X(K)) | X(K + 1) |
|---|---|---|---|---|---|
| 0 | 1.0 | −1.0 | 2 | −.5 | 1.5 |
| 1 | 1.5 | | | | |

### 3.3 AN EXAMPLE WITH A DISCUSSION OF CONVERGENCE

In this example we apply Newton's Method to compute SQRT(A), but similar remarks are applicable for A ** (1/K) when A > 0.

The roots of F(X) = X ** 2 − A = 0, A > 0, are X = ± SQRT(A). The corresponding Newton-Raphson Iteration Formula is

(3.3.1)          $X(N + 1) = .5 * (X(N) + A/X(N))$
          $= .5 * (X(N) ** 2 + A)/X(N).$

In the following theorems concerning *convergence* of X(1), X(2), X(3), ..., defined by (3.3.1), let M = SQRT(A) and M1 = −SQRT(A).

**Theorem.**   H1: X(N) > 0     [X(N) < 0]
          H2: X(N + 1) = .5 * (X(N) ** 2 + M ** 2)/X(N)
          [X(N + 1) = .5 * (X(N) ** 2 + M1 ** 2)/X(N)]
          C: X(N + 1) ≥ M.     [X(N + 1) ≤ M1]

*Proof.*   ERROR $= M - X(N + 1)$

$$= M - .5 * (X(N) ** 2 + M ** 2)/X(N)$$

(3.3.2)      $$= (2 * M * X(N) - X(N) ** 2 - M ** 2)/(2 * X(N))$$

$$= -(X(N) - M) ** 2/(2 * X(N)) \leq 0.$$

**Theorem.**   H1: $X(N) > M$

H2: $X(N + 1) = .5 * (X(N) + M ** 2/X(N))$

C: $X(N + 1) < X(N)$.

*Proof.*   $X(N) - X(N + 1) = X(N) - .5 * (X(N) + M ** 2/X(N))$

(3.3.3)                    $$= .5 * (X(N) - M ** 2/X(N))$$

$$= (.5/X(N)) * (X(N) ** 2 - M ** 2) > 0.$$

**Theorem.**   H1: $X(N) > M$

H2: $X(N + 1) = .5 * (X(N) ** 2 + M ** 2)/X(N)$

(3.3.4)      C: $X(N) > X(N + 1) > M$.

*Proof.*   With $X(N) > M$, (3.3.2) becomes a strict inequality and $X(N+1)$ $>M$. Also, $X(N) > X(N + 1)$ by the theorem just proved.

**Theorem.**   H1: $X(0) > 0, X(0) \neq M$.

H2: $X(K), K \in //1, \infty//$, is generated by (3.3.1)

C: $\text{LIM}(X(N)) = M$, as N App $\infty$.

*Proof.*   By (3.3.4), $X(1) > X(2) > X(3) > \cdots > M$, so M is a lower bound for the monotonically decreasing sequence, and the sequence converges. Therefore, $\text{LIM}(X(N) - X(N + 1)) = 0$, as N App $\infty$. By (3.3.3) we have $\text{LIM}((.5/X(N)) * (X(N) ** 2 - M ** 2)) = 0$, as N App $\infty$, and since we know $X(N)$ converges to some $XX > 0$, $\text{LIM}(X(N) ** 2 - M ** 2) = 0$, as N App $\infty$. Since $X(N) > M > 0$, then $\text{LIM}(X(N) - M) = 0$, as N App $\infty$, so $\text{LIM}(X(N)) = M$, as N App $\infty$.

### 3.4 NEWTON'S METHOD WHEN F'(X(K)) IS SMALL

The iteration formula (3.2.1) for Newton's Method may define a sequence $X(1), X(2), X(3), \ldots$, which converges slowly or not at all when $F'(X(K))$ is small near a zero of $F(X)$. Here we discuss only the three cases indicated in

Figure 3.4.1, where $F(X)$ and $F'(X)$ are small and $F''(X)$ is not. Let $X = C$ be such that $F'(C) = 0$.

In Case I, $X = C$ is not a solution of $F(X) = 0$, and there is no solution near C. A sequence $X(1)$, $X(2)$, $X(3)$, ..., defined by (3.2.1) may appear to be converging to $X = C$, while oscillating about C (successive elements lie on op-

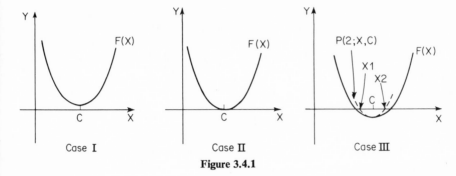

| Case I | Case II | Case III |

**Figure 3.4.1**

posite sides of C). If an element $X(M)$ lies so close to C that the tangent line through $(X(M), F(X(M)))$ intersects the X-axis at $X(M + 1)$ far from C, the series may appear to diverge, or appear to converge to C again, or it may converge to a zero of $F(X)$.

In Case II, $X = C$ is a multiple solution of $F(X) = 0$. The convergence may be too slow to be practical[1] and if $F'(X(M)) << F(X(M))$, then $X(M + 1)$ will be very different from $X(M)$.

In Case III, $X = C$ is close to two nearby solutions. The remarks for Case II apply here too.

Even when we do not know we have one of these three cases, if the sequence defined by Newton's Method converges too slowly, does not converge due to oscillations,[2] or seems to be converging but then some $X(M + 1)$ is very different from $X(M)$, we sometimes *try* the following method (an algorithm for the cases of Figure 3.4.1).

1. Find[3] C such that $F'(C) = 0$.

2. Examine $F(C)$ and $F''(C)$: if $F(C) = 0$ we have Case II, and $X = C$ is a solution of $F(X) = 0$; if $F(C) \neq 0$ and $F''(C) \neq 0$ and they have the same sign we have Case I, and there is no solution near C; if $F(C) \neq 0$ and $F''(C)$ has sign opposite to that of $F(C)$, then we have Case III and there are two solutions of $F(X) = 0$ close to C.

---

[1]In an electronic computer code for Newton's Method we usually include a maximum number of iterations allowed before transferring to an error HALT or EXIT.

[2]If the method suggested doesn't work, one might try a new $X(0)$ somewhere between the oscillations.

[3]Except when $F''(X)$ is not close to zero near C, finding C may be as difficult as the original problem.

3. If $F(C) \neq 0$ and the sign of $F''(C)$ is different from that of $F(C)$, we write $PF(2; X, C) = 0$ in the form

(3.4.1)          $X = C \pm SQRT(-2 * F(C)/F''(C))$,

which defines two numbers X1 and X2, the intersections of $Y = PF(2; X, C)$ and the X-axis, to be used as first guesses in Newton's Method in another attempt to compute zeros of $F(X)$. We hope $F(X1) << F'(X1)$, etc.

## EXERCISES

1. Given $F(X) = X ** 4 - X ** 2 + S = 0$ where $S$ is small and positive. With $X(0) = S ** 2$ use Newton's Method to compute $X(1)$. Compare $F(X(0))$ with $F(X(1))$.

*Note.* If $S = 0$ the roots are $X = 0, 0, 1, -1$. Discuss convergence of the generated sequence for various choices of $S$.

*Answer.* If          $S = .1$ and $X(0) = S ** 2 = .01$,

$$X(1) \doteq 1/(2 * S) = 5$$

then

$$F(X(0)) = S ** 8 - S ** 4 + S \doteq S = .1$$
$$F(X(1)) \doteq F(1/(2 * S)) = F(5) = 600.1.$$

2. For the function in Exercise 1 use (3.4.1) to get a new first guess $X(0) > 0$ and compute $X(1)$ using Newton's Method. Discuss convergence of the generated sequence for various choices of $S$.

*Answer.* $C = 0$ and $X(0) = 0 + SQRT(-2 * S/(-2)) = SQRT(S)$.
          $X(1) = SQRT(S) - S * SQRT(S)/(4 * S - 2)$.

## 3.5 OTHER METHODS FOR FINDING ROOTS OF F(X) = 0

We have discussed Newton's Method first, and in some detail, because it is an iteration process which can be shown to converge for a nontrivial class of functions, because the important Taylor Polynomials enter into the discussion, and because Newton's Method has a natural extension for finding simultaneous solutions of systems of equations. See §3.6.

However, the fact that we can prove a few theorems about Newton's Method is *not* sufficient reason to conclude that it is the only, or the best, method for finding zeros of functions.

For example, Newton's Method is a special case of the iteration process defined by

(3.5.1)        $X(N + 1) = X(N) - F(X(N))/M,$

where $X(N + 1)$ is the X-intercept of the line through $(X(N), F(X(N)))$ with slope M.

A frequently used iteration process of *successive linear interpolations* is defined by (3.5.1) with M equal the slope of the line through $(X(N), F(X(N)))$ and $(X(N - P), F(X(N - P)))$, $P = 1$ or 2 or 3 or ..., where $F(X(N - P))$

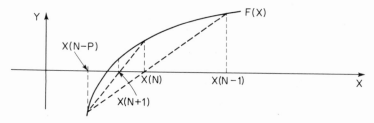

**Figure 3.5.1**

was the last tabulated value of $F(X)$, corresponding to an element of the sequence $X(1), X(2), X(3), \ldots$, which had sign different from $F(X(N))$. See Figure 3.5.1. If $F'(X)$ is difficult (expensive) to evaluate, this method may be better than Newton's Method.

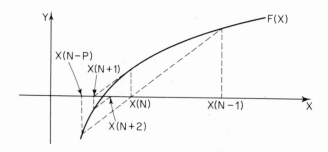

**Figure 3.5.2**

If $F'(X)$ does not change much near a zero of $F(X)$, we might use (3.5.1) with M a constant, say the average of the values of $F'(X)$ at a point where $F(X)$ is positive and at a point where $F(X)$ is negative. See Figure 3.5.2.

Another iteration process is defined by taking

$$X(N + 1) = .5 * (X(N) + X(N - P)),$$

where $X(N - P)$ is the last element of the sequence at which $F(X)$ has a sign different from the sign of $F(X(N))$.

The reader should be able to define several variations of these iteration processes. Proofs of theorems concerning convergence of these methods will not be so easy.

Sometimes $F(X) = 0$ can be written in the form

(3.5.2)              $$F(X) = G(X) - P(X) = 0,$$

where we are able to solve the simultaneous system

(3.5.3)              $$\begin{cases} Y = G(X) \\ Y = P(X). \end{cases}$$

A special case of the method of §3.8, below, may lead to a solution of this system.

Write $Y = P(X)$ in the form[1]

$$X = PP(Y)$$

and generate a sequence $X(1), X(2), X(3), \ldots$, using

(3.5.4)              $$\begin{cases} Y(N) = G(X(N)) \\ X(N + 1) = PP(Y(N)), \end{cases}$$

where a first guess $X(0)$ is obtained, say, by graphing $Y = G(X)$ and $Y = P(X)$, and reading the coordinates of the intersection of these curves. It may happen that it is *inconvenient* to write the inverse, $X = PP(Y)$, for $Y = P(X)$ but we may be able to replace $X(N + 1) = PP(Y(N))$ in (3.5.4) with one (or more) application of Newton's Method to the equation $Y(N) = P(X)$ to obtain the iteration process defined by

---

[1]Instead, we may write the inverse, $X = GG(Y)$, for $Y = G(X)$, and define the iteration by $Y(N) = P(X(N))$ and $X(N + 1) = GG(Y(N))$. Note the example associated with Figures 3.5.3a, b.

(3.5.5) $\quad\begin{cases} Y(N) = G\,(X(N)) \\ X(N+1) = PPP\,(X(N),\,Y(N)) \\ \qquad = X(N) - (P\,(X(N)) - Y(N))/P'\,(X(N)). \end{cases}$

The following example illustrates the effect of using *two* iteration processes, (3.5.4) and $(Y(N) = P\,(X(N))$ and $X(N+1) = GG\,(Y(N)))$, to find the zeros of $F(X) = X ** 3 - 2 * X$.

**Example.** Find the zeros of $F(X) = X ** 3 - 2 * X$, [or, equivalently, find the roots of $F(X) = 0$].

SOLUTION. Clearly, $F(X) = X * (X ** 2 - 2)$ so that the zeros of $F(X)$ are $X = 0, \pm SQRT(2)$. To *compute* a solution of $F(X) = 0$, we might write equivalent equation

E1: $.5 * F(X) = .5 * X ** 3 - X = 0$,

or

E2: $- .5 * F(X) = X - .5 * X ** 3 = 0$

and choose the corresponding system S1 or S2, (3.5.3),

$$\text{S1:} \begin{cases} Y = G(X) = .5 * X ** 3 \\ Y = P(X) = X \end{cases}, \text{ or } \text{ S2:} \begin{cases} Y = X \\ Y = .5 * X ** 3 \end{cases}$$

and define corresponding iteration formula, (3.5.4),

$$\text{I1:} \begin{cases} Y(N) = G\,(X(N)) = .5 * X(N) ** 3 \\ X(N+1) = PP\,(Y(N)) = Y(N). \end{cases}$$

or

$$\text{I2:} \begin{cases} Y(N) = X(N) \\ Y(N) = .5 * X(N+1) ** 3 \quad \text{solved for } X(N+1). \end{cases}$$

From Figure 3.5.3a, it is clear that iteration process I1 defines: for

$$-SQRT(2) < X(0) < SQRT(2),$$

a sequence $X(K)$, $K \in //1, \infty//$, such that

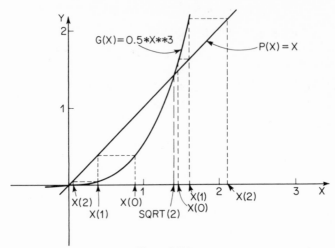

**Figure 3.5.3a**

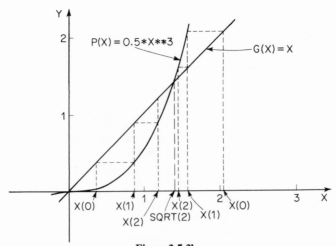

**Figure 3.5.3b**

$$\text{LIM}\big(X(K)\big) = 0, \text{ as K App } \infty \, ;$$

and for $|X(0)| >$ SQRT(2), a sequence $X(K)$, $K \in //1, \infty//$, such that

$$\text{LIM}\big(|X(K)|\big) = + \infty, \text{ as K App } \infty.$$

That is, if $|X(0)| >$ SQRT(2) then the sequence generated by **I1** *diverges*. From Figure 3.5.3b, it is clear that iteration process I2 is such that

$$\text{for } X(0) > 0, \text{ LIM}(X(K)) = + \text{SQRT}(2), \text{ as K App } \infty,$$
$$\text{and for } X(0) < 0, \text{ LIM}(X(K)) = - \text{SQRT}(2), \text{ as K App } \infty.$$

Neither iteration process produces all three roots. Of course, I2 may be considered just another way to compute SQRT(2).

*Note.* Here, (3.5.5) for S2, in place of I2, defines a sequence such that

$$\text{for } X(0) > 0, \text{ LIM}(X(K)) = + \text{SQRT}(2), \text{ as K App } \infty,$$
$$\text{and for } X(0) < 0, \text{ LIM}(X(K)) = - \text{SQRT}(2), \text{ as K App } \infty.$$

Finally, we give a brief outline of the *Graeffe Root-Squaring Process* with an interpretation for the special case where $F(X)$ is a real polynomial of degree N with distinct real roots satisfying[2] $|X1| > |X2| > \cdots > |XN|$. For a more complete description of the process see [2].

MOTIVATION

The product of the real polynomials

$$F(X) = \sum A(K) * X ** K, K \in //0, N//,$$
$$= A(N) * (X - X1) * (X - X2) * \cdots * (X - XN)$$

and

$$(-1) ** N * F(-X) = \sum A(K) * (-1) ** N * (-X) ** K, K \in //0, N//,$$
$$= \sum A(K) * (-1) ** (N+K) * X ** K, K \in //0, N//,$$
$$= (-1) ** N * A(N) * (-X - X1)$$
$$* (-X - X2) * \cdots * (-X - XN)$$
$$= A(N) * (X + X1) * (X + X2) * \cdots * (X + XN)$$

is a new polynomial

---

[2]The $(N - 1)th$ root is named XNM1. Similarly, below, the $(M - 1)th$ function of the set F1, F2, F3, ..., FM, is named FMM1.

(3.5.6a)      $F1(Y) = F1(X ** 2) = (-1) ** N * F(X) * F(-X)$

                $= A(N) ** 2 * (X ** 2 - X1 ** 2) * (X ** 2 - X2 ** 2)$

                $* \cdots * (X ** 2 - XN ** 2),$

where $F1(Y)$ is a polynomial of degree N in $Y = X ** 2$ with zeros $X1 ** 2$, $X2 ** 2, \ldots, XN ** 2$. If $|X1| + |X2| \geq 1$, then $X1 ** 2$ and $X2 ** 2$ are *more separated* than are $|X1|$ and $|X2|$ in the usual sense

$$X1 ** 2 - X2 ** 2 > |X1| - |X2|.$$

If $|X1| + |X2| < 1$, then $X1 ** 2$ and $X2 ** 2$ are *not* more separated in this sense. But as long as $|X1| > |X2|$, we say $X1 ** 2$ and $X2 ** 2$ are *more separated* than $|X1|$ and $|X2|$ *in the sense that* either

(3.5.6b)          $X1 ** 2/(X2 ** 2) > |X1|/|X2|,$ or

            $X2 ** 2/(X1 ** 2) > |X2|/|X1|.$

We say that $F1(Y)$ is obtained from $F(X)$ by one *root-squaring*. Similarly (by another root-squaring),

$$F2(Z) = F2(Y ** 2) = (-1) ** N * F1(Y) * F1(-Y)$$

is a polynomial of degree N in $Z = Y ** 2 = X ** 4$ with zeros $X1 ** 4$, $X2 ** 4, \ldots, XN ** 4$, which are more separated, (3.5.6b), than the zeros of $F1(Y)$. After M root-squarings $(F0(X) \equiv F(X))$

(3.5.7)      $FM(U) = FM(V ** 2) = (-1) ** N * FMM1(V) * FMM1(-V)$

               $= \sum B(K) * U ** K, K \in //0, N//,$

is a polynomial of degree N in $U = X ** (2 ** M)$ with zeros $X1 ** (2 ** M)$, $X2 ** (2 ** M), \ldots, XN ** (2 ** M)$. The zeros of $FM(U)$ are related to the coefficients $B(K), K \in //0, N//$, by

(3.5.8)    $B(N - 1)/B(N) = -(X1 ** (2 ** M) + X2 ** (2 ** M) + \cdots$

                     $+ XN ** (2 ** M))$

            $= -X1 ** (2 ** M) * (1 + (X2/X1) ** (2 ** M)$

                $+ \cdots + (XN/X1) ** (2 ** M))$

            $= -X1 ** (2 ** M)$

                $* (1 + ORDB ((X2/X1) ** (2 ** M)))$

(3.5.8)    $B(N-2)/B(N) = + ((X1 * X2) ** (2 ** M)$
$+ (X1 * X3) ** (2 ** M)$
$+ \cdots + (XNM1 * XN) ** (2 ** M))$
$= + (X1 * X2) ** (2 ** M)$
$* (1 + (X3/X2) ** (2 ** M) + \cdots$
$+ ((XNM1 * XN)/(X1 * X2)) ** (2 ** M))$
$= + (X1 * X2) ** (2 ** M)$
$* (1 + ORDB((X3/X2) ** (2 ** M)))$
$B(N-3)/B(N) = - ((X1 * X2 * X3) ** (2 ** M) + \cdots)$
$= - (X1 * X2 * X3) ** (2 ** M)$
$* (1 + ORDB((X4/X3) ** (2 ** M)))$
$$\vdots$$
$B(0)/B(N) = (-1) ** N * (X1 * X2 * \cdots * XN) ** (2 ** M).$

Now, if the X1, X2, ..., XN, satisfy $|X1| > |X2| > |X3| > \cdots > |XN|$, and if M is *sufficiently large*, then

(3.5.9)        $X1 ** (2 ** M) \doteq -B(N-1)/B(N),$
$X2 ** (2 ** M) \doteq -B(N-2)/B(N-1), \ldots,$ and
$XN ** (2 ** M) \doteq -B(0)/B(1).$

All of the zeros of FM(U) are nonnegative and the appropriate sign for the 2 ** M*th* root of XK ** (2 ** M) must be obtained by substitution in the original polynomial F(X).

THE ALGORITHM

The coefficients of the polynomial

$$F1(Y) = F1(X ** 2) = \sum B(K) * Y ** K, K \in //0, N//,$$

obtained from the given polynomial

$$F(X) = \sum A(K) * X ** K, K \in //0, N//,$$

by one root-squaring, may be computed using the following short-hand scheme. If a sequence of polynomials is being generated to determine the roots of F(X), then after each root-squaring the ratios (3.5.9) are computed. The relative error test is usually used to check for convergence of corresponding

| F(X): | A(N) | A(N − 1) | A(N − 2) | A(N − 3) | ⋯ |
|---|---|---|---|---|---|
| (−1) ** N * F(−X): | A(N) | −A(N − 1) | A(N − 2) | −A(N − 3) | ⋯ |

| A(N) ** 2 | −A(N − 1) ** 2 | A(N − 2) ** 2 | −A(N − 3) ** 2 | ⋯ |
|---|---|---|---|---|
| | +2 * A(N) * A(N − 2) | −2 * A(N − 1) * A(N − 3) | +2 * A(N − 2) * A(N − 4) | ⋯ |
| | | +2 * A(N) * A(N − 4) | −2 * A(N − 1) * A(N − 5) | ⋯ |
| | | | +2 * A(N) * A(N − 6) | ⋯ |

[sum terms in each column with A(N − K) = 0 if K > N]

| F1(Y): | B(N) | B(N − 1) | B(N − 2) | B(N − 3) | ⋯ |
|---|---|---|---|---|---|

ratios. Unfortunately, it frequently happens that the magnitudes of the coefficients, B(J), J ∈ //0, N//, involved in (3.5.9) become so different so quickly that overflow in execution of a computer program occurs *before* convergence is achieved.

This method is often used *with* other iteration methods. A few root-squarings with (3.5.9) frequently lead to usable first guesses, X(0), to be used in Newton's Method; and after a translation of axis so that the close roots are greater than unity, one or two root-squarings will usually separate two *close* roots, see §3.4, so that Newton's Method may be applied to F1(Y) or F2(Z).

### 3.6 NEWTON'S METHOD FOR TWO FUNCTIONS OF TWO VARIABLES

The obvious extension of Newton's Method for the pair of equations

(3.6.1)
$$F(X, Y) = 0$$
$$G(X, Y) = 0$$

is to solve successively the pair of equations[1]

(3.6.2)
$$PF\big(1; (X(N + 1), Y(N + 1)), (X(N), Y(N))\big)$$
$$= F(X(N), Y(N)) + PAR ** (1,)F(X(N), Y(N)) * \Delta X(N)$$
$$+ PAR ** (,1)F(X(N), Y(N)) * \Delta Y(N) = 0$$

[1]For certain classroom presentations we invent local abbreviations. Here, we write PDFX(N) for PAR ** (1,) F(X(N), Y(N)), etc. However, at this point we are probably using the standard mathematical notation in classroom presentations.

$$PG\big(1; \big(X(N+1), Y(N+1)\big), \big(X(N), Y(N)\big)\big)$$

(3.6.2)     $= G\big(X(N), Y(N)\big) + PAR ** (1,) G\big(X(N), Y(N)\big) * \Delta X(N)$

$\qquad + PAR ** (,1)G\big(X(N), Y(N)\big) * \Delta Y(N) = 0,$

linear in $\Delta X(N) \equiv X(N+1) - X(N)$, and $\Delta Y(N) \equiv Y(N+1) - Y(N)$, for
$N \in //0, \infty//$, where $\big(X(0), Y(0)\big)$ is a given first guess at a solution of (3.6.1).
A geometric interpretation of this method is given in the next section.

The system (3.6.2) may be solved by Cramer's Rule to give

$$\Delta X(N) = \frac{\begin{vmatrix} -F\big(X(N), Y(N)\big) & PAR ** (,1)F\big(X(N), Y(N)\big) \\ -G\big(X(N), Y(N)\big) & PAR ** (,1)G\big(X(N), Y(N)\big) \end{vmatrix}}{\begin{vmatrix} PAR ** (1,)F\big(X(N), Y(N)\big) & PAR ** (,1)F\big(X(N), Y(N)\big) \\ PAR ** (1,)G\big(X(N), Y(N)\big) & PAR ** (,1)G\big(X(N), Y(N)\big) \end{vmatrix}}$$

and

$$\Delta Y(N) = \frac{\begin{vmatrix} PAR ** (1,)F\big(X(N), Y(N)\big) & -F\big(X(N), Y(N)\big) \\ PAR ** (1,)G\big(X(N), Y(N)\big) & -G\big(X(N), Y(N)\big) \end{vmatrix}}{\begin{vmatrix} PAR ** (1,)F\big(X(N), Y(N)\big) & PAR ** (,1)F\big(X(N), Y(N)\big) \\ PAR ** (1,)G\big(X(N), Y(N)\big) & PAR ** (,1)G\big(X(N), Y(N)\big) \end{vmatrix}}$$

provided the (denominator) determinant

(3.6.3)     $D(X, Y) = PAR ** (1,)F(X, Y) * PAR ** (,1)G(X, Y)$

$\qquad - PAR ** (,1)F(X, Y) * PAR ** (1,)G(X, Y)$

is not zero at $(X, Y) = \big(X(N), Y(N)\big)$.

Thus, the iteration formulas

$$X(N+1) = X(N)$$

$\qquad + \big(-F\big(X(N), Y(N)\big) * PAR ** (,1) G\big(X(N), Y(N)\big)$

$\qquad + PAR ** (,1)F\big(X(N), Y(N)\big) * G\big(X(N), Y(N)\big)\big)/$

$\qquad\qquad D\big(X(N), Y(N)\big)$

(3.6.4)

$$Y(N+1) = Y(N)$$

$\qquad + \big(-PAR ** (1,)F\big(X(N), Y(N)\big) * G\big(X(N), Y(N)\big)$

$\qquad + F\big(X(N), Y(N)\big) * PAR ** (1,)G\big(X(N), Y(N)\big)\big)/$

$\qquad\qquad D\big(X(N), Y(N)\big)$

define a sequence $\big(X(N+1), Y(N+1)\big)$, $N \in //0, \infty//$, provided

$$D(X(N), Y(N)) \neq 0 \text{ for each N.}$$

*Sometimes* the sequence converges componentwise to a number pair $(X1, Y1)$, which satisfies the original equations. That is,

$$\text{LIM}(X(N)) = X1, \text{ as N App } \infty, \text{ LIM}(Y(N)) = Y1, \text{ as N App } \infty,$$

and $F(X1, Y1) = 0$ and $G(X1, Y1) = 0$.

A *first guess* $(X(0), Y(0))$ may be obtained by sketching the curves $F(X, Y) = 0$, $G(X, Y) = 0$, and $D(X, Y) = 0$ as indicated in Figure 3.7.2. For example, a sketch of $F(X, Y) = 0$ may be obtained in the region R of the X, Y-plane where a zero of $F(X, Y)$ is expected, by:

1. *Choose* a set $A(K)$, $K \in //0, N//$, of first coordinates of points in R and a set $B(K)$, $K \in //0, M//$, of second coordinates of points in R;
2. *Compute* for each $A(K)$ corresponding $Y(A(K))$, and for each $B(K)$ compute corresponding $X(B(K))$ such that

$$F(A(K), Y(A(K))) = 0 \text{ and } F(X(B(K)), B(K)) = 0;$$

3. *Plot* the points $(A(K), Y(A(K)))$ and $(X(B(K)), B(K))$ obtained in (2); and
4. Using your best judgement, *sketch* arcs of $F(X, Y) = 0$ through the points plotted in (3). A first guess $(X(0), Y(0))$ for an iteration of the above type is obtained by *reading* from the graph the coordinates of the intersection(s) of the sketched estimates to $F(X, Y) = 0$ and $G(X, Y) = 0$. If a sketch of $D(X, Y) = 0$ comes close to this point, then the method of §3.7 may lead to a solution of (3.6.1).

### EXERCISES

1. Use the grid $\{(A(K), B(K)) | A(K) = B(K) \equiv K/10, K \in //5, 10//\}$ and the method suggested above to sketch the curves $F(X, Y) = X ** 2 + Y ** 2 -1 = 0$ and $G(X, Y) = Y - X ** 2 = 0$. Use your sketches to read-off an estimate $(X(0), Y(0))$ to a simultaneous solution of the two equations.

2. Find estimates to the simultaneous solution of

$$F(X, Y) = X ** 2 + Y ** 2 - 1 = 0$$
$$G(X, Y) = Y - X ** 2 = 0$$

near $(X(0), Y(0)) = (.7, .6)$ by executing three times the operations indicated in (3.6.4) using the following schematic. $\Delta X(K) = X(K + 1) - X(K)$ and $\Delta Y(K) = Y(K + 1) - Y(K)$ are, respectively, the fractional parts of the first and second equation in (3.6.4). The numerators and denominator of these fractions are signed determinants of matrices obtained from the second and third rows of the schematic by covering an appropriate column. The desired solution is $(X, Y) = (SQRT(T), T)$, where $T = .5 * (-1 + SQRT(5))$.

| X(K) | Y(K) | |
|---|---|---|
| PAR ∗∗ (1,) F(X(K), Y(K)) | PAR ∗∗ (,1) F(X(K), Y(K)) | F(X(K), Y(K)) |
| PAR ∗∗ (1,)G(X(K), Y(K)) | PAR ∗∗ (,1)G(X(K), Y(K)) | G(X(K), Y(K)) |
| D(X(K), Y(K)) | ΔX(K) | ΔY(K) |

| X(0) = .7 | Y(0) = .6 | |
|---|---|---|
| 1.4 | 1.2 | −.15 |
| −1.4 | 1 | .11 |
| 3.08 | .282/3.08 = .092 | .056/3.08 = .018 |

| X(1) = .792 | Y(1) = .618 | |
|---|---|---|

## 3.7 SPECIAL CASE WHEN D(X, Y) IS NEAR ZERO

If, near a solution of the system (3.6.1),

$$(3.7.1) \qquad D(X, Y) = \begin{vmatrix} PAR ** (1,) F(X, Y) & PAR ** (,1)F(X, Y) \\ PAR ** (1,)G(X, Y) & PAR ** (,1)G(X, Y) \end{vmatrix}$$

is small when compared with corresponding values of the numerator of either fraction in equations (3.6.4), then we may find the generated sequence $(X(N), Y(N))$, $N \in //1, \infty //$, behaving something like those discussed in §3.4. In this section we discuss some of the implications of $D(X, Y) = 0$, and present a checklist (similar to that given in §3.4) indicating a method to *try* if $D(X, Y)$ is small near a solution.

More important than the title subject of this section is the presentation of some geometric interpretations of the functions and equations involved. See Figures 3.7.1 and 3.7.2.

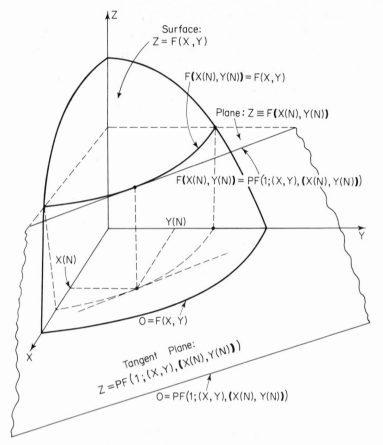

**Figure 3.7.1**

The equations (3.6.1) may be considered the intersection of the surfaces

$$Z = F(X, Y), \text{ and } Z = G(X, Y)$$

with the plane $Z = 0$, the X, Y-plane. Either of the surfaces may intersect the X, Y-plane in one or several curves and/or one or several distinct points — or the surface may not intersect the X, Y-plane at all. In any case we refer to the equation $0 = F(X, Y)$ as a curve in the $Z = 0$ plane, and to $ZZ(= \text{constant})$ $= F(X, Y)$ as a curve in the $Z = ZZ$ plane.

The *tangent plane* to $Z = F(X, Y)$ at the point $(X(N), Y(N), F(X(N), Y(N)))$ is defined by

(3.7.2)        $$Z = PF(1; (X, Y), (X(N), Y(N)))$$

and it intersects the X, Y-plane in a line [compare the first equation in(3.6.2)], not at all [PAR ∗∗ (1,)F (X(N), Y(N)) = PAR ∗∗ (,1)F (X(N), Y(N)) = 0 and F (X(N), Y(N)) ≠ 0], or the tangent plane *is* the X, Y-plane [PAR ∗∗(1,) F (X(N), Y(N)) = PAR ∗∗ (,1)F (X(N), Y(N)) = F (X(N), Y(N)) = 0].

Thus D (X(N), Y(N)) = 0 unless *each* equation in (3.6.2) defines a line. If these lines are parallel, then

$$-\text{PAR} ** (1,)\text{F} (\text{X(N), Y(N)}) / \text{PAR} ** (,1)\text{F} (\text{X(N), Y(N)})$$
$$= -\text{PAR} ** (1,)\text{G} (\text{X(N), Y(N)}) / \text{PAR} ** (,1)\text{G} (\text{X(N), Y(N)}),$$

or

$$-\text{PAR} ** (,1)\text{F} (\text{X(N), Y(N)}) / \text{PAR} ** (1,)\text{F} (\text{X(N), Y(N)})$$
$$= -\text{PAR} ** (,1)\text{G} (\text{X(N), Y(N)}) / \text{PAR} ** (1,)\text{G} (\text{X(N), Y(N)}),$$

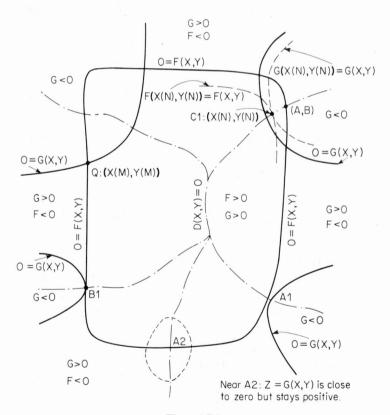

**Figure 3.7.2**

and again $D(X(N), Y(N)) = 0$. So, as we knew all the time, (3.6.2) has a unique solution if and only if $D(X(N), Y(N)) \neq 0$.

The intersection of the surface $Z = F(X, Y)$ and the plane $Z = F(X(N), Y(N))$ is a curve $F(X(N), Y(N)) = F(X, Y)$. Similarly, in the $Z = G(X(N), Y(N))$ plane there is the curve $G(X(N), Y(N)) = G(X, Y)$. If $D(X(N), Y(N)) \neq 0$, the tangent plane (3.7.2) cuts the plane $Z = F(X(N), Y(N))$ in a line, the tangent to $F(X(N), Y(N)) = F(X, Y)$ at $(X(N), Y(N))$. Then, the slopes of $F(X(N), Y(N)) = F(X, Y)$ and $G(X(N), Y(N)) = G(X, Y)$ at $(X(N), Y(N))$ are the slopes of the first and second lines, respectively, of (3.6.2).

If either curve $F(X(N), Y(N)) = F(X, Y)$ or $G(X(N), Y(N)) = G(X, Y)$ has a singular point[1] at $(X(N), Y(N))$, or if both curves have the same slope at $(X(N), Y(N))$, then $D(X(N), Y(N)) = 0$.

The X, Y-plane in Figure 3.7.2 may be considered the $Z = 0$ plane that has the curves $0 = F(X, Y)$ and $0 = G(X, Y)$. The curves $D(X, Y) = 0$ consist of precisely those points $(U, V)$ at which the curves $F(U, V) = F(X, Y)$ and $G(U, V) = G(X, Y)$, [the projections onto the $Z = 0$ plane of the corresponding curves in the $Z = F(U, V)$ and $Z = G(U, V)$ planes], have parallel tangents, or PAR ** (1,)F(U, V) = PAR ** (,1)F(U, V) = 0, or PAR ** (1,)G(U, V) = PAR ** (,1)G(U, V) = 0. The symbols $F > 0$, $G < 0$, etc. indicate the regions where the surfaces $Z = F(X, Y)$ and $Z = G(X, Y)$ lie above, below, etc. the $Z = 0$ plane. The interpretations "shore line" for $F = 0$, "above sea level" for $F > 0$, etc. usually help in these discussions.

The remainder of this section is intended as an outline of a method for the four special cases (A1: no solution; A2: no solution; B1: a multiple solution; C1: two distinct solutions close together) indicated in Figure 3.7.2 — analogous to those discussed in §3.4. If, at a point like Q: $(X(M), Y(M))$, the curves $0 = F(X, Y)$ and $0 = G(X, Y)$ intersect and $D(X(M), Y(M))$ is not close to zero, then the method defined by (3.6.4) should be used.

Specifically, we assume that in the region in which we suspect there is a solution of (3.6.1) and in which we have found $D(X, Y)$ to be small [so that iteration with (3.6.4) gives a sequence $(X(K), Y(K))$, $K \in //1, \infty//$, which does not converge fast enough or appears to diverge], the curve $D(X, Y) = 0$ *intersects* either $F(X, Y) = 0$ or $G(X, Y) = 0$. Then either

---

[1]$(X(N), Y(N))$ is a *singular point* of the curve $F(X(N), Y(N)) = F(X, Y)$ if there does not exist a neighborhood of $(X(N), Y(N))$ in which it is possible to represent one variable as a single-valued function of the other variable. PAR ** (1,)F(X(N), Y(N)) = PAR ** (,1)F(Y(N), X(N)) = 0 is a *necessary* condition that $(X(N), Y(N))$ be a singular point of the curve. The condition is *not* sufficient. For example, $(X - Y) ** 2 = 0$ has no singular points, yet PAR ** (1,)F(X, Y) = PAR ** (,1)F(X, Y) = 0 for every point on the curve (line).

(3.7.3a)    $DF(X, Y) = \begin{vmatrix} PAR \ast\ast (1,)F(X, Y) & PAR \ast\ast (,1)F(X, Y) \\ PAR \ast\ast (1,)D(X, Y) & PAR \ast\ast (,1)D(X, Y) \end{vmatrix}$

or

(3.7.3b)    $DG(X, Y) = \begin{vmatrix} PAR \ast\ast (1,)G(X, Y) & PAR \ast\ast (,1)G(X, Y) \\ PAR \ast\ast (1,)D(X, Y) & PAR \ast\ast (,1)D(X, Y) \end{vmatrix}$

is not close to zero there.

*Note.* Near A2 in Figure 3.7.2 we have $DG(X, Y) = 0$ at a minimum point of $Z = G(X, Y)$.

In the following *method* we suppose $DF(X, Y)$ is not small in the region of interest.

1. Find a solution (A, B) of

$$F(X, Y) = 0 \text{ and } D(X, Y) = 0$$

   by the method of §3.6.

2. Compute $G(A, B)$. (i) If $G(A, B) = 0$, then (A, B) is the desired multiple solution. (ii) If $G(A, B) \neq 0$, then we suggest that a sketch like that in Figure 3.7.2 be made for the region in question to determine if a solution is possible.

3. If we suspect that there are two distinct solutions of (3.6.1) close to (A, B), then *new* first guesses (X1, Y1) and (X2, Y2) at a solution of (3.6.1) to be used in the method (3.6.4) are obtained as follows: Let the surfaces $Z = F(X, Y)$ and $Z = G(X, Y)$ be replaced by the Taylor Polynomial estimates $Z = PF(2; (X, Y), (A, B))$ and $Z = PG(2; (X, Y), (A, B))$. The intersections of these surfaces with the $Z = 0$ plane are two curves (conics)

(3.7.4a)    $0 = PF(2; (X, Y), (A, B))$

$= F(A, B) + PAR \ast\ast (1,)F(A, B) \ast \Delta X$

$+ PAR \ast\ast (,1)F(A, B) \ast \Delta Y$

$+ .5 \ast PAR \ast\ast (2,)F(A, B) \ast \Delta X \ast\ast 2$

$+ PAR \ast\ast (1, 1)F(A, B) \ast \Delta X \ast \Delta Y$

$+ .5 \ast PAR \ast\ast (,2)F(A, B) \ast \Delta Y \ast\ast 2$

(3.7.4b)    $0 = PG\,(2; (X, Y), (A, B))$

$\quad = G(A, B) + PAR ** (1,)G(A, B) * \Delta X$

$\quad + PAR ** (,1)G(A, B) * \Delta Y$

$\quad + .5 * PAR ** (2,)G(A, B) * \Delta X ** 2$

$\quad + PAR ** (1, 1)G(A, B) * \Delta X * \Delta Y$

$\quad + .5 * PAR ** (,2)G(A, B) * \Delta Y ** 2,$

where $F(A, B) = 0$, $\Delta X = X - A$, and $\Delta Y = Y - B$. The intersections of these curves are $(X1, Y1)$ and $(X2, Y2)$.

We conclude this section with a description of a particular method for solving (3.7.4a) and (3.7.4b).

Since   $D(A, B) = 0$ and $DF(A, B) \neq 0$, then

$PAR ** (1,)G(A, B)/PAR ** (1,)F(A, B)$

$= PAR **(,1)G(A, B)/PAR ** (,1)F(A, B) = \text{constant} \equiv K1.$

When we multiply (3.7.4a) by K1 and subtract this from (3.7.4b) we get

(3.7.5)    $0 = G(A, B) + AA * \Delta X ** 2 + BB * \Delta X * \Delta Y$

$\quad + CC * \Delta Y ** 2,$

where    $AA = .5 * (PAR ** (2,)G(A, B) - K1 * PAR ** (2,)F(A, B))$

$\quad BB = PAR ** (1, 1)G(A, B) - K1 * PAR ** (1, 1)F(A, B)$

$\quad CC = .5 * (PAR ** (,2)G(A, B) - K1 * PAR ** (,2)F(A, B)).$

Setting $\Delta Y = T * \Delta X$, noting $F(A, B) = 0$, and solving for the T in the third term, (3.7.4a) becomes

$T = - PAR ** (1,)F(A, B)/PAR ** (,1)F(A, B)$

$\quad - (.5 * \Delta X/PAR ** (,1)F(A, B)) * (PAR ** (2,)F(A, B)$

$\quad + 2 * T * PAR ** (1, 1)F(A, B) + T ** 2 * PAR ** (,2)F(A, B))$

and (3.7.5) becomes

$\Delta X = \pm \text{SQRT}\,(-G(A, B)/(AA + BB * T + CC * T ** 2)).$

The iteration process (one of the type discussed in the following section) consists of solving successively the equations

(3.7.6a)     $\Delta X(N + 1) = \pm$ SQRT$(-G(A, B)/(AA + BB * T(N)$
             $+ CC * T(N) ** 2))$

(3.7.6b)     $T(N + 1) = -$ PAR $** (1,)F(A, B)/$PAR $** (,1)F(A, B)$
             $- (.5 * \Delta X(N)/$PAR $** (,1)F(A, B))$
             $* ($PAR $** (2,)F(A, B)$
             $+ 2 * T(N) * $PAR $** (1, 1)F(A, B)$
             $+ T(N) ** 2 * $PAR $** (,2)F(A, B))$

to define two sequences, one for each choice of sign in (3.7.6a), $(\Delta XP(M),$
$TP(M))$ and $(\Delta XN(M), TN(M))$, $M \in //1, \infty//$, say with $TP(0) = TN(0) =$
$-$PAR $** (1,)F(A, B)/$PAR $** (,1)F(A, B)$ and $\Delta XP(0) = \Delta XN(0) = 0$.

Sometimes these sequences converge to $(\Delta X1, T1)$ and $(\Delta X2, T2)$ which
define *new first guesses* $(X1, Y1) = (\Delta X1 + A, T1 * \Delta X1 + B)$ and $(X2, Y2)$
$= (\Delta X2 + A, T2 * \Delta X2 + B)$.

For a particular problem, convergence may be improved if we set $\Delta X =$
$T * \Delta Y$ and derive iteration formulas corresponding to (3.7.6a) and (3.7.6b)
for $\Delta Y(N + 1)$ and $T(N + 1)$.

**EXERCISES**

**1.** For

$$F(X, Y) = X ** 2 + Y ** 2 - 1 = 0$$
$$G(X, Y) = (X - 1.95) ** 2 + Y ** 2 - 1 = 0,$$

*sketch*, corresponding to Figure 3.7.2, $F(X,Y) = 0$, $G(X, Y) = 0$, and
$D(X, Y) = 0$. Starting with (3.7.3a), *execute* the three steps indicated to
compute estimates $(X1, Y1)$ and $(X2, Y2)$ to be used as first guesses in the
method of §3.6. Use (3.7.6a, 6b) to compute $(X1, Y1)$ and $(X2, Y2)$.

**2.** Discuss the solvability of

$$F(X, Y) = X ** 2 + Y ** 2 - 1 = 0$$
$$G(X, Y) = (X - S) ** 2 + Y ** 2 - 1 = 0$$

for various choices of S where $|S| < 3$.

## 3.8 ANOTHER ITERATION PROCESS FOR F(X, Y) = 0, G(X, Y) = 0

If we can write F(X, Y) = 0, and G(X, Y) = 0, respectively, in the form

(3.8.1)
$$X = FF(X, Y)$$
$$Y = GG(X, Y),$$

where

(3.8.2)
$$|PAR ** (1,)FF(X, Y)| + |(PAR ** (,1)FF(X, Y)| < 1,$$

and
$$|PAR ** (1,)GG(X, Y)| + |(PAR ** (,1)GG(X, Y)| < 1$$

in the vicinity of a solution of (3.8.1), then the iteration process

(3.8.3)
$$X(N + 1) = FF (X(N), Y(N))$$
$$Y(N + 1) = GG (X(N), Y(N))$$

sometimes defines a sequence $(X(N), Y(N))$, $N \in //1, \infty//$, such that

LIM (X(N)) = X1, as N App ∞,

LIM (Y(N)) = Y1, as N App ∞, and

F(X1, Y1) = 0 and G(X1, Y1) = 0.

  For, with F(X, Y) = X − FF(X, Y) = 0 and

G(X, Y) = Y − GG(X,Y) = 0, we can write

PF(1; (X(N + 1), Y(N + 1)), (X(N), Y(N))) = 0, and

PG(1; (X(N + 1), Y(N + 1)), (X(N), Y(N))) = 0, in the form

(3.8.4)
$$X(N + 1) = FF (X(N), Y(N))$$
$$+ PAR ** (1,)FF (X(N), Y(N)) * (X(N + 1) − X(N))$$
$$+ PAR ** (,1)FF (X(N), Y(N)) * (Y(N + 1) − Y(N))$$
$$Y(N + 1) = GG (X(N), Y(N))$$
$$+ PAR ** (1,)GG (X(N), Y(N)) * (X(N + 1) − X(N))$$
$$+ PAR **(,1)GG (X(N), Y(N)) * (Y(N + 1) − Y(N)).$$

Now if X(N + 1) − X(N) and Y(N + 1) − Y(N) are small, with (3.8.2) we conclude that the last two terms of each equation in (3.8.4) are *small*, and when neglected give (3.8.3).

Sometimes convergence is improved if we use new data as soon as they are computed

(3.8.5)

$$X(N + 1) = FF(X(N), Y(N))$$
$$Y(N + 1) = GG(X(N + 1), Y(N)).$$

Convergence is obtained (in the set of real numbers) if the first guess $(X(0), Y(0))$ is close enough to the solution $(X1, Y1)$.

### EXERCISES

**1.** For $F(X,Y) = Y - X ** 3 + X **2 = 0$ and $G(X, Y) = Y ** 2 - X = 0$, write (3.8.3)

$$X(N + 1) = Y(N) ** 2 = GG(X(N), Y(N))$$
$$Y(N + 1) = X(N) ** 3 - X(N) ** 2 = FF(X(N), Y(N)).$$

(i) With this choice for (3.8.3) find the region where conditions (3.8.2) are satisfied. (ii) Can this choice for (3.8.3) be used to obtain estimates which converge to the solution $(X, Y) = (0, 0)$? Execute a few steps in the iteration with $(X(0), Y(0)) = (.1, 0)$. (iii) Can this choice for (3.8.3) be used to obtain estimates which converge to the solution with $X > 1$? Try a few steps in the iteration with $(X(0), Y(0)) = (1.1, 1.0)$. Try other first guesses. *Answer.* (i) $|Y| < .5$ and $-\frac{1}{3} < X < 1$.

**2.** For $F(X, Y) = Y - X ** 3 + X ** 2 = 0$ and $G(X, Y) = Y ** 2 - X = 0$ make *other choices* for (3.8.3), not the choice used in Exercise 1, and discuss possible convergence of the iteration.

### 3.9 COMPLEX ZEROS OF REAL POLYNOMIALS

Thus far we have considered only methods for finding real zeros of real functions. In this section we describe a method for finding pairs of zeros—possibly conjugate complex pairs of zeros—of real polynomials using only *real* arithmetic.

We seek real numbers P and Q such that $X ** 2 + P * X + Q$ is a factor of

$$(3.9.1) \quad F(X) = A(0) * X ** N + A(1) * X ** (N - 1) + \cdots$$
$$+ A(N - 1) * X + A(N).$$

The zeros of $X ** 2 + P * X + Q$ are then zeros of $F(X)$.

There are many methods for finding $P$ and $Q$. We discuss the Bairstow Iteration Process where the quotient $F(X)/(X ** 2 + P * X + Q)$ is written

$$(3.9.2) \quad F(X)/(X ** 2 + P * X + Q)$$
$$= B(0) * X ** (N - 2) + B(1) * X ** (N - 3) + \cdots$$
$$+ B(N - 3) * X + B(N - 2)$$
$$+ B(N - 1) * X ** (-1) + B(N) * X ** (-2)$$
$$+ B(N + 1) * X ** (-3) + \cdots.$$

That is, the remainder is represented as an infinite series.

Using synthetic division we have

| $-P$ | $-Q$ | $A(0)$ | $A(1)$ | $A(2)$ | $A(3)$ | $\cdots$ | $A(N - 1)$ | $A(N)$ | $0$ | $\cdots$ |
|---|---|---|---|---|---|---|---|---|---|---|
| | | | | $-Q * B(0)$ | $-Q * B(1)$ | $\cdots$ | $-Q * B(N - 3)$ | $-Q * B(N - 2)$ | $-Q * B(N - 1)$ | $\cdots$ |
| $(3.9.3)$ | | | $-P * B(0)$ | $-P * B(1)$ | $-P * B(2)$ | $\cdots$ | $-P * B(N - 2)$ | $-P * B(N - 1)$ | $-P * B(N)$ | $\cdots$ |
| | | $B(0)$ | $B(1)$ | $B(2)$ | $B(3)$ | $\cdots$ | $B(N - 1)$ | $B(N)$ | $B(N + 1)$ | $\cdots,$ |

where $B(K) = A(K) - P * B(K - 1) - Q * B(K - 2)$, $K \in //0, \infty//$, with $B(-1) = B(-2) \equiv 0$ and $A(K) \equiv 0$ for $K > N$. Clearly, $B(K) = 0$ for $K > N$ if $B(N - 1) = B(N) = 0$, in which case $X ** 2 + P * X + Q$ is a factor of $F(X)$.

The $B(K)$ depend on the choice of $P$ and $Q$ in the division. Thus, the problem here is to find $P$ and $Q$ so that

$$B(N - 1) \equiv B(N - 1; P, Q) = 0$$
$$(3.9.4)$$
$$B(N) \equiv B(N; P, Q) = 0.$$

To solve this system we apply Newton's Method for functions of two variables discussed in §3.6.

If $(P(0), Q(0))$ is the first guess at a solution of (3.9.4), then a sequence of estimates $(P(K), Q(K))$, $K \in //1, \infty//$, is defined by

$$B(N - 1; P(K), Q(K)) + PAR ** (1,)B(N - 1; P(K), Q(K)) * \Delta P(K)$$
$$+ PAR ** (,1)B(N - 1; P(K), Q(K)) * \Delta Q(K) = 0$$
$$(3.9.5)$$
$$B(N; P(K), Q(K)) + PAR ** (1,)B(N; P(K), Q(K)) * \Delta P(K)$$
$$+ PAR ** (,1)B(N; P(K), Q(K)) * \Delta Q(K) = 0,$$

where $\Delta P(K) \equiv P(K + 1) - P(K)$ and $\Delta Q(K) \equiv Q(K + 1) - Q(K)$. Since PAR $** (1,)B(N - 1; P, Q)$ involves PAR $** (1,)B(N - 2; P, Q)$, and PAR $**$ $(1,)B(N - 3; P, Q)$ and PAR $** (1,)B(N - 2; P, Q)$ involve PAR $** (1,)B(N - 4; P, Q)$, etc. the calculation of the coefficients in (3.9.5) would be complicated except for the existence of relations between these partial derivatives and certain coefficients defined by a second synthetic division—much as $F'(X(N))$ was computed by a second synthetic division in Exercise 3 of §3.2.

We write the *polynomial part* of the quotient in (3.9.2) divided by $X ** 2 + P * X + Q$ as

(3.9.6)
$$(B(0) * X ** (N - 2) + B(1) * X ** (N - 3) + \cdots$$
$$+ B(N - 3) * X + B(N - 2)) / (X ** 2 + P * X + Q)$$
$$= C(0) * X ** (N - 4) + C(1) * X ** (N - 5) + \cdots$$
$$+ C(N - 5) * X + C(N - 4) + C(N - 3) * X ** (-1)$$
$$+ C(N - 2) * X ** (-2) + \cdots .$$

As in (3.9.3), synthetic division gives

| $- P$ | $-Q$ | B(0) | B(1) | B(2) | $\cdots$ | B(N − 3) | B(N − 2) | 0 | 0 | $\cdots$ |
|---|---|---|---|---|---|---|---|---|---|---|
| | | | $-Q * C(0)$ | $\cdots$ | | $-Q * C(N - 5)$ | $-Q * C(N - 4)$ | $-Q * C(N - 3)$ | $-Q * C(N - 2)$ | $\cdots$ |
| (3.9.7) | | | $-P * C(0)$ | $-P * C(1)$ | $\cdots$ | $-P * C(N - 4)$ | $-P * C(N - 3)$ | $-P * C(N - 2)$ | $-P * C(N - 1)$ | $\cdots$ |
| | | C(0) | C(1) | C(2) | $\cdots$ | C(N − 3) | C(N − 2) | C(N − 1) | C(N) | $\cdots$ |

where $C(K) = B(K) - P * C(K - 1) - Q * C(K - 2)$, $K \in //0, \infty//$, with $C(-1) = C(-2) \equiv 0$ and $B(K) \equiv 0$ for $K > N - 2$. It can be shown, see [3], that

$$\text{PAR} ** (1,)B(N - 1; P(K), Q(K)) = \text{PAR} ** (,1)B(N; P(K), Q(K))$$
$$= -C(N - 2; P(K), Q(K)),$$
$$\text{PAR} ** (,1)B(N - 1; P(K), Q(K)) = -C(N - 3; P(K), Q(K)),$$

and

$$\text{PAR} ** (1,)B(N; P(K), Q(K)) = -C(N - 1; P(K), Q(K)).$$

The linear system (3.9.5) now takes the form

(3.9.8)
$$C(N - 2; P(K), Q(K)) * \Delta P(K)$$
$$+ C(N - 3; P(K), Q(K)) * \Delta Q(K) = B(N - 1; P(K), Q(K))$$
$$C(N - 1; P(K), Q(K)) * \Delta P(K)$$
$$+ C(N - 2; P(K), Q(K)) * \Delta Q(K) = B(N; P(K), Q(K)).$$

The Bairstow Iteration Process consists then of solving successively the system (3.9.8), with coefficients defined by the two synthetic divisions (3.9.3) and (3.9.7), to define a sequence $(P(K + 1), Q(K + 1)) = (P(K) + \Delta P(K), Q(K) + \Delta Q(K))$, $K \in //0, \infty//$, which may converge to a solution $(P1, Q1)$ of (3.9.4). If such a $(P1, Q1)$ is obtained, then (3.9.1) can be written

$$F(X) = (X ** 2 + P1 * X + Q1) * (B(0) * X ** (N - 2)$$
$$+ B(1) * X ** (N - 3) + \cdots + B(N - 3) * X + B(N - 2)),$$

and the roots of $X ** 2 + P1 * X + Q1 = 0$ are also roots of $F(X) = 0$.

### EXERCISES

**1.** Use the Bairstow process (3.9.3), (3.9.7), and (3.9.8) with

$$X ** 4 - 3 * X ** 3 + 20 * X ** 2 + 44 * X + 54 = 0$$

and first guess $(P(0), Q(0)) = (2, 2)$ to compute new estimate $(P(1), Q(1))$.

SOLUTION

| $-2 -2\|$ | $+1$ | $-3$ | $+20$ | $+44$ | $+54$ |
|---|---|---|---|---|---|
|  |  | $-2$ | $+10$ | $-56$ |  |
|  |  | $-2$ | $+10$ | $-56$ | $+4$ |
|  | $+1$ | $-5$ | $+28$ | $-2$ | $+2$ |

| $-2 -2\|$ | $+1$ | $-5$ | $+28$ |
|---|---|---|---|
|  |  | $-2$ | $+14$ |
|  |  | $-2$ | $+14$ | $-80$ |
|  | $+1$ | $-7$ | $+40$ | $-66$ |

$$40 * \Delta P(1) - 7 * \Delta Q(1) = -2$$
$$-66 * \Delta P(1) + 40 * \Delta Q(1) = 2$$
$$\Delta P(1) = P(1) - P(0) \doteq -.0580$$
$$\Delta Q(1) = Q(1) - Q(0) \doteq -.0457$$
$$P(1) \doteq 1.94, Q(1) \doteq 1.95.$$

**2.** Use the Bairstow Process to find $(P(2), Q(2))$ for the polynomial equation in Exercise 1, above, with $(P(1), Q(1)) = (1.94, 1.96)$.

*Answer.*   (P(2), Q(2)) = (1.9413, 1.9538).

3. With **(P(2), Q(2))** from Exercise 2 compute B(0), B(1), and B(2) in (3.9.3). Then compute the corresponding estimates to roots of the original polynomial in Exercise 1. That is, find roots of

$$X ** 2 + P(2) * X + Q(2) = 0$$

and

$$B(0) * X ** 2 + B(1) * X + B(2) = 0.$$

Substitute one of these (complex) roots into the original 4*th* degree polynomial.

*Answer.*   (B(0), B(1), B(2)) = (1, −4.9413, 27.6387).


### SUGGESTED READING

1. Uspensky, J. V. (1948): *Theory of Equations.* McGraw-Hill Book Company, New York. (Page 174).
2. Scarborough, J. B. (1962): *Numerical Mathematical Analysis.* The Johns Hopkins Press, Baltimore. (Chapter XI.)
3. Hildebrand, F. B. (1956): *Introduction to Numerical Analysis.* McGraw-Hill Book Company, New York. (Page 474.)

# 4  SYSTEMS OF LINEAR EQUATIONS

## 4.1 MOTIVATION

A first (semester) course in elementary numerical analysis often requires such extensive laboratory computing that we do not get far into a study of linear systems.[1] Except for an exceptional class, we do not consider eigenvalue problems at all. We do consider methods in later chapters which involve parameters defined as solutions of linear systems. Also, matrix notation and terminology simplify the presentation so that attention is focused on the method and its applications.

We present this chapter with two purposes in mind.

Our first purpose is to present in the following three sections of this chapter some definitions and notation involved in a study of linear systems, and a practical method (Gauss Elimination) for solving linear systems. We include some examples that suggest an important source of linear systems with interpretations of the solution. Probably, most of §4.2 can be left as "assigned reading" and referred to when needed in later sections.

The second purpose is the inclusion of more elementary material on linear systems (we include one section on linear programming, emphasizing the involvement with underdetermined linear systems). This material can be taken with the introduction to eigenvalues in Chapter 5 to form a part of a second (semester) course in elementary numerical analysis.

Most schools offer a sophomore course in linear systems and matrices, but this is usually not a prerequisite for the elementary numerical analysis sequence.

[1]After §4.4 (if time permits, after §4.5) we usually skip to Chapter 6.

The material presented here is not adequate to replace the linear systems course, but it is useful as a reference for the many applications to follow in this text. Our third (semester) course in elementary numerical analysis usually consists of selected topics in this text *expanded* by student presentations of material contained in books listed in Suggested Reading, notably [6], [8], and [10]. Some favorite choices are linear programming, gradient methods, and eigenvalue problems.

## 4.2 SOME DEFINITIONS AND NOTATION

The *linear system*, M equations in N unknowns,

$$(4.2.1) \qquad \sum A(I, J) * X(J), J \in //1, N//, = B(I), \text{ for each } I \in //1, M//,$$

written in expanded form

$$A(1, 1) * X(1) + A(1, 2) * X(2) + \cdots + A(1, N) * X(N) = B(1)$$
$$A(2, 1) * X(1) + A(2, 2) * X(2) + \cdots + A(2, N) * X(N) = B(2)$$
$$(4.2.2) \qquad \vdots \qquad\qquad \vdots \qquad\qquad\qquad \vdots \qquad\qquad \vdots$$
$$A(M, 1) * X(1) + A(M, 2) * X(2) + \cdots + A(M, N) * X(N) = B(M)$$

may have one solution, infinitely many solutions, or no solution at all. A vector $XX = (XX(1), XX(2), \ldots, XX(N))$ is a *solution* of the linear system (4.2.2) if the components of XX satisfy *each* equation in the system (4.2.2).

The array

$$(4.2.3) \qquad \begin{bmatrix} A(1, 1) & A(1, 2) & \cdots & A(1, N) \\ A(2, 1) & A(2, 2) & \cdots & A(2, N) \\ \vdots & \vdots & & \vdots \\ A(M, 1) & A(M, 2) & \cdots & A(M, N) \end{bmatrix} \equiv A$$

is called the *matrix of coefficients* A of the linear system (4.2.2), or (4.2.1). The *column matrices* (also called vectors)

$$(4.2.4) \qquad \begin{bmatrix} X(1) \\ X(2) \\ \vdots \\ X(N) \end{bmatrix} \equiv X, \quad \text{and} \quad \begin{bmatrix} B(1) \\ B(2) \\ B(3) \\ \vdots \\ B(M) \end{bmatrix} \equiv B$$

are called the *unknown vector* X and the *column of constants* B, respectively, of (4.2.2).

The row-by-column definition of matrix multiplication applied to the left member of the *matrix equation* $A * X = B$ gives

$$(4.2.5) \quad A * X = \begin{bmatrix} A(1,1) & A(1,2) & \cdots & A(1,N) \\ A(2,1) & A(2,2) & \cdots & A(2,N) \\ \vdots & \vdots & & \vdots \\ A(M,1) & A(M,2) & \cdots & A(M,N) \end{bmatrix} * \begin{bmatrix} X(1) \\ X(2) \\ \vdots \\ X(N) \end{bmatrix}$$

$$= \begin{bmatrix} \sum A(1,J) * X(J), J \in //1, N//, \\ \sum A(2,J) * X(J), J \in //1, N//, \\ \vdots \\ \sum A(M,J) * X(J), J \in //1, N//, \end{bmatrix} = \begin{bmatrix} B(1) \\ B(2) \\ \vdots \\ B(M) \end{bmatrix} = B.$$

Two matrices are *equal* if they have the same dimension (number of rows and columns) *and* corresponding elements are equal. The matrix of coefficients (4.2.3) has dimension $MbyN$. The unknown vector X has dimension $Nby1$, and the column of constants B is an $Mby1$ matrix.

The product $A * X$ in (4.2.5) is an $Mby1$ matrix, and $A * X = B$ if and only if corresponding elements of the matrices in the last equality of (4.2.5) are equal. That is,

$$\sum A(1,J) * X(J), J \in //1, N//, = B(1)$$
$$\sum A(2,J) * X(J), J \in //1, N//, = B(2)$$
$$\vdots \qquad\qquad\qquad \vdots$$
$$\sum A(M,J) * X(J), J \in //1, N//, = B(M)$$

hold simultaneously. Thus, the linear system (4.2.2), or (4.2.1), is *equivalent* to the matrix equation (4.2.5) in the sense that the components of *any* solution $XX = (XX(1), XX(2), \ldots, XX(N))$ of (4.2.2) are elements of a corresponding solution

$$X = XX = \begin{bmatrix} XX(1) \\ XX(2) \\ \vdots \\ XX(N) \end{bmatrix}$$

of the matrix equation (4.2.5), i.e., $A * XX = B$, and conversely.

A few *functions* defined on matrices are order (ORDER), transpose

(TRAN), conjugate (CONJ), determinant (DET), rank (RANK), adjoint (ADJ), and inverse (INV).

Some *names* associated with *properties* of matrices are real, complex, zero, dimension, row-dimension, square, column, symmetric, Hermitian, singular, nonsingular, diagonal, scalar, unit, orthogonal, unitary, positive definite, dominant diagonal, and ill-conditioned.

Some *parts* of matrices are named. A matrix consists of *elements, rows* (of elements), *columns* (of elements), and *diagonals* (of elements). We say that the element $A(I, J)$ is in the $I$*th* row and the $J$*th* column of the matrix A. The *principal* (or main) *diagonal* consists of those elements of A in the form $A(I, I)$.

A matrix is *real* (*complex*) if all of its elements are real (complex) numbers. The zero matrix has all its elements equal zero. If the row-dimension (number of rows) equals column-dimension, call it M, then the matrix is *square* with *order* M. The *transpose* of the matrix A in (4.2.3) is

$$
\text{TRAN(A)} = \begin{bmatrix} A(1, 1) & A(2, 1) & \cdots & A(M, 1) \\ A(1, 2) & A(2, 2) & \cdots & A(M, 2) \\ \vdots & \vdots & & \vdots \\ A(1, N) & A(2, N) & \cdots & A(M, N) \end{bmatrix}.
$$

That is, TRAN(A) is obtained from A by *interchanging* the rows and columns of A, so that the $(I, J)$*th* element of TRAN(A) is $A(J, I)$. If $A = \text{TRAN(A)}$, then A is *symmetric* (and square).

If the elements of A are complex numbers, then the *conjugate of A* is the complex matrix CONJ(A) obtained from A by defining the $(I, J)$*th* element of CONJ(A) to be the complex conjugate of $A(I, J)$. The matrix A is *Hermitian* if $A = \text{TRAN(CONJ(A))}$.

A *diagonal matrix* is a square matrix with all off-diagonal elements equal zero. A *scalar matrix* is a diagonal matrix with all diagonal elements equal the same constant. A *unit matrix* is any scalar matrix with diagonal elements unity. We denote any unit matrix by I and understand its order by the context. A scalar matrix is denoted by the scalar on the diagonal, or by that scalar times a unit matrix.

The *sum* (and *difference*) of matrices A and B is defined if the matrices A and B have the *same dimension*. The $(I, J)$*th* element of the sum C is

$$
C(I, J) = A(I, J) + B(I, J).
$$

The *product* of matrices A and B is defined if the column-dimension of the left factor equals the row-dimension of the right factor. In particular, the row-by-column product $C = A * B$ of the M$by$P matrix A and the P$by$N matrix B is an M$by$N matrix which has $(I, J)$*th* element

$$C(I, J) = \sum A(I, K) * B(K, J), K \in //1, P//.$$

That is, we sum the products of elements of the I*th* row of A times corresponding elements of the J*th* column of B. In particular, a *scalar* T (an M*by*M matrix) *times* the M*by*N matrix A is the M*by*N matrix T * A with (I, J)*th* element

$$(T * A)(I, J) = T * A(I, J),$$

where T in the right member is a number. Also,

$$TRAN(A * B) = TRAN(B) * TRAN(A).$$

*Division* of matrices is *not* defined, but some square matrices have multiplicative inverses. The matrix B is *the inverse* of A, written B = INV(A), if

$$B * A = A * B = I.$$

It is possible to define a left inverse and a right inverse for matrices, but we will not use these concepts here.

A square matrix A, real or complex, is *orthogonal*, [*unitary*], if and only if TRAN(A) = INV(A), [TRAN(CONJ(A)) = INV(A)].

A real [complex Hermitian] square matrix A is *positive definite* if the quadratic form [Hermitian form Q(X, X) = TRAN(CONJ(X)) * A * X]

$$Q(X, X) = TRAN(X) * A * X$$

$$= [X(1)\, X(2) \cdots X(N)] * \begin{bmatrix} A(1,1) & A(1,2) & \cdots & A(1,N) \\ A(2,1) & A(2,2) & \cdots & A(2,N) \\ \vdots & \vdots & & \vdots \\ A(N,1) & A(N,2) & \cdots & A(N,N) \end{bmatrix}$$

$$* \begin{bmatrix} X(1) \\ X(2) \\ \vdots \\ X(N) \end{bmatrix}$$

$$= \sum\sum A(I, J) * X(I) * X(J), I \in //1, N//, J \in //1, N//,$$

is positive for every X $\neq$ 0. Also, the matrix A is *positive semidefinite, negative definite*, or *negative semidefinite* if Q(X, X) is nonnegative, negative, or nonpositive, respectively, for every X $\neq$ 0. The matrix A is *definite* if Q(X, X) $\neq$ 0 for every X $\neq$ 0.

Associated with every square matrix A of order N there is unique complex number (real number if A is real) called the *determinant of order N* of A, written

$$(4.2.6) \quad DET(A) = \begin{vmatrix} A(1, 1) & A(1, 2) & A(1, 3) & \cdots & A(1, N) \\ A(2, 1) & A(2, 2) & A(2, 3) & \cdots & A(2, N) \\ \vdots & \vdots & \vdots & & \vdots \\ A(N, 1) & A(N, 2) & A(N, 3) & \cdots & A(N, N) \end{vmatrix}.$$

That is, determinant is a single-valued function defined *on* the space of N*by*N matrices *to* the complex numbers. The classical definition (see [1]) of the *number* DET(A) which is the image of A represents DET(A) as the sum of N! terms, each of which is a product of N elements of A. That is, an application of this definition to compute DET(A) could require $(N - 1) * N!$ multiplications and $N! - 1$ additions. Instead of this classical definition of DET(A), we present the *method of minors* for computing DET(A). The calculation of DET(A) by the method of minors requires $N! * \sum (1/K!)$, $K \in //1, N - 1//$, $[<N! * EXP(1)]$ multiplications and $N! - 1$ additions. In §4.4, we shall see that the Gauss Elimination Process can be used to compute DET(A) using only $N * (N ** 2 - 1)/3 + (N - 1)$ multiplications and $N * (N**2 - 1)/3$ additions. The latter method (or variations of it) is usually used in computer programs to compute DET(A) when $ORDER(A) \geq 4$. Classroom examples usually involve matrices of order four or less, so the method of minors is useful there.

The *cofactor* of the element A(I, J) of a matrix A of order N is

$$COF(A(I, J)) = (-1) ** (I + J) * MINOR(A(I, J)),$$

where MINOR(A(I, J)) is the *determinant* of the $(N - 1) by (N - 1)$ submatrix of A obtained by striking out (removing) the I*th* row and the J*th* column of A. If B is the matrix of cofactors, i.e., $B(I, J) = COF(A(I, J))$, then the transpose of this *matrix* of cofactors is called the *adjoint* of A, written $ADJ(A) = TRAN(B)$, see (4.2.8), below.

The *method of minors* defines DET(A) as a linear combination of cofactors of any row or any column of A. For each I or $J \in //1, N//$,

$$(4.2.7) \quad DET(A) = \sum A(I, K) * COF(A(I, K)), K \in //1, N//,$$
$$= \sum A(K, J) * COF(A(K, J)), K \in //1, N//.$$

The first sum is DET(A) *expanded* by the I*th* row, and the second sum is

DET(A) *expanded* by the J*th* column of (4.2.6). For example, the fourth order determinant DET(A), expanded by the first column, is written as a linear combination of four determinants of order three.

$$
\text{DET(A)} = \begin{vmatrix}
A(1, 1) & A(1, 2) & A(1, 3) & A(1, 4) \\
A(2, 1) & A(2, 2) & A(2, 3) & A(2, 4) \\
A(3, 1) & A(3, 2) & A(3, 3) & A(3, 4) \\
A(4, 1) & A(4, 2) & A(4, 3) & A(4, 4)
\end{vmatrix}
$$

$$
= A(1, 1) * COF(A(1, 1)) + A(2, 1) * COF(A(2, 1))
$$
$$
+ A(3, 1) * COF(A(3, 1)) + A(4, 1) * COF(A(4, 1)).
$$

$$
COF(A(1, 1)) = (-1) ** (1 + 1) * \begin{vmatrix}
A(2, 2) & A(2, 3) & A(2, 4) \\
A(3, 2) & A(3, 3) & A(3, 4) \\
A(4, 2) & A(4, 3) & A(4, 4)
\end{vmatrix}.
$$

$$
COF(A(2, 1)) = (-1) ** (2 + 1) * \begin{vmatrix}
A(1, 2) & A(1, 3) & A(1, 4) \\
A(3, 2) & A(3, 3) & A(3, 4) \\
A(4, 2) & A(4, 3) & A(4, 4)
\end{vmatrix}, \text{ etc.}
$$

The signed third-order determinant COF(A(2, 1)) expanded by the first row becomes a linear combination of three determinants of order two.

$$
COF(A(2, 1)) = -A(1, 2) * \begin{vmatrix}
A(3, 3) & A(3, 4) \\
A(4, 3) & A(4, 4)
\end{vmatrix}
$$
$$
+ A(1, 3) * \begin{vmatrix}
A(3, 2) & A(3, 4) \\
A(4, 2) & A(4, 4)
\end{vmatrix}
$$
$$
- A(1, 4) * \begin{vmatrix}
A(3, 2) & A(3, 3) \\
A(4, 2) & A(4, 3)
\end{vmatrix}.
$$

The first of these second-order determinants is just

$$
\begin{vmatrix}
A(3, 3) & A(3, 4) \\
A(4, 3) & A(4, 4)
\end{vmatrix} = A(3, 3) * A(4, 4) - A(3, 4) * A(4, 3).
$$

Thus, the method of minors is a process by which a determinant of order N is "replaced" by a linear combination of determinants of order N − 1, and each of these determinants of order N − 1 is replaced by a linear combination of determinants of order N − 2, etc. until DET(A) is written as a linear combination of determinants of order 2, and these second-order determinants are evaluated by the usual "cross-multiply" formula. Then, we use the distributive property of the real-number system to sum the N! terms (products of N elements of A) to get the number DET(A).

A square matrix A is *singular* if DET(A) = 0, and *nonsingular* if DET(A) ≠ 0.

An M*by*N matrix A has *rank* P, written RANK(A) = P, if there is a nonsingular submatrix of A of order P, obtained from A by deleting some (M − P) rows and (N − P) columns, while every such submatrix of A of order P + 1 is singular. The determinant (4.2.6) has *rank* Q if A has rank Q.

If the N*th* order matrix A has rank N, i.e., A is nonsingular, then the inverse of A is the matrix defined by the formula

$$(4.2.8) \quad \text{INV(A)} = \text{ADJ(A)}/\text{DET(A)}$$

$$= 1/\text{DET(A)} * \begin{bmatrix} \text{COF}(A(1,1)) & \cdots & \text{COF}(A(N,1)) \\ \text{COF}(A(1,2)) & \cdots & \text{COF}(A(N,2)) \\ \vdots & & \vdots \\ \text{COF}(A(1,N)) & \cdots & \text{COF}(A(N,N)) \end{bmatrix}.$$

Direct calculation of A * INV(A) and INV(A) * A gives the identity matrix I when we use (4.2.7) and (4.2.10), below.

*Note.* If A and B are N*th* order nonsingular matrices, then INV(A * B) = INV(B) * INV(A).

Now we list some useful properties of determinant. All matrices are assumed to be of order N.

1. If the elements of a row (or column) of A have a common factor K, then

$$\text{DET(A)} = \begin{vmatrix} K * AA(1,1) & K * AA(1,2) & \cdots & K * AA(1,N) \\ A(2,1) & A(2,2) & \cdots & A(2,N) \\ \vdots & \vdots & & \vdots \\ A(N,1) & A(N,2) & \cdots & A(N,N) \end{vmatrix}$$

$$= K * \begin{vmatrix} AA(1,1) & AA(1,2) & \cdots & AA(1,N) \\ A(2,1) & A(2,2) & \cdots & A(2,N) \\ \vdots & \vdots & & \vdots \\ A(N,1) & A(N,2) & \cdots & A(N,N) \end{vmatrix}.$$

This is easily verified by expanding the determinants by the first row.

2. If B is obtained from A by interchanging the first and second rows of A, then $DET(B) = -DET(A)$.

   *Hint.* Expand DET(B) by the second row and expand DET(A) by the first row. In general, if B is obtained from A by interchanging *any two* rows (or columns) of A, then $DET(B) = -DET(A)$.

   *Note.* An odd number of adjacent interchanges will execute the desired interchange.

3. If any two rows (or columns) of A are equal, then $DET(A) = 0$.

   *Hint.* Interchange the two equal rows and apply (2), above.

4. If any two rows (or columns) of A are proportional, then $DET(A) = 0$.

   *Hint.* Factor out the constant of proportionality and apply (3).

5. If A, B, and C are equal except possibly in their P*th* row, and if for each $J \in //1, N//$, we have $A(P, J) = B(P, J) + C(P, J)$, then $DET(A) = DET(B) + DET(C)$.

   *Hint.* Expand each determinant by the P*th* row. Similar statements hold with the word row replaced by column.

6. If one row (column) of A is multiplied by a constant and added to another row (column) of A to define B, then $DET(A) = DET(B)$. For example,

(4.2.9)

$$DET(A) = \begin{vmatrix} A(1,1) & A(1,2) & \cdots & A(1,N) \\ A(2,1) & A(2,2) & \cdots & A(2,N) \\ \vdots & \vdots & & \vdots \\ A(N,1) & A(N,2) & \cdots & A(N,N) \end{vmatrix}$$

$$= \begin{vmatrix} A(1,1) & A(1,2) & \cdots & A(1,N) \\ A(2,1) + K*A(1,1) & A(2,2) + K*A(1,2) & \cdots & A(2,N) + K*A(1,N) \\ \vdots & \vdots & & \vdots \\ A(N,1) & A(N,2) & \cdots & A(N,N) \end{vmatrix}$$

$$= DET(B).$$

   *Hint.* Apply (5) to the second row of DET(B), then use (1) and (3).

7. $RANK(A) = R$ if and only if *some* $N - R$ rows of A are linear combinations of the remaining R rows. See [2] and §4.3, below.

8. The sum of products of elements of one row (column) of A by the corresponding cofactors of another row (column) is zero.

(4.2.10)     $\sum A(I, K) * COF(A(J, K))$, $K \in //1, N//$, and $I \neq J, = 0$.

*Hint.* The sum in (4.2.10) is equivalent to DET(A) when the I*th* and J*th* rows of A are equal.

9. If $A = B * C$, then DET(A) = DET(B) $*$ DET(C), and

$$RANK(A) \leq MIN(RANK(B), RANK(C)).$$

10. If A is positive definite, then DET(A) $> 0$.

We conclude this section with some geometric considerations. Our discussion is generally restricted to the plane E2 (Euclidean 2-space) and E3. A generalization to Euclidean N-space (EN) is obtained when we replace the terms line and number pair in E2, and line, plane, and triple in E3, by hyperplane and N-tuple in EN. Each equation in (4.2.2) defines a *hyperplane*.

One linear equation in two unknowns [with, say, $A(1, 1) \neq 0$]

(4.2.11a)          $A(1, 1) * X(1) + A(1, 2) * X(2) = B(1)$

defines a line in X(1), X(2)-space. Another linear equation

(4.2.11b)          $A(2, 1) * X(1) + A(2, 2) * X(2) = B(2)$

may define the *same* line as the first line. In this case there are infinitely many number pairs $(XX(1), XX(2))$ which satisfy *both* equations (4.2.11a, b), and we say that there is a one-parameter family of solutions of the system (4.2.11a, b).

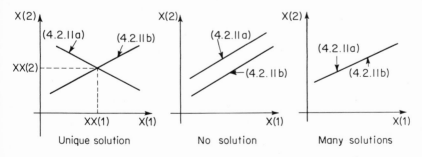

Figure 4.2.1

If the lines defined by (4.2.11a) and (4.2.11b) are parallel but not coincident, then *no* number pair $(XX(1), XX(2))$ satisfies *both* equations, and the system (4.2.11a, b) has no solution. In this case, we say that the system is inconsistent.

If the lines defined by (4.2.11a, b) *intersect*, then they have one point in common, and its coordinates $(XX(1), XX(2))$ define *the unique* solution of the system (4.2.11a, b).

Two linear systems are said to be *equivalent* if they have the same solution set. For example, the solution set for a given equation is the same as the solution set for the equation obtained from the given equation by dividing both sides of the equation by any nonzero constant. Also, the solution set for the system (4.2.11a, b) is the *same* as the solution set for the system

$$(4.2.12) \qquad \begin{aligned} A(1, 1) * X(1) + \quad A(1, 2) * X(2) &= B(1) \\ AA(2, 1) * X(1) + AA(2, 2) * X(2) &= BB(2), \end{aligned}$$

where the second equation of (4.2.12) is defined to be (4.2.11b) plus a constant times (4.2.11a). When the system has a unique solution, we have all used such operations on equations to *eliminate* a variable from one of the given equations to obtain an equivalent "triangular" system

$$(4.2.13) \qquad \begin{aligned} X(1) + C(1, 2) * X(2) &= C(1) \\ X(2) &= C(2), \end{aligned}$$

or even a "diagonal" system

$$(4.2.14) \qquad \begin{aligned} X(1) + 0 * X(2) &= D(1) \\ X(2) &= D(2). \end{aligned}$$

The second equation in (4.2.13) defines a line which is parallel to a coordinate axis. Each line in (4.2.14) is parallel to a coordinate axis. The Gauss Elimination Process in §4.4, below, is a generalization of this technique.

The corresponding discussion for three equations in three unknowns is easy.

$$(4.2.15) \qquad \begin{aligned} A(1, 1) * X(1) + A(1, 2) * X(2) + A(1, 3) * X(3) &= B(1) \\ A(2, 1) * X(1) + A(2, 2) * X(2) + A(2, 3) * X(3) &= B(2) \\ A(3, 1) * X(1) + A(3, 2) * X(2) + A(3, 3) * X(3) &= B(3). \end{aligned}$$

Each equation in (4.2.15) defines a plane in E3. The three planes could be coincident, in which case there is a two-parameter family of solutions (triples of coordinates of points on the plane). If at least two planes are parallel, but not coincident, then *no* point lies on all three planes. In this case, the system (4.2.15) has no solution, and the system is inconsistent. If two planes intersect, they intersect in a line. If this line lies in the third plane, then there is a line (one-parameter family) of solutions of the system (4.2.15). If this line intersects the third plane, then that point corresponds to *the unique* solution of (4.2.15).

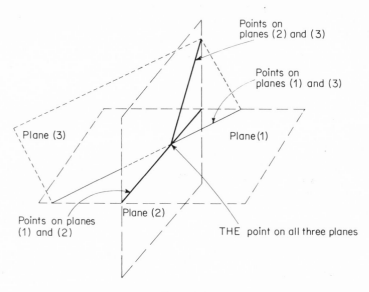

**Figure 4.2.2**

If the system (4.2.15) has a unique solution, then we can use an elimination method to replace (4.2.15) by an equivalent "triangular" (or a "diagonal") linear system where at least one new equation corresponds to a plane parallel to a coordinate plane, etc.

The reader should attempt a corresponding discussion for N equations in N unknowns, using "hyperplane" for plane, etc.

We now give one geometric interpretation for the problem of finding a solution X of the matrix equation $A * X = B$, corresponding to (4.2.15).

$$A * X = \begin{bmatrix} A(1,1) & A(1,2) & A(1,3) \\ A(2,1) & A(2,2) & A(2,3) \\ A(3,1) & A(3,2) & A(3,3) \end{bmatrix} * \begin{bmatrix} X(1) \\ X(2) \\ X(3) \end{bmatrix} = \begin{bmatrix} B(1) \\ B(2) \\ B(3) \end{bmatrix} = B.$$

Let the elements of the column matrix B be the coordinates of the terminal end of a vector B1 with heel at the origin. We say B1 has coordinates $(B(1), B(2), B(3))$. Similarly, a vector X1 has coordinates $(X(1), X(2), X(3))$, a point in E3. The operator A1 (associated with the matrix A) maps every vector X1 with coordinates $(X(1), X(2), X(3))$ into a vector Y1 with coordinates $(Y(1), Y(2), Y(3))$, where each $Y(K) = \sum A(K, J) * X(J), J \in //1, 3//$. Then the problem is to *find* a vector X1 with coordinates $(XX(1), XX(2), XX(3))$ which maps under A1 into a specified vector Y1 = B1.

If the linear system (4.2.15) is homogeneous (B = 0), then we ask for all vectors X1 which map under A1 into the origin. This set of vectors X1 is called the *null space* of A1.

The eigenvalue problems of Chapter 5 may be interpreted as asking for vectors X1 which map under A1 into a constant times itself, L * X1. That is, we ask for a vector which maps under A1 into a vector with the same or opposite direction, and whose magnitude is changed by the factor $|L|$.

### 4.3 CRAMER'S RULE. SOME REMARKS ON EXISTENCE AND UNIQUENESS OF SOLUTIONS

Suppose the first equation of the system of N equations in N unknowns (with corresponding matrix equation A * X = B)

$$A(1, 1) * X(1) + A(1, 2) * X(2) + \cdots + A(1, N) * X(N) = B(1)$$
$$A(2, 1) * X(1) + A(2, 2) * X(2) + \cdots + A(2, N) * X(N) = B(2)$$
(4.3.1)  $\quad \vdots \qquad\qquad \vdots \qquad\qquad\qquad \vdots \qquad\qquad \vdots$
$$A(N, 1) * X(1) + A(N, 2) * X(2) + \cdots + A(N, N) * X(N) = B(N)$$

is multiplied by the cofactor $COF(A(1, 1))$ of $A(1, 1)$, the second equation is multiplied by $COF(A(2, 1))$, etc., and the N*th* equation is multiplied by $COF(A(N, 1))$. If the resulting equations are added, then [using (4.2.10) and (4.2.7)] we get

(4.3.2)    $\sum A(I, 1) * COF(A(I, 1)) * X(1), I \in //1, N//, = X(1) * DET(A)$
$= \sum B(I) * COF(A(I, 1)), I \in //1, N//.$

Similarly, for each K, if the I*th* equation is multiplied by $COF(A(I, K))$, for $I \in //1, N//$, and if the resulting equations are summed, then we get, for each $K \in //1, N//$,

(4.3.3) $\sum A(I, K) * COF(A(I, K)) * X(K), I \in //1, N//,$

$= X(K) * DET(A) = \sum B(I) * COF(A(I, K)), I \in //1, N//.$

Thus, if $DET(A) \neq 0$, then *the* solution of (4.3.1) is, for each $K \in //1, N//,$

(4.3.4) $X(K) = 1/DET(A) * \sum B(I) * COF(A(I, K)), I \in //1, N//.$

Since, in (4.3.2), the last sum $\sum B(I) * COF(A(I, 1)), I \in //1, N//,$ is the determinant (expanded by the first column)

$$\begin{vmatrix} B(1) & A(1, 2) & A(1, 3) & \cdots & A(1, N) \\ B(2) & A(2, 2) & A(2, 3) & \cdots & A(2, N) \\ \vdots & \vdots & \vdots & & \vdots \\ B(N) & A(N, 2) & A(N, 3) & \cdots & A(N, N) \end{vmatrix},$$

and since the sum in (4.3.4) is the determinant (expanded by the K*th* column) of the matrix formed from A by replacing its K*th* column by the column of constants, then the solution (4.3.4) of (4.3.1) may be written as a set of N quotients of N*th* order determinants. This representation of the solution of (4.3.1) is called *Cramer's Rule*. This method was used to solve the linear system in §3.6.

Solution of (4.3.1) by Cramer's Rule involves evaluation of $N + 1$ determinants of order N. Of course, if the method of minors is used to evaluate the determinants, we may expand DET(A) by a column, say the first, and the cofactors $COF(A(I, 1))$ required in (4.3.4) need not be recomputed. Even with other tricks to reduce the computing when applying Cramer's Rule, if $N > 3$ we have better (more economical) methods for solving (4.3.1). In practice, the elimination process presented in the next section (and variations of it) is preferred to Cramer's Rule.

We turn now to the more general form (4.2.2), M equations in N unknowns.

(4.3.5) $\sum A(I, J) * X(J), J \in //1, N//, = B(I),$ for each $I \in //1, M//.$

If each $B(I) = 0, I \in //1, M//,$ then (4.3.5) is called a *homogeneous* linear system, and *one* solution of the homogeneous system is $X = (0, 0, \ldots, 0),$ called the *trivial solution*. The reader should show that if $X = (X(1), X(2), \ldots, X(N))$ is *any* solution of a homogeneous linear system, then $K * X =$

$(K * X(1), K * X(2), \ldots, K * X(N))$ is also a solution, for any constant K. In Chapter 5 we seek *nontrivial* solutions of an important class of homogeneous linear equations which involve a parameter.

We have seen that "square" linear systems, with *constant* $B(I)$, $I \in //1, N//$, have a solution (4.3.4) if $DET(A) \neq 0$. Also, homogeneous linear systems have at least one solution $(X = 0)$.

We now list some theorems concerning the solvability of the linear system (4.3.5). These statements involve the rank of the *augmented matrix*

$$(A|B) = \begin{bmatrix} A(1,1) & A(1,2) & \cdots & A(1,N) & B(1) \\ A(2,1) & A(2,2) & \cdots & A(2,N) & B(2) \\ \vdots & \vdots & & \vdots & \vdots \\ A(M,1) & A(M,2) & \cdots & A(M,N) & B(M) \end{bmatrix}.$$

We write $R = RANK(A)$, and $R1 = RANK((A|B))$.

**Theorem 1.** The linear system (4.3.5) *has* a solution if and only if $R = R1$.

**Theorem 2.** $R \leq R1$.

*Note.* If $R < R1$, we say the system is *inconsistent*.

**Theorem 3.** The linear system (4.3.5) has a *unique* solution if and only if $N = R = R1$.

In particular, if $M = N$, then (4.3.1) has a unique solution if and only if A is nonsingular $[DET(A) \neq 0]$.

**Theorem 4.** If $R = R1$, then *some* R unknowns may be represented in terms of the remaining $N - R$ unknowns. That is, there is an $(N - R)$-parameter family of solutions where the parameters may be assigned any real values. Also, *some* $M - R$ equations are linear combinations of the remaining R equations. See [2].

**Example 1.** Let (4.3.5) be such that $R = R1 < N$, and let the R*by*R submatrix in the upper left corner of A be nonsingular. Then write the first R equations, for each $I \in //1, R//$,

(4.3.6)     $\sum A(I, J) * X(J), J \in //1, R//$,

$= B(I) - \sum A(I, J) * X(J), J \in //R + 1, N//$,

or in matrix form

$$(4.3.7) \quad AA * XX = \begin{bmatrix} A(1,1) & A(1,2) & \cdots & A(1,R) \\ A(2,1) & A(2,2) & \cdots & A(2,R) \\ \vdots & \vdots & & \vdots \\ A(R,1) & A(R,2) & \cdots & A(R,R) \end{bmatrix} * \begin{bmatrix} X(1) \\ X(2) \\ \vdots \\ X(R) \end{bmatrix}$$

$$= \begin{bmatrix} B(1) - \sum A(1,J) * X(J), J \in //R+1, N//, \\ B(2) - \sum A(2,J) * X(J), J \in //R+1, N//, \\ \vdots \\ B(R) - \sum A(R,J) * X(J), J \in //R+1, N//, \end{bmatrix} = BB.$$

Since $DET(AA) \neq 0$, $INV(AA)$ exists. Also, the unique solution of (4.3.7) is given by

$$(4.3.8) \qquad XX = INV(AA) * AA * XX = INV(AA) * BB,$$

where the components of $XX$ are linear combinations of elements of $BB$ which are linear combinations of the $X(J)$, $J \in //R+1, N//$. Also, $XX$ is a solution of the (neglected) system, for each $I \in //R+1, N//$,

$$\sum A(I,J) * X(J), J \in //1, R//, = B(I) - \sum A(I,J) * X(J), J \in //R+1, N//,$$

since these equations are linear combinations of those in (4.3.6). Note that the solution (4.3.8) involves the $N - R$ parameters $X(J)$, $J \in //R+1, N//$. *Underdetermined* linear systems (with more unknowns than equations) are considered in linear programming problems in §4.9, below.

**Example 2.** Define the polynomial of degree 2 which passes through the three points $(-H, F(-H))$, $(0, F(0))$, $(H, F(H))$. We require that the polynomial form

$$(4.3.9) \qquad P(X; A, B, C) = A * X ** 2 + B * X + C$$

satisfy the conditions

$$
\begin{aligned}
& P(-H; A, B, C) = F(-H) \\
(4.3.10) \qquad & P(0; A, B, C) = F(0) \\
& P(H; A, B, C) = F(H),
\end{aligned}
$$

to obtain the linear system

$$
\begin{aligned}
& (-H) ** 2 * A + (-H) * B + C = F(-H) \\
(4.3.11) \qquad & (0) ** 2 * A + \quad (0) * B + C = F(0) \\
& (H) ** 2 * A + \quad (H) * B + C = F(H).
\end{aligned}
$$

The corresponding matrix equation is

$$
\begin{bmatrix} H**2 & -H & 1 \\ 0 & 0 & 1 \\ H**2 & H & 1 \end{bmatrix} * \begin{bmatrix} A \\ B \\ C \end{bmatrix} = \begin{bmatrix} F(-H) \\ F(0) \\ F(H) \end{bmatrix}.
$$

The solution of the linear system is

(A, B, C)

$$
= \left( \big( F(H) - 2 * F(0) + F(-H) \big) / (2 * H ** 2), \big( F(H) - F(-H) \big) / (2 * H), F(0) \right).
$$

The reader should verify that the polynomial P(X; A, B, C), with the A, B, and C of the solution (A, B, C) substituted, agrees with F(X) at the specified points X = −H, 0, and H.

**Example 3.** Define the coefficients A, B, and C of the linear form (here, a functional: real-valued function of the function F)

(4.3.12)     $T(F) = \int F(X)$, over $X \in (-H, H)$,

$$
- \big( A * F(-H) + B * F(0) + C * F(H) \big)
$$

subject to the conditions

$$
T(F) = 0, \text{ for } F(X) \equiv 1.
$$
(4.3.13)     $T(F) = 0, \text{ for } F(X) = X.$
$$
T(F) = 0, \text{ for } F(X) = X ** 2.
$$

With $F(X) \equiv 1$, the condition $T(F) = 0$ becomes

$$
\int 1, \text{ over } X \in (-H, H), = A * 1 + B * 1 + C * 1
$$

or

$$
A + B + C = 2 * H.
$$

The condition $T(F) = 0$, for $F(X) = X$ becomes

$$
\int X, \text{ over } X \in (-H, H), = A * (-H) + B * (0) + C * (H),
$$

or

$$
-H * A + H * C = H ** 2/2 - (-H) ** 2/2 = 0.
$$

Also, the condition $T(F) = 0$, for $F(X) = X ** 2$ becomes

$$\int X ** 2, \text{ over } X \in (-H, H), = A * (-H) ** 2 + B * 0 + C * H ** 2,$$

or

$$H ** 2 * (A + C) = H ** 3/3 - (-H) ** 3/3 = 2/3 * H ** 3.$$

Then, the coefficients A, B, and C are defined by the linear system

$$
\begin{aligned}
A + B + C &= 2 * H \\
-A \qquad + C &= 0 \\
A \qquad + C &= 2/3 * H.
\end{aligned}
$$

(4.3.14)

The solution of (4.3.14) is $(A, B, C) = (H/3, 4 * H/3, H/3)$. The form (4.3.12) with the solution $(A, B, C)$ substituted defines Simpson's Rule, where $T(F)$ denotes the truncation error of the estimate

$$\int F(X), \text{ over } X \in (-H, H), \doteq H/3 * \big(F(-H) + 4 * F(0) + F(H)\big).$$

This corresponds to the second numerical integration formula in Table 10.2.1. Also, see Exercise 5, below.

### EXERCISES

**1.** Discuss the solvability of the linear system

$$
\begin{aligned}
X(1) - 2 * X(2) - X(3) &= 1 \\
2 * X(1) + \quad X(2) + X(3) &= -2 \\
4 * X(1) - 3 * X(2) - X(3) &= 0.
\end{aligned}
$$

Use Cramer's Rule to solve the system. Compare Example 1 with $R = 2$.

**2.** Discuss the solvability of the linear system obtained from the system in Exercise 1 by replacing the last equation by

$$4 * X(1) - 3 * X(2) - X(3) = 1.$$

**3.** Provide the details for Example 2.

**4.** Provide the details for Example 3.

**5.** With P(X; A, B, C) defined in Example 2, (with the values of A, B, and C substituted) compute

$$W = \int P(X; A, B, C), \text{ over } X \in (-H, H).$$

Compare W with the estimate in Example 3.

### 4.4. GAUSS ELIMINATION

In this section we first consider the linear system (4.3.1) of N equations in N unknowns, and assume DET(A) $\neq$ 0 so that the system has a unique solution. We indicate how the Gauss Elimination Method may be applied to obtain this solution. A part of this process is sufficient to compute DET(A). Then we indicate how the Gauss Elimination Method can be applied to the more general system (4.2.2) of M equations in N unknowns to select a maximal subsystem of linearly independent equations and to determine if the system is consistent.

We suppose the linear system (4.3.1) has DET(A) $\neq$ 0, and that the equations have been arranged so that the coefficient A(1, 1) $\neq$ 0. In practice, it often happens that we work with linear systems where *each* equation has *one* coefficient much larger in magnitude than the other coefficients in the equation (not counting the constant term). Sometimes we are able to rewrite the system with these largest elements "on the diagonal" of the matrix of coefficients. If for each I $\in$ //1, N//,

(4.4.1a)      $|A(I, I)| > \sum |A(I, J)|, J \in //1, N//$, and $J \neq I$,

*and* for each J $\in$ //1, N//,

(4.4.1b)      $|A(J, J)| > \sum |A(I, J)|, I \in //1, N//$, and $I \neq J$,

then the matrix of coefficients is said to have the property *dominant diagonal.*

If in (4.3.1) the coefficient A(1, 1) $\neq$ 0, then we may write the equivalent linear system [it has the same solution as (4.3.1)]

$$X(1) + A1(1, 2) * X(2) + \cdots + A1(1, N) * X(N) = B1(1)$$
$$A1(2, 2) * X(2) + \cdots + A1(2, N) * X(N) = B1(2)$$
(4.4.2)      $\qquad \vdots \qquad\qquad\qquad \vdots \qquad\qquad \vdots$
$$A1(N, 2) * X(2) + \cdots + A1(N, N) * X(N) = B1(N),$$

where

$$A1(1, J) = A(1, J)/A(1, 1), \text{ for each } J \in //2, N//,$$

$$B1(1) = B(1)/A(1, 1),$$

and for each $I \in //2, N//$,

$$A1(I, J) = A(I, J) - A(I, 1) * A1(1, J), \text{ for each } J \in //2, N//,$$

$$B1(I) = B(I) - A(I, 1) * B1(1).$$

This *elimination* of $X(1)$ from all the equations of (4.3.1) except the first was accomplished as follows:

1. Divide the first equation through by $A(1, 1)$ (the coefficient used as the divisor is called the *pivot* of the elimination); and
2. For each $I \in //2, N//$, multiply the new first equation by $A(I, 1)$ and subtract the resulting equation from the I*th* equation.

The determinant of the matrix of coefficients in (4.3.1) is $A(1, 1)$ times the corresponding determinant in (4.4.2); see properties 1 and 6 in §4.2. The solution of (4.4.2) is also the solution of (4.3.1).

If $A1(2, 2) \neq 0$, then $A1(2, 2)$ may be used as a pivot in the elimination of $X(2)$ from equations 3 through N of (4.4.2) to obtain

$$X(1) + A1(1, 2)*X(2) + A1(1, 3)*X(3) + \cdots + A1(1, N)*X(N) = B1(1)$$

$$X(2) + A2(2, 3)*X(3) + \cdots + A2(2, N)*X(N) = B2(2)$$

(4.4.3)
$$A2(3, 3)*X(3) + \cdots + A2(3, N)*X(N) = B2(3)$$
$$\vdots \qquad \qquad \vdots \qquad \qquad \vdots$$
$$A2(N, 3)*X(3) + \cdots + A2(N, N)*X(N) = B2(N).$$

If $A1(2, 2) = 0$, then the second through the N*th* equations of (4.4.2) can be rearranged to give a nonzero coefficient of $X(2)$ in the $A1(2, 2)$ position which can be used as a pivot. Each time the positions of two equations are interchanged the determinants of the matrices of coefficients before and after the changes are opposite in sign.

This elimination process is repeated until we obtain the triangular form [we assumed $DET(A) \neq 0$]

$$X(1) + A1(1, 2) * X(2) + A1(1, 3) * X(3) + \cdots$$

$$+ A1(1, N) * X(N) = B1(1)$$

$$X(2) + A2(2, 3) * X(3) + \cdots$$

(4.4.4)
$$+ A2(2, N) * X(N) = B2(2)$$
$$\vdots$$

$$X(N - 1) + ANM1(N - 1, N) * X(N) = BNM1(N - 1)$$

$$X(N) = BN(N).$$

The obvious method (called *back-substitution*) for solving the system (4.4.4) is: (i) Substitute $X(N) = BN(N)$ into the $(N - 1)th$ equation to determine $X(N - 1)$; (ii) Substitute $X(N)$ and $X(N - 1)$ into the $(N - 2)th$ equation to determine $X(N - 2)$; etc. This method for computing (4.4.4), followed by its solution by back-substitution, is called the *Gauss Elimination Method* to solve (4.3.1).

**Example 1.** Use Gauss Elimination to solve the system

$$A + B + C = -1$$
$$A \qquad\quad = 1$$
$$A - B + C = 3.$$

SOLUTION. The first elimination, (4.4.2), gives

$$A + B + C = -1 \qquad \text{Pivot: } A(1, 1) = 1.$$
$$-B - C = 2$$
$$-2 * B \qquad = 4.$$

The second elimination, (4.4.3), gives first

$$A + B + C = -1$$
$$B + C = -2 \qquad \text{Pivot: } A1(2, 2) = -1.$$
$$-2 * B \qquad = 4,$$

then

$$A + B + C = -1$$
$$B + C = -2$$
$$2 * C = 0.$$

Finally, we get, (4.4.4)

$$A + B + C = -1$$
$$B + C = -2$$
$$C = 0. \qquad \text{Pivot: } A2(3, 3) = 2.$$

Back-substitution gives

$$C = 0, \quad B = -2, \quad A = 1.$$

The determinant of the matrix of coefficients is

$$A(1, 1) * A1(2, 2) * A2(3, 3) = (1) * (-1) * (2) = -2.$$

**Example 2.** Using Gauss Elimination, solve

$$C + B + A = -1$$
$$A = 1$$
$$C - B + A = 3.$$

*Note.* This is the system in Example 1 with the *positions* of the first and third variables interchanged.

SOLUTION. The first elimination, (4.4.2), gives

$$C + B + A = -1 \qquad \text{Pivot: } A(1, 1) = 1.$$
$$A = 1$$
$$-2 * B \qquad = 4.$$

Here, $A1(2, 2) = 0$ so that a row interchange (or column interchange, described below) is in order to obtain a nonzero pivot in the $A1(2, 2)$ position. We write

$$C + B + A = -1$$
$$-2 * B \qquad = 4$$
$$A = 1.$$

The second elimination results in the form (4.4.4)

$$C + B + A = -1$$
$$B \qquad = -2 \qquad \text{Pivot: } A1(2, 2) = -2.$$
$$A = 1. \qquad \text{Pivot: } A2(3, 3) = 1.$$

Back-substitution gives

$$A = 1, \quad B = -2, \quad C = 0.$$

The determinant of the matrix of coefficients is $-1$ (due to the execution of one row interchange) times the product of the pivots; i.e.,

$$DET(A) = (-1) ** 1 * (1) * (-2) * (1) = 2.$$

We can save many strokes of the pen by writing, at each stage of the elimination process, just the coefficients of the equations involved. See Exercise 2, below. In §4.5 we describe a method (*Crout Reduction*) equivalent to the Gauss Elimination Method, which begins with the augmented matrix (A|B) for (4.3.1), obtains the coefficients in (4.4.4), records them in corresponding positions of the array (A|B), and uses the other positions in (A|B) as storage for intermediate calculations (including all the pivot elements).

Not counting possible interchanges of equations (rows) $N * (N + 1) * (2 * N + 1)/6$ multiplications and $N * (N ** 2 - 1)/3$ additions[1] are required to obtain the form (4.4.4), and $N * (N - 1)/2$ multiplications and $N * (N - 1)/2$ additions are required for a back-substitution. If no row interchanges are necessary, then $N * (N ** 2 + 3 * N - 1)/3$ multiplications and $N * (N - 1) * (2 * N + 5)/6$ additions are required to solve (4.3.1) by the Gauss Elimination Method.

Since the determinant of the matrix of coefficients in (4.4.4) is unity, then DET(A), assumed not zero, for (4.3.1) is $(-1) ** M$ times the product of the pivot elements used to obtain (4.4.4) from (4.3.1), where M is the number of row interchanges executed in the process. And, since the Gauss Elimination Method can be applied to any square matrix A, neglecting calculations involving the column of constants, and since back-substitution is not required to *determine* the pivots, then calculation of DET(A) by this method requires $N * (N ** 2 - 1)/3$ multiplications and $N * (N ** 2 - 1)/3$ additions to determine the pivots *and* $N - 1$ multiplications to compute the product of the pivots.

If DET(A) = 0, then at some point in the Gauss Elimination Method, say when we seek a pivot to eliminate X(K) from the $(K + 1)th$ through the $Nth$ equations, we find either that the $Kth$ equation reduces[2] to $0 = L$, *or* that the coefficient of X(K) is zero in each of the $Kth$ through the $Nth$ equations. In the first case, with $L = 0$, it is clear that the $Kth$ equation is a linear combination of the preceeding $K - 1$ equations. In the latter case we are left with $N - K + 1$ equations in $N - K$ unknowns, and if the original system (4.3.1) is consistent, then at least one of this set of $N - K + 1$ equations is a linear combination of the others in the set.

---

[1] When *counting* arithmetic operations for this method we count a division as a multiplication and count a subtraction as an addition, assuming that the execution times for a multiplication and a division (an addition and a subtraction) are about the same on an electronic computer with these operations built-in. Here we do *not* count those operations that always generate 1 (on the diagonal) or 0 (below the 1) in the column corresponding to the variable being eliminated.

[2] If $L \neq 0$, then the original system is not consistent. The most important practical problem here is to decide when a number is considered zero.

We have seen how row (equation) interchanges could be useful in finding a pivot for an elimination. We could also execute a *column* interchange by rewriting *all* equations (including those from which certain other variables have already been eliminated) with the positions of the variables with their respective coefficients interchanged. For example, if in (4.4.2) we have $A1(2, 2) = 0$ and $A1(2, 3) \neq 0$, we might write the equivalent system

$$X(1) + A1(1, 3)*X(3) + A1(1, 2)*X(2) + \cdots + A1(1, N)*X(N) = B1(1)$$
$$A1(2, 3)*X(3) + A1(2, 2)*X(2) + \cdots + A1(2, N)*X(N) = B1(2)$$

(4.4.5)

$$A1(N, 3)*X(3) + A1(N, 2)*X(2) + \cdots + A1(N, N)*X(N) = B1(N)$$

and use $A1(2, 3)$ as a pivot to eliminate $X(3)$ from the third through the $Nth$ equations.

In practice, we attempt to avoid using as pivots numbers which should be zero, but are not zero due to round-off errors experienced when computing with number systems like those discussed in Chapter 1. Also, we try to avoid using for pivots numbers that are small compared to other numbers used in the calculation, as this tends to increase (i) the range of numbers involved, (ii) the effect of round-off, and (iii) the probability of overflow.

Thus, we might include in a code that uses the Gauss Elimination Method (or any of several equivalent processes) a search for *largest pivot*. For the $Kth$ elimination, *search* the $Kth$ equation (and/or the first column of the $Kth$ through the $Nth$ equations) for the coefficient largest in magnitude, and after the appropriate column (or row) interchange use this largest coefficient as pivot. If the largest pivot is zero, then the variable corresponding to the first column in this subsystem (if it appears explicitly in the first $K - 1$ equations) is an independent parameter in the solution, and terms involving this parameter are transposed to the side of the equation containing the constants. Then we examine the next equation (and next column) for a largest pivot. Of course, if $\text{DET}(A) \neq 0$, then no zero largest pivot is found.

When a search for a largest pivot is included, the Gauss Elimination Method can be used (i) to determine whether or not the system (4.3.1) or (4.2.2) is consistent; (ii) to determine the rank of a matrix; (iii) to compute $\text{DET}(A)$ for (4.3.1); (iv) to determine a largest linearly independent subset of the system (4.2.2); (v) when $\text{DET}(A) \neq 0$, to find the unique solution of (4.3.1); and (vi) after execution of (iv) to solve (4.3.7) for the $(N - R)$-parameter family of solutions to (4.2.2). For, if after any elimination one equation becomes $0 = L$ where $L \neq 0$, then the system is not consistent. And, for (4.3.1),

DET(A) is $(-1)**M$ times the product of the pivots where M represents the number of row interchanges in addition to the number of column interchanges, etc.

**EXERCISES**

**1.** (a) Write in detail the matrix equation corresponding to the system (4.3.1). (b) Write the matrix equation corresponding to the system after the first and third equations are interchanged. (c) Write the matrix equation corresponding to the system after a column interchange involving the second and N*th* column.

**2.** Starting with the augmented matrix (A|B) for the system (4.3.1), describe, with appropriate remarks concerning variables associated with their columns, the operations on rows and columns of (A|B) required to obtain the augmented matrix for the system (a) obtained from (4.3.1) by interchanging the first and second equations, (b) (4.4.2), (c) (4.4.3), (d) (4.4.5), (e) (4.4.4), and (f) back-substitution from (4.4.4).

*Hint.* For (f): In back-substitution we multiply the N*th* equation in (4.4.4) by ANM1(N − 1, N) and subtract this from the (N − 1)*th* equation, then multiply the N*th* equation by ANM2(N − 2, N) and multiply the *new* (N − 1)*th* equation by ANM2(N − 2, N − 1) and subtract both of these from the (N − 2)*th* equation, etc.

**3.** The *Jordan Elimination Method* is like Gauss Elimination except that at the same time X(K) is being eliminated from the N − K equations below the K*th* equation we also eliminate X(K) from the first K − 1 equations, so that each off-diagonal coefficient in (4.4.4) is zero, and *no* back-substitution is required to solve (4.4.4). Describe the Jordan Elimination Method in terms of operations on rows and columns of augmented matrices. See Exercise 2.

## 4.5. CROUT REDUCTION. MATRIX INVERSION

Crout Reduction is a name associated with a short-hand version of Gauss Elimination. The methods differ only in the manner in which (4.4.4) is computed. Execution of Crout Reduction requires the *same* number of multiplications and additions as does execution of Gauss Elimination.

The remarks of §4.4 concerning interchange of rows and/or columns to determine (largest) pivots, calculation of determinants, determining a largest linearly independent subset of a given linear system, and solving linear systems using the Gauss Elimination Process are applicable here for Crout Reduction. We do not repeat their statements but illustrate some of them in examples.

In this section, we assume that the augmented matrix, $(A|B)$, for the linear system, for each $I \in //1, N//$,

$$(4.5.1) \qquad \sum A(I, J) * X(J), J \in //1, N//, = B(I), \qquad [A * X = B],$$

is stored in the computer.

$$(4.5.2) \qquad (A|B): \begin{array}{cccccc} A(1,1) & A(1,2) & A(1,3) & \cdots & A(1,N) & B(1) \\ A(2,1) & A(2,2) & A(2,3) & \cdots & A(2,N) & B(2) \\ A(3,1) & A(3,2) & A(3,3) & \cdots & A(3,N) & B(3) \\ \vdots & \vdots & \vdots & & \vdots & \vdots \\ A(N,1) & A(N,2) & A(N,3) & \cdots & A(N,N) & B(N) \end{array}$$

We compute elements of a new matrix "B," with the same dimension as $(A|B)$, and store "B" in the storage cells originally occupied by $(A|B)$.

$$(4.5.3) \qquad \text{"B":} \begin{array}{cccccc} A(1,1) & A1(1,2) & A1(1,3) & \cdots & A1(1,N) & B1(1) \\ C(2,1) & A1(2,2) & A2(2,3) & \cdots & A2(2,N) & B2(2) \\ C(3,1) & C(3,2) & A2(3,3) & \cdots & A3(3,N) & B3(3) \\ \vdots & \vdots & \vdots & & \vdots & \vdots \\ C(N,1) & C(N,2) & C(N,3) & \cdots & ANM1(N,N) & BN(N) \end{array}$$

The elements $A(1, 1), A1(2, 2), A2(3, 3), \ldots, ANM1(N, N)$ *on* the principal diagonal of "B" are the *pivot* elements involved in a solution of (4.5.1) by Gauss Elimination. The elements *above* the principle diagonal in "B" are the coefficients in (4.4.4), so that after computing "B," only a back-substitution is required to solve (4.5.1). The elements of "B" *below* the principal diagonal are recordings of *intermediate calculations.*

The elements of "B" are computed one block at a time in the sequence indicated by the circled numbers in the blocks of (4.5.4).

(4.5.4)     "B":

| A(1, 1) | A1(1, 2) | A1(1, 3) | A1(1, 4) | ② A1(1, N) | B1(1) |
|---|---|---|---|---|---|
| C(2, 1) | A1(2, 2) | A2(2, 3) | A2(2, 4) | ④ A2(2, N) | B2(2) |
| C(3, 1) | C(3, 2) | A2(3, 3) | A3(3, 4) | ⑥ A3(3, N) | B3(3) |
| ⋮ ① | ⋮ ③ | ⋮ ⑤ | | | ⋮ |
| C(N, 1) | C(N, 2) | C(N, 3) | | ... | BN(N) |

Block (1):  $A1(1, 1) = A(1, 1)$, and $C(K, 1) = A(K, 1)$, for $K \in //2, N//$.

Block (2):  $A1(1, K) = A(1, K)/A(1, 1)$, for $K \in //2, N//$,

and $B1(1) = B(1)/A(1, 1)$.

Block (3):  $A1(2, 2) = A(2, 2) - C(2, 1) * A1(1, 2)$

$C(K, 2) = A(K, 2) - C(K, 1) * A1(1, 2)$, for $K \in //3, N//$.

Block (4):  $A2(2, K) = (A(2, K) - C(2, 1) * A1(1, K))/A1(2, 2)$,

for $K \in //3, N//$,

$B2(2) = (B(2) - C(2, 1) * B1(1))/A1(2, 2)$.

Block (5):  $A2(3, 3) = A(3, 3) - C(3, 1) * A1(1, 3) - C(3, 2) * A2(2, 3)$

$C(K, 3) = A(K, 3) - C(K, 1) * A1(1, 3)$

$- C(K, 2) * A2(2, 3)$, for $K \in //4, N//$.

Block (6):  $A3(3, K) = (A(3, K) - C(3, 1) * A1(1, K)$

$- C(3, 2) * A2(2, K))/A2(3, 3)$,

for $K \in //4, N//$,

$B3(3) = (B(3) - C(3, 1) * B1(1) - C(3, 2) * B2(2))/A2(3, 3)$.

To complete the $J$th column, Block $(2 * J - 1)$: Compute

(4.5.5a)     $AJM1(J, J) = A(J, J) - C(J, 1) * A1(1, J) - C(J, 2) * A2(2, J)$

$- \cdots - C(J, J - 1) * AJM1(J - 1, J)$,

and for each $K \in //J + 1, N//$,

(4.5.5b)     $C(K, J) = A(K, J) - C(K, 1) * A1(1, J) - C(K, 2) * A2(2, J)$

$- \cdots - C(K, J - 1) * AJM1(J - 1, J)$.

To complete the $I$th row, Block $(2 * I)$: Compute for each $K \in //I + 1, N//$,

(4.5.6a)     $AI(I, K) = 1/AIM1(I, I) * (A(I, K) - C(I, 1) * A1(1, K)$
$- C(I, 2) * A2(2, K) - \cdots$
$- C(I, I - 1)* AIM1(I - 1, K))$,

and

(4.5.6b)     $BI(I) = 1/AIM1(I, I) * (B(I) - C(I, 1) * B1(1) - C(I, 2) * B2(2)$
$- \cdots - C(I, I - 1) * BIM1(I - 1))$.

Each element of "B" is defined using only elements in the row and column that contain the element being computed. All the elements of the first column of "B" are computed [*copied* from (A|B)]; then all other elements of the first row are computed; then all other elements of the second column are computed; then all other elements of the second row are computed, etc. *When we follow this sequence*, if an element of "B" has been computed, then the element in the corresponding row and column of (A|B) is no longer needed to complete the calculation of "B." Thus the newly computed element of "B" may be stored in the storage cell containing the corresponding element of (A|B). The only other *workspace* required to compute "B" is that needed to compute inner products, as in (4.5.5a, b) and (4.5.6a, b).

When the calculation of "B" is complete, the elements C(I, J) of "B" below the principal diagonal are no longer needed, and these storage cells are available for use as *workspace* when executing the back-substitution to solve (4.4.4), and thus obtain a solution of (4.5.1).

**Example 1.** Using Crout Reduction, solve (compare Example 1 of §4.4)

$$A * X = \begin{bmatrix} 1 & 1 & 1 \\ 1 & 0 & 0 \\ 1 & -1 & 1 \end{bmatrix} * \begin{bmatrix} X(1) \\ X(2) \\ X(3) \end{bmatrix} = \begin{bmatrix} -1 \\ 1 \\ 3 \end{bmatrix} = B.$$

SOLUTION.

$$
\begin{array}{cccc}
 & 1 & 1 & 1 & -1 \\
(A|B): & 1 & 0 & 0 & 1 \\
 & 1 & -1 & 1 & 3
\end{array}
$$

*Note.* We generate a separate matrix "B," but ask the reader to recall that in a computer program, or when executing Crout Reduction with chalk on a blackboard (where it is easy to erase numbers), one would probably want to replace elements of (A|B) with corresponding elements of "B" as they are computed.

After execution of the operations indicated above for Blocks (1) through (6) with N = 3, we get

$$
\begin{array}{cccc}
1 & 1 & 1 & -1 \\
\text{"B": } 1 & -1 & -1/(-1) & 2/(-1). \\
1 & -2 & 2 & 0/2
\end{array}
$$

Thus (4.4.4) becomes

$$X(1) + (1) * X(2) + (1) * X(3) = (-1)$$
$$X(2) + (1) * X(3) = (-2)$$
$$X(3) = (0),$$

and back-substitution gives

$$X(3) = 0, \quad X(2) = -2, \quad X(1) = 1.$$

*Note.* DET(A) = (1) * (−1) * (2) = −2, the product of elements on the principal diagonal of "B."

**Example 2.** Using Crout Reduction, solve (compare Example 1, above, and Example 2 of §4.4)

$$
A * X = \begin{bmatrix} 1 & 1 & 1 \\ 0 & 0 & 1 \\ 1 & -1 & 1 \end{bmatrix} * \begin{bmatrix} X(3) \\ X(2) \\ X(1) \end{bmatrix} = \begin{bmatrix} -1 \\ 1 \\ 3 \end{bmatrix} = B.
$$

SOLUTION *A.*

$$
\begin{array}{ccccc}
& 1 & 1 & 1 & -1 \\
(A|B): & 0 & 0 & 1 & 1 \\
& 1 & -1 & 1 & 3
\end{array}
$$

We compute Blocks (1), (2), and (3).

$$
\begin{array}{cccc}
& 1 & 1 & 1 & -1 \\
\text{"B": } & 0 & 0 & & \\
& 1 & -2 & &
\end{array}
$$

Since the number in A1(2, 2) position is zero, we cannot execute the operations indicated in Block (4). Thus, a row or column interchange is in order. *For a row interchange* we rewrite $(A|B)$ *and* the incomplete "B" with their second and third rows interchanged.

$$
(A|B): \quad
\begin{array}{rrrr}
1 & 1 & 1 & -1 \\
1 & -1 & 1 & 3 \\
0 & 0 & 1 & 1
\end{array}
$$

M = 1. (M = 1 indicates that a row *or* a column interchange has been executed.)

$$
\text{"B":} \quad
\begin{array}{rr}
1 & 1 \\
1 & -2 \\
0 & 0
\end{array}
\qquad
\begin{array}{r}
1 \\
\\
\end{array}
\qquad
\begin{array}{r}
-1 \\
\\
\end{array}
$$

M = 1.

We *continue* with the calculation of "B." Note that *no recalculation* of elements of "B" is required after a row interchange.

$$
\text{"B":} \quad
\begin{array}{cccc}
1 & 1 & 1 & -1 \\
1 & -2 & 0/(-2) & 4/(-2) \\
0 & 0 & 1 & 1/1
\end{array}
\qquad M = 1.
$$

Then (4.4.4) becomes

(4.5.7)
$$
\begin{aligned}
X(3) + (1) * X(2) + (1) * X(1) &= (-1) \\
X(2) + (0) * X(1) &= (-2) \\
X(1) &= (1),
\end{aligned}
$$

where $X(1) = 1, X(2) = -2, X(3) = 0$. And $DET(A) = (-1) ** M * (1) * (-2) * (1) = 2$, where A is the matrix of coefficients *before* the row interchange.

SOLUTION *B*. Proceed as in Solution *A* until a row or column interchange is found to be necessary. *For a column interchange,* those elements in the last Block computed before the interchange *do* require recalculation. We interchange the second and third columns of $(A|B)$ and of "B."

$$
(A|B): \quad
\begin{array}{rrrr}
1 & 1 & 1 & -1 \\
0 & 1 & 0 & 1 \\
1 & 1 & -1 & 3
\end{array}
\qquad M = 1.
$$

$$
\text{"B":} \quad
\begin{array}{rrr}
1 & 1 & 1 \quad -1 \\
0 & \cancel{0} \\
1 & \cancel{-2}
\end{array}
\qquad M = 1.
$$

Now we *delete the result of the previous calculation of Block* (*3*) and proceed with the calculation of "B" by calculating new elements in Block (3), etc., to get

$$
\begin{array}{cccc}
1 & 1 & 1 & -1 \qquad M = 1. \\
\text{"B": } \ \ 0 & 1 & 0/1 & 1/1 \\
1 & 0 & -2 & 4/(-2)
\end{array}
$$

Now (4.4.4) becomes [*note the interchange of positions of variables* $X(2)$ *and* $X(1)$ due to the interchange of columns two and three in $(A|B)$]

$$
X(3) + (1) * X(1) + (1) * X(2) = (-1)
$$
(4.5.8)
$$
X(1) + (0) * X(2) = (1)
$$
$$
X(2) = (-2),
$$

where $X(2) = -2, X(1) = 1, X(3) = 0$. And $DET(A) = (-1) ** M *(1) * (1) *$ $(-2) = 2$, where A is the matrix of coefficients *before* the column interchange in $(A|B)$.

If "B" *has been computed* for $A * X = B$, and if it is desired to change the column of constants from B to C and solve $A * X = C$, then "B" for $A * X = C$ has the same first N columns as the above *computed* "B," and the formulas (4.5.6b) for BI(I) in Block $(2 * I), I \in //1, N//$, are used to compute $CI(I), I \in //1, N//$, to obtain the last column of the new "B."

**Example 3.** Using the "B" of Example 1, apply Crout Reduction to solve

$$
A * X = \begin{bmatrix} 1 & 1 & 1 \\ 1 & 0 & 0 \\ 1 & -1 & 1 \end{bmatrix} * \begin{bmatrix} X(1) \\ X(2) \\ X(3) \end{bmatrix} = \begin{bmatrix} 1 \\ 0 \\ 0 \end{bmatrix} = C.
$$

SOLUTION.

$$
\begin{array}{ccccc}
& 1 & 1 & 1 & 1 \\
(A|C): & 1 & 0 & 0 & 0 \\
& 1 & -1 & 1 & 0
\end{array}
$$

We know the first three columns of "B" from Example 1, so

$$
\begin{array}{ccccc}
& 1 & 1 & 1 & C1(1) \\
\text{"B": } & 1 & -1 & 1 & C2(2) \\
& 1 & -2 & 2 & C3(3),
\end{array}
$$

where C1(1), C2(2), and C3(3) are given by the formulas for B1(1), B2(2), and B3(3) in Blocks, (2), (4), and (6) respectively. Thus,

$$
\text{"B"}: \quad
\begin{array}{cccc}
1 & 1 & 1 & 1 \\
1 & -1 & 1 & -1/(-1) \\
1 & -2 & 2 & 1/2
\end{array}
$$

and (4.4.4) becomes

$$X(1) + (1) * X(2) + (1) * X(3) = (1)$$
$$X(2) + (1) * X(3) = (1)$$
$$X(3) = (1/2)$$

so that $X(3) = 1/2, X(2) = 1/2, X(1) = 0$.

It is now clear that Crout Reduction can be applied to solve the matrix equation

$$
(4.5.9) \qquad A * X =
\begin{bmatrix}
A(1,1) & A(1,2) & A(1,3) \\
A(2,1) & A(2,2) & A(2,3) \\
A(3,1) & A(3,2) & A(3,3)
\end{bmatrix}
$$

$$
* \begin{bmatrix}
X(1,1) & X(1,2) & \cdots & X(1,K) \\
X(2,1) & X(2,2) & \cdots & X(2,K) \\
X(3,1) & X(3,2) & \cdots & X(3,K)
\end{bmatrix}
$$

$$
= \begin{bmatrix}
B(1,1) & B(1,2) & \cdots & B(1,K) \\
B(2,1) & B(2,2) & \cdots & B(2,K) \\
B(3,1) & B(3,2) & \cdots & B(3,K)
\end{bmatrix} = B
$$

by writing

$$
\text{(A|B):} \quad
\begin{array}{ccccccc}
A(1,1) & A(1,2) & A(1,3) & B(1,1) & B(1,2) & \cdots & B(1,K) \\
A(2,1) & A(2,2) & A(2,3) & B(2,1) & B(2,2) & \cdots & B(2,K) \\
A(3,1) & A(3,2) & A(3,3) & B(3,1) & B(3,2) & \cdots & B(3,K)
\end{array}
$$

and using (4.5.5a, b) and (4.5.6a, b) to compute

$$
\text{"B"}: \quad
\begin{array}{ccccccc}
A(1,1) & A1(1,2) & A1(1,3) & B1(1,1) & B1(1,2) & \cdots & B1(1,K) \\
C(2,1) & A1(2,2) & A2(2,3) & B2(2,1) & B2(2,2) & \cdots & B2(2,K) \\
C(3,1) & C(3,2) & A2(3,3) & B3(3,1) & B3(3,2) & \cdots & B3(3,K).
\end{array}
$$

We solve, for each $J \in //1, K//$,

$$X(1, J) + A1(1, 2) * X(2, J) + A1(1, 3) * X(3, J) = B1(1, J)$$

(4.5.10)     $$X(2, J) + A2(2, 3) * X(3, J) = B2(2, J)$$

$$X(3, J) = B3(3, J)$$

to obtain in $Jth$ column of the solution matrix X. If *no* column interchanges are executed in the calculation of "B", then the back-substitution equations appear as indicated in (4.5.10). If column interchanges *are* executed when computing "B", then the corresponding back-substitution equations will have the positions of some variables interchanged [compare (4.5.7) and (4.5.8) of Example 2]. In any case, the *elements* of the columns of the solution matrix, X, are determined by back-substitution in systems like (4.5.10), possibly with the *positions* of some variables changed.

This is one of the better elementary methods for computing X = INV(A). [Assuming DET(A) $\neq$ 0, we choose B = I, the identity matrix with the dimensions of A.]

If in (4.5.9) we have K > N, or if INV(A) is needed for other purposes, then INV(A) should be computed and used to solve (4.5.9). See (4.3.8).

**Example 4.** Using Crout Reduction, compute INV(A) where

$$A = \begin{bmatrix} 1 & 1 & 1 \\ 1 & 0 & 0 \\ 1 & -1 & 1 \end{bmatrix}.$$

SOLUTION

$$(A|I): \quad \begin{matrix} 1 & 1 & 1 & 1 & 0 & 0 \\ 1 & 0 & 0 & 0 & 1 & 0 \\ 1 & -1 & 1 & 0 & 0 & 1 \end{matrix}$$

(We could use the first three columns of "B" from Example 1 or the first four columns from Example 3.)

$$\text{"B":} \quad \begin{matrix} 1 & 1 & 1 & 1 & 0 & 0 \\ 1 & -1 & -1/(-1) & -1/(-1) & 1/(-1) & 0/(-1) \\ 1 & -2 & 2 & 1/2 & -2/2 & 1/2 \end{matrix}$$

Back-substitution using (4.5.10) gives [note the remarks following (4.5.10) concerning possible column interchanges in the calculation of "B"; none are required here]

| J | X(1, J) | X(2, J) | X(3, J) |
|---|---------|---------|---------|
| 1 | 0 | 1/2 | 1/2 |
| 2 | 1 | 0 | −1 |
| 3 | 0 | −1/2 | 1/2 |

$$\text{and INV(A)} = X = \begin{bmatrix} 0 & 1 & 0 \\ 1/2 & 0 & -1/2 \\ 1/2 & -1 & 1/2 \end{bmatrix}.$$

The *obvious check* on the *quality* of a computed solution is: (i) Substitute the computed solution into the left side of the equations (4.5.1), i.e., compute A * X; and (ii) Compare the numbers computed in (i) with the given constants in B. (In the next section we discuss another measure of the quality of a computed solution.) Clearly, this check requires that we *complete* the process of solving the system before executing the check. If an error in arithmetic, a computational error, is committed and not detected when executing the method of solution, then considerable effort could be wasted.

We now describe a technique for detecting computational errors when executing Gauss Elimination or Crout Reduction. The probability of machine error is so small that we do *not* recommend that such checks for computing errors be incorporated in electronic computer programs. However, a check like this one may be useful to the operator of a desk calculator. This *computational error check* is applicable to systems like (4.5.1) or (4.5.9).

*Computation.*

1. Append a column (called the *check column* for the calculation) to the right of (A|B), where each element in the check column is the *sum* of the other elements in its row of (A|B).
2. Compute "B", treating the check column as if it were just another column of B.
3. Compute by back-substitution the solution, $(XC(1), XC(2), \ldots, XC(N))$, using the column of "B" that corresponds to the check column.

*Interpretation.*

1. Each element of "B" in the column corresponding to the check column should be +1 *more* than the sum of the other elements in its row in "B" *to the right* of the principal diagonal.
2. In the case (4.5.1), if X = TRAN[X(1)X(2) ⋯ X(N)] is the solution of A * X = B, then (note step 3 in computation) we should have

$$XC(J) = X(J) + 1, \text{ for each } J \in //1, N//.$$

**Example 5.** Solve the linear system in Example 1 and include a check column.

SOLUTION.

Check
column

| | 1 | 1 | 1 | −1 | 2 |
|---|---|---|---|---|---|
| (A\|B): | 1 | 0 | 0 | 1 | 2 |
| | 1 | −1 | 1 | 3 | 4 |

| | 1 | 1 | 1 | −1 | 2 | *Note.* | $2 = 1 + (1 + 1 - 1)$ |
|---|---|---|---|---|---|---|---|
| "B": | 1 | −1 | 1 | −2 | 0/(−1) | | $0 = 1 + (1 - 2)$ |
| | 1 | −2 | 2 | 0 | 2/2 | | $1 = 1 + (0)$ |

$$\big(X(1), X(2), X(3)\big) = (1, -2, 0)$$
$$\big(XC(1), XC(2), XC(3)\big) = (2, -1, 1).$$

*Note.* $XC(1) = 2 = 1 + X(1)$, $XC(2) = -1 = 1 + X(2)$,
$XC(3) = 1 = 1 + X(3)$.

## EXERCISES

**1.** Use Crout Reduction to compute INV(A) for A given in Example 2, above. Use a row interchange and keep a check column.

**2.** Same as Exercise 1, but use a column interchange.

### 4.6. INHERENT ERROR

In §4.5 it was noted that a check on the *quality* of a computed solution XX could be made by substituting it in the original linear system.[1] Also *computational errors* committed when executing Crout Reduction, or Gauss Elimination, may be detected *before* completing the calculation of the computed solution by using a check column.

---

[1] It is not difficult to construct examples to show that the requirement that the elements of A ∗ XX agree with corresponding elements of B to K significant digits is *neither* a necessary *nor* a sufficient condition that the elements of XX agree with corresponding elements of the exact solution X of A ∗ X = B to K significant digits.

In this section we describe two methods (see [3] and [4]) that may be used to obtain an estimate of the *quality obtainable* in a computed solution. The linear systems considered here are assumed to have unique solutions.

Specifically, we develop a relation between the solution, $X = (X(1), X(2), \ldots, X(N))$, of a given linear system

(4.6.1)
$$\sum A(I, J) * X(J), J \in //1, N//, = B(I), \text{ for each } I \in //1, N//,$$
$$A * X = B \text{ (matrix equation)}$$

and the solution, $X + \Delta X = (X(1) + \Delta X(1), X(2) + \Delta X(2), \ldots, X(N) + \Delta X(N))$ of the linear system (4.6.2) obtained from the given system by changing the coefficients[2] by a specified amount.

(4.6.2)
$$\sum (A(I, J) + \Delta A(I, J)) * (X(J) + \Delta X(J)), J \in //1, N//,$$
$$= B(I) + \Delta B(I), \text{ for each } I \in //1, N//.$$
$$(A + \Delta A) * (X + \Delta X) = B + \Delta B.$$

The change, $\Delta X$, in the solution due to the changes in the coefficients is called the *inherent error* of the solution. In this definition and in the following derivation of estimates to the inherent error of the solution of (4.6.1), we *assume that no round-off errors are committed when solving the systems.* Thus inherent error is inherent in the system itself and does not depend on the method used to solve the system. If it is not economical to solve (4.6.1) by computing INV (A), (see the remark preceeding Example 4 of §4.5), then a method like Crout Reduction is recommended for the solution of the linear systems involved here.

From (4.6.2), if we know the solution, X, of (4.6.1), then the inherent error, $\Delta X$, of the solution of (4.6.1) is the solution of

(4.6.3)    $$(A + \Delta A) * \Delta X = B + \Delta B - (A * X + \Delta A * X) = \Delta B - \Delta A * X.$$

We define an *estimate*, $\Delta X1$, to a solution of (4.6.3) by assuming that $\Delta A * \Delta X$ has elements that are insignificant relative to the other elements involved in (4.6.3). Thus, define

(4.6.4)    $$A * \Delta X1 = \Delta B - \Delta A * X \equiv C, \text{ or } \Delta X1 = INV(A) * C.$$

To *compute* a solution of (4.6.4) we need to know X, $\Delta A$, and $\Delta B$ explicitly.

In practice, the *elements* of $\Delta A$ and $\Delta B$ are not known explicitly, but they may be known to satisfy relations like

---

[2]In most applications the A(I, J) are in *doubt* by $\Delta A(I, J)$ due to the method used to obtain the matrix A, say, from an experiment and/or round-off of data.

(4.6.5) $$|\Delta A(I, J)| \le E, \text{ and } |\Delta B(I)| \le E,$$

so that the elements of the vector C in (4.6.4) satisfy

(4.6.6) $$|C(I)| \le (1 + \sum|X(J)|, J \in //1, N//,) * E \equiv K.$$

Now we can define a vector, $\Delta X2$, whose elements are upper bounds for corresponding elements of $\Delta X1$ [assuming that INV(A) is available (4.2.8)]

(4.6.7) $$\begin{aligned}|\Delta X1(I)| &= 1/|DET(A)| * |\sum COF(A(J, I)) * C(J), J \in //1, N//, |\\ &\le 1/|DET(A)| * \sum|COF(A(J, I))| * |C(J)|, J \in //1, N//,\\ &\le 1/|DET(A)| * \sum|COF(A(J, I))| * K, J \in //1, N//,\\ &= K/|DET(A)| * \sum|COF(A(J, I))|, J \in //1, N//,\\ &= K * S(I) \equiv \Delta X2(I),\end{aligned}$$

where the S(I) are called the *measures of sensitivity* of the solution of (4.6.4). The S(I) are *bounds* on the changes in the $\Delta X1(I)$ when C is a column vector with elements any real numbers with magnitudes less than or equal to unity. Also, the $\Delta X2(I)$ are bounds on the changes in $\Delta X1(I)$ when C in (4.6.4) is any real column vector with each $|C(I)| \le K$.

*Note.* The S(I) depend only on A; K is a function of the solution, X, thus a function of B.

Thus, *under the assumption* that $\Delta A * \Delta X$ in (4.6.3) is so small that the solution, $\Delta X1$, of (4.6.4) is for all practical purposes a solution of (4.6.3), *the magnitudes of the elements of the inherent error vector*, $\Delta X$, *do not exceed the corresponding elements of the vector* $\Delta X2$.

(4.6.8) $$|\Delta X(I)| \doteq |\Delta X1(I)| \le \Delta X2(I).$$

*Note.* When DET(A) is very small [compared to elements of ADJ(A)], we would expect some of the elements of $\Delta X2$ to be large [see (4.6.7)].

The following is a method for computing [without using INV(A)] *another bound* (also denoted by $\Delta X2$) on the inherent error of the solution of (4.6.1). The method is described using Crout Reduction, but other equivalent processes could be used.

A vector $\Delta X2$ whose elements satisfy $|\Delta X1(I)| \leq \Delta X2(I)$, where $\Delta X1$ is the solution of (4.6.4) with elements of $\Delta A$, $\Delta B$, and C satisfying (4.6.5) and (4.6.6) is obtained as follows:

1. Compute a vector, S, (the elements are also called measures of sensitivity) by applying to

(4.6.9)      $A * S = T$      (T is a column vector with entries *unity*),

the following *modified Crout Reduction* process. Compute the first N columns of "B" by the usual Crout Reduction process, *but* compute the last column of "B" and execute back-substitution using [compare (4.5.6b), and the I*th* equation in (4.4.4), respectively]

(4.6.10)     $BI(I) = 1/|AIM1(I, I)| * (1 + |C(I, 1)| * B1(1)$
$+ \ |C(I, 2)| * B2(2) + \cdots$
$+ \ |C(I, I - 1)| * BIM1(I - 1))$

(4.6.11)     $S(I) = BI(I) + \sum|AI(I, J)| * S(J), J \in //I + 1, N//.$

That is, go through the motions of using Crout Reduction for the last column of "B" and back-substitution, but assume that all numbers are nonnegative and always add. We compare (4.6.10) with (4.5.6b), and (4.6.11) with back-substitution in the Crout Reduction Process, and see that the $|S(I)| \geq |\Delta X1(I)|$ whenever the $|C(I)| \leq 1$ in (4.6.4).

2. Compute a solution of (4.6.1), and then compute K, (4.6.6).
3. The bound $\Delta X2$ has elements [which are related to elements of $\Delta X1$ and $\Delta X$ as indicated in (4.6.8)]

$$\Delta X2(I) = K * S(I).$$

**Example.** Use Milne's Method to compute a bound on the inherent error of the solution to (see Example 1 of §4.5)

$$A * X = \begin{bmatrix} 1 & 1 & 1 \\ 1 & 0 & 0 \\ 1 & -1 & 1 \end{bmatrix} * \begin{bmatrix} X(1) \\ X(2) \\ X(3) \end{bmatrix} = \begin{bmatrix} -1 \\ 1 \\ 3 \end{bmatrix} = B.$$

SOLUTION. We compute the solution, X, and the measures of sensitivity, S, at the same time. (i) Append a column of ones to the right of $(A|B)$; (ii) Apply Crout Reduction to compute the column of "B" corresponding to B; and (iii) Apply the *modified* Crout Reduction described in Milne's Method, (4.6.10), to obtain the column of "B" corresponding to the column of ones.

|          |   |    |         |          | Inherent error column |          |
|----------|---|----|---------|----------|------|----------|
|          | 1 | 1  | 1       | −1       | 1    |          |
| $(A|B)$: | 1 | 0  | 0       | 1        | 1    |          |
|          | 1 | −1 | 1       | 3        | 1    |          |
|          | 1 | 1  | 1       | −1       | 1    | [=1/1]   |
| "B":     | 1 | −1 | −1/(−1) | 2/(−1)   | 2/1  | [=(1 + 1)/1] |
|          | 1 | −2 | 2       | 0/2      | 6/2  | [=(1 + 1 + 4)/2] |

The modified back-substitution, (4.6.11), for the measures of sensitivity gives

$$S(3) = 3, \quad S(2) = 2 + (1) * (3) = 5, \quad S(1) = 1 + (1) * (5) + (1) * (3) = 9.$$

The solution of $A * X = B$, see Example 1 of §4.5, is $X(1) = 1, X(2) = -2$, $X(3) = 0$. Thus, (4.6.6),

$$K = (1 + |1| + |-2| + |0|) * E = 4 * E,$$

where E is a bound on the error in the representation of elements of A and B in $A * X = B$. Then (whenever we are justified in neglecting the term $\Delta A * \Delta X$) the *inherent error of the solution* of $A * X = B$ due to an uncertainty, not exceeding E, in the elements of A and B satisfies

$$|\Delta X(1)| \leq S(1) * K = 9 * 4 * E = 36 * E$$
$$|\Delta X(2)| \leq S(2) * K = 5 * 4 * E = 20 * E$$
$$|\Delta X(3)| \leq S(3) * K = 3 * 4 * E = 12 * E.$$

*Note.* INV(A) was computed in Example 4 of §4.5, so the cofactors required in (4.6.7) are available. If we form a matrix with elements the absolute value of elements of INV(A), we may compute the measures of sensitivity in (4.6.7) by

$$\begin{bmatrix} S(1) \\ S(2) \\ S(3) \end{bmatrix} = \begin{bmatrix} 0 & 1 & 0 \\ 1/2 & 0 & 1/2 \\ 1/2 & 1 & 1/2 \end{bmatrix} * \begin{bmatrix} 1 \\ 1 \\ 1 \end{bmatrix} = \begin{bmatrix} 1 \\ 1 \\ 2 \end{bmatrix}.$$

Then, *another bound* on the inherent error of the solution of $A * X = B$ in this example is $\Delta X2$ with components

$$\Delta X2(1) = S(1) * 4 * E = 4 * E,$$

$$\Delta X2(2) = S(2) * 4 * E = 4 * E,$$

$$\Delta X2(3) = S(3) * 4 * E = 8 * E.$$

In this example $DET(A) = -2$. When the magnitude of $DET(A)$ is *very small* relative to the magnitudes of elements of $ADJ(A)$, the coefficient of E in some element of $\Delta X2$ is much *larger* [implying that the solution of (4.6.1) is *less* reliable].

We conclude this section with a list of more terminology concerning the quality of a solution of

$$A * X = B.$$

A *solution* X is *stable* if the inherent error $\Delta X$ in (4.6.3) is "small" whenever $\Delta A$ and $\Delta B$ are "small." Unfortunately, we do not have a precise characterization of "small." An inverse matrix INV(A) is *stable* if the elements of $(INV(A + \Delta A) - INV(A))$ are "small" whenever the elements of $\Delta A$ are "small." There are many measures of the *condition* of the matrix A. Sometimes one measure of the condition of A gives useful information (e.g., about the stability of the solution X) while other measures of condition are noncommittal. A not very precise, but often-used, measure of the condition of A is a measure of the stability of INV(A); that is, A is *ill-conditioned* if INV(A) is *unstable*. Other measures of condition of A are the *condition numbers* of Turing, Todd, and Faddeev (see [5]) which involve the elements of A explicitly. An analysis of the condition of a linear system that does *not* neglect $\Delta A * \Delta X$ is given in [6a], and uses a condition number that involves a Euclidean norm facilitating meaningful geometric interpretations.

### EXERCISES

**1.** Compute INV(A1) and INV(A2) for

$$A1 = \begin{bmatrix} 1 & 1 \\ 1 & 1.0001 \end{bmatrix}, \quad \text{and} \quad A2 = \begin{bmatrix} 1 & 1 \\ 1 & .9999 \end{bmatrix}.$$

Can you conclude that INV(A1) is or is not stable? Note that DET(A1) is "small" compared to elements of ADJ(A1).

**2.** With A1 and A2 given in Exercise 1, discuss the stability of the solution X of A1 $*$ X $=$ B where TRAN(B) $=$ [1  2]. In particular, compute the solutions of A1 $*$ X $=$ B and A2 $*$ X $=$ B.

*Note.* The linear equations corresponding to A1 $*$ X $=$ B define lines that are "almost parallel." The system corresponding to A2 $*$ X $=$ B defines lines with the slope of one line changed "a little" but the intersection is changed "a lot" (when compared with the lines associated with A1 $*$ X $=$ B).

### 4.7. RELAXATION. GAUSS-SEIDEL ITERATION

When N is very large, some of the methods previously discussed for solving

$$(4.7.1) \qquad \sum A(I, J) * X(J), J \in //1, N//, = B(I), \text{ for each } I \in //1, N//,$$

are *not* practical. Iteration methods are useful when solving linear systems with large, sparse matrices where elimination is out of the question. Gauss-Seidel Iteration is stressed because of its relation to other iteration methods and its frequent involvement in studies of numerical solutions of differential equations.

In this section we briefly discuss a class of *iteration* methods that explicitly involve the given data (elements of A and B). A first guess (X(0, 1), X(0, 2), ..., X(0, N)) is chosen,[1] and we define a sequence of vectors

$$(4.7.2) \qquad (X(K, 1), X(K, 2), \ldots, X(K, N)), \text{ for } K \in //1, \infty//,$$

which hopefully converges componentwise to a solution of the linear system (4.7.1). That is, for each I $\in$ //1, N//,

$$(4.7.3) \qquad \text{LIM}(X(K, I)) = XX(I), \text{ as } K \text{ App } \infty,$$

where XX $=$ (XX(1), XX(2), ..., XX(N)) is a solution of (4.7.1). Then, we describe one of these methods which is particularly well suited to execution on electronic digital computers, and which is known to converge for an important class of linear systems.

If X0 $=$ (X(0, 1), X(0, 2), ..., X(0, N)) is a first guess at a solution of (4.7.1), then a measure of the error of the estimate to a solution by X0 is given by the *residuals*, for each I $\in$ //1, N//,

---

[1]Any computed solution of (4.7.1) may be used as a first guess. Frequently the components of a first guess are chosen to be X(0, I) = 1, for each I $\in$ //1, N//.

$$R(0, I) = \sum A(I, J) * X(0, J), J \in //1, N//, -B(I).$$

Various methods for generating sequences, (4.7.2), of estimates to a solution of (4.7.1) so that (it is hoped) the residuals, for each $I \in //1, N//$,

(4.7.4)          $$R(K, I) = \sum A(I, J) * X(K, J), J \in //1, N//, -B(I),$$

satisfy, for each $I \in //1, N//$,

(4.7.5)          $$LIM(R(K, I)) = 0, \text{ as } K \text{ App } \infty,$$

are called *relaxation methods*.

As a *first step* in most relaxation methods we rewrite (shift) the equations in (4.7.1), possibly interchanging the row-order of some of the equations and/ or the column-positions of some variables in all of the equations, in the form

(4.7.6)
$$\sum AS(I, J) * XS(J), J \in //1, N//, = BS(I), \text{ for each } I \in //1, N//,$$
$$AS * XS = BS,$$

so that the absolute value of each diagonal element, $|AS(I, I)|$, of AS is as large as possible relative to the magnitudes of other elements in its row and column of AS. Some *art* is usually involved in choosing the form (4.7.6). Relaxation methods of the type discussed here work best when AS of (4.7.6) is (i) *dominant diagonal* [for each I, $|AS(I, I)| \gg |AS(I, J)|$ and $|AS(I, I)| \gg |AS(J, I)|$ for each $J \in //1, N//,$] and (ii) *sparse* [many off-diagonal elements of AS are *zero*].

In the remainder of this section we suppose that the linear system has been written so that the matrix of coefficients is as nearly dominant diagonal as possible. In particular, we assume that $A(I, I) \neq 0, I \in //1, N//$.

One much-used relaxation method defines the sequence (4.7.2) as follows: Given the estimate $(X(K, 1), X(K, 2), \ldots, X(K, N))$. Use the I*th* equation in (4.7.1) to define $X(K + 1, I)$ by

(4.7.7)   $$X(K + 1, I) = 1/A(I, I) * (B(I)$$
$$- \sum A(I, J) * X(K, J), J \in //1, N//, \text{ and } J \neq I,).$$

That is, for each $I \in //1, N//$, in (4.7.4), *change* $X(K, I)$ so that $R(K, I) = 0$. Thus, obtain the new estimate

$$(X(K + 1, 1), X(K + 1, 2), \ldots, X(K + 1, N)).$$

Another important relaxation method, called *Gauss-Seidel Iteration*, is similar to (4.7.7) but uses new data as soon as they are available. Here, the components of the (K + 1)*th* estimate are defined by, for each I ∈ //1, N//,

$$(4.7.8) \quad X(K + 1, I) = 1/A(I, I) * (B(I)$$
$$- \sum A(I, J) * X(K + 1, J), J \in //1, I - 1//,$$
$$- \sum A(I, J) * X(K, J), J \in //I + 1, N//,).$$

If the matrix of coefficients in (4.7.6) is symmetric (Hermitian) and positive definite, then Gauss-Seidel Iteration can be shown (see [7]) to define a sequence, (4.7.2), which converges, (4.7.3), to a solution of (4.7.6), and thus to a solution of (4.7.1).

One class of linear systems where A is Hermitian, positive definite, dominant diagonal, and with many off-diagonal zeros, arises in the study of numerical solutions of differential equations. See Examples 4 and 7 of §11.1, below.

## EXERCISES

1. Write in expanded form the linear systems and formulas involved in this section.

2. Construct an example of a linear system with a dominant diagonal matrix of coefficients. Solve your system using Gauss-Seidel Iteration.

### 4.8 COMPLEX AND EQUIVALENT REAL LINEAR SYSTEMS

Throughout this section we write I ≡ SQRT(−1).

The complex linear system [corresponding to the real system (4.2.2)], for each K ∈ //1, M//,

$$(4.8.1) \quad \sum (A(K, J) + I * B(K, J)) * (X(J) + I * Y(J)), J \in //1, N//,$$
$$= (C(K) + I * D(K))$$

can be written (by equating the real part of each side of the equality in each equation, etc.) as 2 * M real equations in 2 * N real unknowns, for each K ∈ //1, M//,

$$(4.8.2) \quad \sum (A(K, J) * X(J) - B(K, J) * Y(J)), J \in //1, N//, = C(K)$$
$$\sum (B(K, J) * X(J) + A(K, J) * Y(J)), J \in //1, N//, = D(K).$$

With A and B the obvious M$by$N matrices, and

$$X = \begin{bmatrix} X(1) \\ X(2) \\ \vdots \\ X(N) \end{bmatrix}, \quad Y = \begin{bmatrix} Y(1) \\ Y(2) \\ \vdots \\ Y(N) \end{bmatrix}, \quad C = \begin{bmatrix} C(1) \\ C(2) \\ \vdots \\ C(M) \end{bmatrix}, \quad D = \begin{bmatrix} D(1) \\ D(2) \\ \vdots \\ D(M) \end{bmatrix},$$

the system (4.8.2) has corresponding (partitioned) matrix equation

$$(4.8.3) \quad \begin{bmatrix} A & -B \\ B & A \end{bmatrix} * \begin{bmatrix} X \\ Y \end{bmatrix} = \begin{bmatrix} C \\ D \end{bmatrix},$$

where the $(2 * M)by(2 * N)$ matrix of coefficients, the unknown column vector, and the column of constants are *partitioned* into the submatrices indicated. Clearly, (4.8.3) may be written as the pair of matrix equations

$$A * X - B * Y = C$$
$$B * X + A * Y = D,$$

which correspond to the system (4.8.2).

Thus, if X and Y satisfy (4.8.3), then

$$X + I * Y = (X(1) + I * Y(1), X(2) + I * Y(2), \ldots, X(N) + I * Y(N))$$

is a solution of (4.8.1).

### EXERCISE

**1.** Use the method of this section to solve the complex linear system

$$-2 * (X(1) + I * Y(1)) + I * (X(2) + I * Y(2)) = 1 + I * 2$$
$$-2 * I * (X(1) + I * Y(1)) + 1 * (X(2) + I * Y(2)) = 2 + I * 3.$$

Write (4.8.2) and (4.8.3) explicitly. Check your solution by substitution in each of (4.8.1), (4.8.2), and (4.8.3).

*Answer.* $X(1) + I * Y(1) = -1 + I * 0$, and $X(2) + I * Y(2) = 2 + I * 1$.

### 4.9. LINEAR PROGRAMMING

In Example 1 of §4.3 we considered the *underdetermined* system of R linear equations in N ($>$R) unknowns, for each $I \in //1, R//$,

$$(4.9.1) \qquad \sum A(I, J) * X(J), J \in //1, N//, = B(I).$$

We noted that if the matrix consisting of the first R columns of the matrix of coefficients for (4.9.1) has determinant not zero, then the last $N - R$ unknowns may be transposed to the right number of (4.9.1) to define the linear system, for each $I \in //1, R//$.

$$
\begin{aligned}
&\sum A(I, J) * X(J), J \in //1, R//, \\
(4.9.2) \qquad &= B(I) - \sum A(I, J) * X(J), J \in //R + 1, N//, \\
&AA * XX = BB
\end{aligned}
$$

which may be solved by Cramer's Rule to define [recall (4.3.8)]

$$(4.9.3) \qquad XX = INV(AA) * BB.$$

Since BB involves $N - R$ unknowns, then (4.9.3) defines the first R unknowns in terms of the remaining $N - R$ unknowns. That is, the underdetermined linear system (4.9.1) has an $(N - R)$-parameter family of solutions.

Generally, a problem in applied mathematics is not considered "well-set" unless the mathematical model has a unique solution. Thus, we expect problems that involve underdetermined linear systems, like (4.9.1), also to involve *additional conditions* that *select* from the $(N - R)$-parameter family of solutions of (4.9.1) *one solution* that is considered *best*.

Linear programming problems have a variety of representations, but they are each equivalent to the problem of finding an $(N + 1)$-tuple, $(Z, X)$, where X is an appropriately-chosen element of the $(N - R)$-parameter family of (N-tuples) solutions of (4.9.1), and Z is the corresponding *value* of a function (called the *objective function*)

$$(4.9.4) \qquad Z = F(X) = \sum C(J) * X(J), J \in //1, N//.$$

The C(J), $J \in //1, N//$, are constants. We usually further restrict the choice of of X by specifying additional conditions. For example, we might require that the components of X be nonnegative. Then, X is in the competition to be chosen *the* X only if it is in S, a proper subset of the (N − R)-parameter family of solutions of (4.9.1). Elements of S are called *feasible solutions*.

A solution of the linear programming problem associated with F(X) and S is any (N + 1)-tuple (ZZ, XX) where XX ∈ S and

(4.9.5)          $ZZ = F(XX) = MIN(F(X))$, over X ∈ S.

XX is called a *minimum feasible solution*. We say *any* (ZZ, XX) because there may be many N-tuples XX in S such that $F(XX) = ZZ$. See the second Note in Example 1, below. When we find that a linear programming problem has many solutions, we may then add a condition to pick one solution. If we can not think of an additional condition that is pertinent to the problem, this additional condition may depend on the method used to solve the linear programming problem (for example, "use the *first* minimum feasible solution that the method produces").

In some contexts it is convenient to define an objective function G(X) which is to be *maximized* over S; then, the condition (4.9.5) is replaced by

(4.9.6)          $ZZ = G(XX) = MAX(G(X))$, over X ∈ S.

For example, in certain problems in economics the objective function G(X) denotes profit from producing X(1) items of one product, X(2) items of another product, etc., and C(1), C(2), etc. are the profits per item of these products. In this example, we would require each $X(J) \geq 0$, and each $C(J) > 0$. We seek a combination $XX = (X(1), X(2), \ldots, X(N))$, which is within our capacity (XX ∈ S), to produce the maximum profit $ZZ = G(XX)$. Since

$MAX(G(X))$, over X ∈ S, $= -MIN(-G(X))$, over X ∈ S,

these linear programming problems could have been defined as minimization problems. To see this, sketch G(X), −G(X), and compare extrema.

We do not present a formal statement of a linear programming problem. Instead, we present three examples to indicate two forms for linear programming problems, one source of these problems, and define some terminology as we proceed. In the first example, the set S is defined by a set of linear inequalities, and we give a geometric argument to solve the linear programming problem. In the second example, we solve the problem of Example 1 by an analytical process that involves an underdetermined system of linear equations (4.9.10a, b, c) which replaces the first three inequalities in (4.9.8). The third example illustrates the application of linear programming to the problem of finding a "best approximation" in the Chebyshev sense. Exercise 3 is a problem in economics.

**Example 1.** Find $(ZZ, XX)$ where $XX = (XX(1), XX(2))$ is in S, and $ZZ = F(XX)$ is the minimum value of

(4.9.7)           $Z = F(X) = -2 * X(1) - X(2)$

as $X = (X(1), X(2))$ varies over the set S defined by the five conditions

$$X(1) + 3 * X(2) \leq 6$$
$$X(1) + X(2) \leq 3$$
(4.9.8)           $$X(1) - X(2) \leq 2$$
$$X(1) \geq 0$$
$$X(2) \geq 0.$$

*Note.* The usual statement of this linear programming problem is: Find a vector $XX = (XX(1), XX(2))$ that minimizes

$$F(X) = -2 * X(1) - X(2)$$

subject to the constraints

[the conditions (4.9.8) are listed].

We have simply included a name (Z) for the value of the objective function, and a name (S) for the set of feasible solutions defined by the constraints.

SOLUTION. We obtain a solution of this linear programming problem by *geometric* considerations. The first inequality

$$X(1) + 3 * X(2) \leq 6$$

defines points $(X(1), X(2))$ on, and on one side of the line

$$X(1) + 3 * X(2) = 6.$$

The appropriate "side" of the line is determined by picking any point *not* on the line and checking to see if the inequality is satisfied. Here, $(X(1), X(2)) = (0, 0)$ satisfies the inequality, so the inequality defines the half-plane on and "below" the line. See Figure 4.9.1. The other inequalities in (4.9.8) define half-planes "below" X(1) +

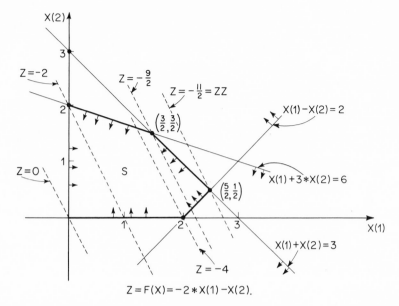

**Figure 4.9.1**

$X(2) = 3$, "above" $X(1) - X(2) = 2$, the "right" half-plane, and the "upper" half-plane respectively. The set S of feasible solutions is the set of points $(X(1), X(2))$ that satisfy *all* inequalities in (4.9.8). That is, S is the *intersection* of all the half-planes defined by the inequalities. This set is *convex* (the line segment joining any two points of S lies entirely in S). In this example, S is a convex simple closed polygon, and its interior. The objective function

$$Z = F(X) = -2 * X(1) - X(2)$$

may be considered a one-parameter family of parallel lines (Z is the parameter). We seek the *smallest* parameter value $Z = ZZ$ that defines a line in the family $F(X) = Z$ where the line $F(X) = ZZ$ includes at least one point XX of S.

*Note.* If the line $F(X) = ZZ$ is *parallel* to a "side" of S, and if a minimizing XX is on that side, then there is a whole line segment of points XX that give the objective function $F(X)$ its minimum value ZZ. That is, the linear programming problem would have an infinite number of solutions $(ZZ, XX)$.

In this example, the line $F(X) = Z$ is *not* parallel to a side of S, so the minimum ZZ defines a line

$$-2 * X(1) - X(2) = ZZ$$

which contains *exactly one* point of S, a *vertex* of the polygon (boundary of S).

From Figure 4.9.1, we see that the unique *solution* of the linear programming problem in this example is (ZZ, XX) where

$$XX = \big(X(1), X(2)\big) = (5/2, 1/2)$$

and

$$ZZ = F(XX) = -2 * (5/2) - (1/2) = -11/2.$$

In general, it is known that a minimum feasible solution XX occurs *at a vertex* of the convex set S. Thus, it is enough to find the (finite) set of vertices of S, compute the corresponding set of values of the objective function F(X), and select the minimum value ZZ of F(X) and a corresponding vector XX.

Various methods have been devised to examine the value of F(X) *at the vertices* of S. In the next example we present one of these applied to the problem in Example 1. The *Simplex Method* (not presented here) is a schematic device equivalent to executing the method of Example 2 (as Crout Reduction is considered an abbreviated version of Gauss Elimination, and synthetic division is equivalent to long division of polynomials). Other methods involve "dual problems." See [8].

Like most fields of applied mathematics, linear programming began as a set of methods to solve particular problems. Mathematization is producing a discipline where more and more problems are yielding to analysis. The present state of the art is indicated in references listed in Suggested Reading at the end of this chapter.

**Example 2.** In this example we apply an analytical method to solve a linear programming problem *equivalent* to the problem in Example 1. The first three inequalities in (4.9.8) are replaced by *equations*. For example, the set of number pairs $\big(X(1), X(2)\big)$ that satisfy

$$X(1) + 3 * X(2) \leq 6$$
$$X(1) \geq 0, \text{ and } X(2) \geq 0,$$

is exactly the set of number pairs $\big(X(1), X(2)\big)$ that are the first two components of triples $\big(X(1), X(2), X(3)\big)$ that satisfy

$$X(1) + 3 * X(2) + X(3) = 6$$
$$X(1) \geq 0, X(2) \geq 0, \text{ and } X(3) \geq 0.$$

We introduced the (nonnegative) *slack variable* X(3) to replace the inequality by an equality. We introduce three slack variables to obtain the following equivalent linear programming problem. Find $(ZZ, XX)$ where

$$XX = \big(XX(1), XX(2), XX(3), XX(4), XX(5)\big)$$

is in S, and $ZZ = F(XX)$ is the minimum value of

(4.9.9a)     $Z = F(X) = -2 * X(1) - X(2) + 0 * X(3) + 0 * X(4) + 0 * X(5)$

as $X = \big(X(1), X(2), X(3), X(4), X(5)\big)$ varies over the set S defined by

(4.9.10a)     $X(1) + 3 * X(2) + X(3) \qquad\qquad = 6$

(4.9.10b)     $X(1) \quad + X(2) \qquad + X(4) \qquad = 3$

(4.9.10c)     $X(1) \quad - X(2) \qquad\qquad\quad + X(5) = 2$

(4.9.10d)     $X(1) \geq 0, \ X(2) \geq 0, \ X(3) \geq 0, \ X(4) \geq 0, \text{ and } X(5) \geq 0.$

It is known that the vertices (*extreme points*) of S correspond to vectors X with *at most* K nonzero components, where K is the number of equations in (4.9.10). Since the minimum feasible solution is a vertex of S, then we only need to look at vertices of S. Thus, we will examine five-tuples that satisfy (4.9.10) and that have *at least* two components equal zero.

SOLUTION. *Step 1.* We begin by choosing $X(1) = X(2) = 0$ in (4.9.10a, b, c). Then, the equations become

$$X(3) \qquad\quad = 6$$
$$X(4) \quad = 3$$
$$X(5) = 2,$$

and we trivially obtain the feasible solution (element of S)

$$X = (0, 0, 6, 3, 2).$$

Since (i) the components of this feasible solution are nonnegative, (ii) at least two components are zero, and (iii) the "columns" of (4.9.10a, b, c) that correspond to nonzero components are linearly independent, then we call this feasible solution a *basic feasible solution*. Basic feasible solutions are vertices (or corners) of S. The basic feasible solution just obtained gives the objective function $F(X)$ the value

$$F(X) = -2*(0) - (0) + 0 * (6) + 0 * (3) + 0 * (2) = 0.$$

*Step 2.* We note that $F(X)$, (4.9.9a), is *reduced* more by a unit of $X(1)$ than by a unit of X(2); so we will choose X(1) as large as possible, consistent with (4.9.10a, b, c, d), and leave X(2) = 0. With X(2) = 0, (4.9.10a, b, c) becomes

$$
\begin{aligned}
X(1) + X(3) &= 6 \\
X(1) \qquad + X(4) &= 3 \\
X(1) \qquad\qquad + X(5) &= 2.
\end{aligned}
$$

We must choose X(3) = 0, or X(4) = 0, or X(5) = 0, have X(1) as large as possible, and still have (4.9.10d) satisfied.

$$
\begin{aligned}
&X(3) = 0, \text{ and } X(1) = 6 \text{ implies } X(4) = -3 < 0. \\
&X(4) = 0, \text{ and } X(1) = 3 \text{ implies } X(5) = -1 < 0. \\
&X(5) = 0, \text{ and } X(1) = 2 \text{ implies } X(3) = 4, \text{ and } X(4) = 1.
\end{aligned}
$$

Therefore, with X(2) = 0, we must choose X(5) = 0. Then (4.9.10a, b, c) becomes

$$
\begin{aligned}
X(1) + X(3) \qquad &= 6 \\
X(1) \qquad + X(4) &= 3 \\
X(1) \qquad\qquad &= 2,
\end{aligned}
$$

which we can solve by Jordan Elimination to obtain

$$
\begin{aligned}
X(1) \qquad\qquad &= 2 \\
X(3) \qquad &= 4 \\
X(4) &= 1.
\end{aligned}
$$

Thus, a new basic feasible solution is

$$
X = (2, 0, 4, 1, 0),
$$

which gives the objective function the value

$$
F(X) = -2 * (2) - (0) + 0 * (4) + 0 * (1) + 0 * (0) = -4.
$$

This is indeed *less* than F(X) for the first basic feasible solution.

*Note.* Instead of writing the several special linear systems that we have in Step 2, we find it convenient to replace (4.9.10a, b, c) by an equivalent linear system obtained by a Gauss Elimination on the X(1)-column, keeping the equation involving X(5) "as is." In this particular case we subtract (4.9.10c) from (4.9.10a), and from (4.9.10b) to obtain

(4.9.11a)      $4 * X(2) + X(3) \qquad\quad - X(5) = 4$

(4.9.11b)      $2 * X(2) \qquad\quad + X(4) - X(5) = 1$

(4.9.11c)      $X(1) - X(2) \qquad\qquad\quad + X(5) = 2.$

We "cover" the $X(2)$ and $X(5)$-columns, and read-off the potentially nonzero components of the new basic feasible solution. From (4.9.11c) we have

$$X(1) = 2 + X(2) - X(5).$$

Thus, the objective function (4.9.9a) can be written

(4.9.9b)      $F(X) = -2 * \big(2 + X(2) - X(5)\big) - X(2)$

$$= -3 * X(2) + 2 * X(5) - 4.$$

Notice, if $X(2) = X(5) = 0$, then $F(X) = -4$, as claimed.

*Step 3.* From (4.9.9b) we see that we can reduce $F(X)$ by increasing $X(2)$, and keeping $X(5) = 0$. With $X(5) = 0$, (4.9.11a, b, c) becomes [we could make the following analysis by "covering" the $X(5)$-column in (4.9.11a, b, c)]

$$4 * X(2) + X(3) \qquad\quad = 4$$
$$2 * X(2) \qquad\quad + X(4) = 1$$
$$X(1) - X(2) \qquad\qquad = 2.$$

We must set $X(1) = 0$, or $X(3) = 0$, or $X(4) = 0$, and find the largest "allowable" $X(2)$.

$X(3) = 0$ and $X(2) = 1$ implies $X(4) = -1 < 0$.

$X(4) = 0$ and $X(2) = 1/2$ implies $X(3) = 2$, and $X(1) = 5/2$.

$X(1) = 0$ and $X(2) = -2$ implies $X(2) < 0$.

The only choice consistent with (4.9.11a, b, c), (4.9.10d), and $X(5) = 0$ is the choice $X(4) = 0$. So we "keep" (4.9.11b) and eliminate $X(2)$ from the other equations to obtain

(4.9.12a)      $+ X(3) - 2 * X(4) + \quad X(5) = 2$

(4.9.12b)      $X(2) \qquad + .5 * X(4) - .5 * X(5) = 1/2$

(4.9.12c)      $X(1) \qquad\quad + .5 * X(4) + .5 * X(5) = 5/2.$

Thus, a new basic feasible solution is

$$X = (5/2, 1/2, 2, 0, 0).$$

From (4.9.12b)

$$X(2) = .5 * (1 - X(4) + X(5)),$$

so the objective function (4.9.9b) can be written

$$(4.9.9c) \qquad F(X) = -3 * .5 * (1 - X(4) + X(5)) + 2 * X(5) - 4$$
$$= 3/2 * X(4) + 1/2 * X(5) - 11/2.$$

When $X(4) = X(5) = 0$, then $F(X) = -11/2$.

*Step 4.* We examine (4.9.9c). Since the coefficients of $X(4)$ and $X(5)$ in $F(X)$ are positive, then *no nonnegative choice* for $X(4)$ and/or $X(5)$ *will reduce* $F(X)$. Thus, the minimum feasible solution of the linear programming problem is (ZZ, XX) where

$$XX = (5/2, 1/2, 2, 0, 0)$$

and

$$F(XX) = -2 * (5/2) - (1/2) + 0 * (2) + 0 * (0) + 0 * (0) = -11/2.$$

SUMMARY. The linear systems (4.9.10a, b, c), (4.9.11a, b, c), and (4.9.12a, b, c) are equivalent. The objective function $F(X)$ in any of the forms (4.9.9a), (4.9.9b), and (4.9.9c) has the *same value* for any X in S, where S is defined by (4.9.10d) and any of the three above linear systems.

*Step 1.* We make an easy (standard) choice for our initial basic feasible solution.

*Step 2.* We examine (4.9.9a) to choose a (then zero) component which when increased will reduce $F(X)$. We choose $X(1)$ as large as possible, consistent with our constraints [including the requirement that $X(3)$ or $X(4)$ or $X(5)$ must be zero]. We rewrite (4.9.10a, b, c) as (4.9.11a, b, c) so that $X(1)$, $X(3)$, and $X(4)$ are easily determined when $X(2) = 0$ and $X(5) = 0$. Thus, we obtain a new basic feasible solution. We use (4.9.11c) to get a new form (4.9.9b) for $F(X)$ that involves the variables $X(2)$ and $X(5)$, so the value of $F(X)$ is easily read-off for the current basic feasible solution.

*Step 3.* We examine (4.9.9b) to choose a (then zero) component which when increased will reduce $F(X)$. We choose $X(2)$ as large as possible, consistent with our constraints. We rewrite (4.9.11a, b, c) as (4.9.12a, b, c) so that the new basic feasible solution can be read-off. We use (4.9.12b) to get a new form (4.9.9c) for $F(X)$ that involves the (then zero) components.

*Step 4.* We observe in (4.9.9c) that the *coefficients* of $X(4)$ and $X(5)$ are positive, so we cannot reduce F(X) by increasing either X(4) or X(5). Thus, we conclude that the last computed basic feasible solution is the minimum feasible solution.

We say (even though the basic feasible solutions in Example 2 are five-tuples) that the first basic feasible solution

$$X = (0, 0, 6, 3, 2), \text{ with } F(X) = 0,$$

"corresponds" to the origin in Figure 4.9.1. The basic feasible solution

$$X = (2, 0, 4, 1, 0), \text{ with } F(X) = -4,$$

"corresponds" to the vertex (2, 0) in Figure 4.9.1. The minimum feasible solution

$$XX = (5/2, 1/2, 2, 0, 0), \text{ with } F(XX) = -11/2,$$

"corresponds" to the vertex (5/2, 1/2) in Figure 4.9.1. Thus, the analysis of Example 2 leads to the "same" solution as that obtained by geometric considerations in Example 1.

If hip-boots are required to wade through Example 2, imagine how discouraging a corresponding analysis would be for a linear programming problem that involved twenty inequalities in a dozen variables; then, (4.9.10) becomes 20 equations in 32 unknowns. Fortunately, the above analysis has been formalized to produce the Simplex Method which can be executed by following a specified set of operations that require little or no understanding of the linear programming problem being solved. Thus, *execution* can be assigned to lower-priced personnel and electronic computers. Justification for the Simplex Method is usually achieved by a study of linear programming problems with the linear system (4.9.10) represented as a matrix equation

$$X(1) * \begin{bmatrix} 1 \\ 1 \\ 1 \end{bmatrix} + X(2) * \begin{bmatrix} 3 \\ 1 \\ -1 \end{bmatrix} + X(3) * \begin{bmatrix} 1 \\ 0 \\ 0 \end{bmatrix} + X(4) * \begin{bmatrix} 0 \\ 1 \\ 0 \end{bmatrix} + X(5) * \begin{bmatrix} 0 \\ 0 \\ 1 \end{bmatrix}$$

$$= \begin{bmatrix} 6 \\ 3 \\ 2 \end{bmatrix},$$

or as a vector equation

$$X(1) * P(1) + X(2) * P(2) + X(3) * P(3) + X(4) * P(4) + X(5) * P(5) = P(0),$$

where, for various choices of coefficients $X(J)$, $J \in //1, 5//$, the vector $P(0)$ is considered a linear combination of the vectors $P(J)$, $J \in //1, 5//$. This formulation has an interesting geometric interpretation, essentially different from that given in Example 1.

**Example 3.** Suppose it is required to find the coefficients A and B of the linear polynomial

(4.9.13a)                    $$P(T) = A * T + B$$

so that the graph of $P(T)$, a line, comes "close" to the points

$$(.2, .1), \qquad (.3, .2), \qquad (.4, .2),$$

and

(4.9.13b)
$$|P(.2) - .1| \leq M$$
$$|P(.3) - .2| \leq M$$
$$|P(.4) - .2| \leq M$$

for the constant M *as small as possible.* See Figure 8.1.1, on p. 259. That is, no line passes through the three points, but we ask for the line that comes closest to the three points in the sense that the maximum error *at* the specified points is a minimum.

*Note.*

$$|W| \leq E \text{ is equivalent to } -E \leq W \leq E$$
$$\text{is equivalent to } W \leq E \text{ } and \text{ } -W \leq E.$$

Thus, the conditions (4.9.13b) may be written in the equivalent form(s)

(4.9.13c)

| | |
|---|---|
| $P(.2) - .1 \leq M$ | $-M + P(.2) \leq .1$ |
| $-P(.2) + .1 \leq M$ | $-M - P(.2) \leq -.1$ |
| $P(.3) - .2 \leq M$ | $-M + P(.3) \leq .2$ |
| $-P(.3) + .2 \leq M$ , or | $-M - P(.3) \leq -.2$ |
| $P(.4) - .2 \leq M$ | $-M + P(.4) \leq .2$ |
| $-P(.4) + .2 \leq M$ | $-M - P(.4) \leq -.2.$ |

The linear programming problem associated with the second set of inequalities in

(4.9.13c), after slack variables have been introduced, may be written in the following form.

Find $(ZZ, XX)$ where

$$XX = (MM, AA, BB, CC1, CC2, CC3, CC4, CC5, CC6)$$

is in S, and $ZZ = F(XX)$ is the minimum value of

(4.9.14a)   $Z = F(X) = 1 * M + 0 * A + 0 * B + 0 * C1 + 0 * C2 + 0 * C3$
$$+ 0 * C4 + 0 * C5 + 0 * C6$$

as $X = (M, A, B, C1, C2, C3, C4, C5, C6)$ varies over the set S defined by

<table>
<tr><td rowspan="6">(4.9.15a)</td><td>$-M + .2 * A + B + C1$</td><td></td><td></td><td>$= .1$</td></tr>
<tr><td>$-M - .2 * A - B \quad + C2$</td><td></td><td></td><td>$= -.1$</td></tr>
<tr><td>$-M + .3 * A + B \qquad + C3$</td><td></td><td></td><td>$= .2$</td></tr>
<tr><td>$-M - .3 * A - B \qquad\qquad + C4$</td><td></td><td></td><td>$= -.2$</td></tr>
<tr><td>$-M + .4 * A + B \qquad\qquad\qquad + C5$</td><td></td><td></td><td>$= .2$</td></tr>
<tr><td>$-M - .4 * A - B \qquad\qquad\qquad\qquad + C6$</td><td></td><td></td><td>$= -.2$</td></tr>
</table>

(4.9.15b)   $M \geq 0, C1 \geq 0, C2 \geq 0, C3 \geq 0, C4 \geq 0, C5 \geq 0, C6 \geq 0,$

but A and B are *not* restricted in sign.

*Note.* In practice, one would probably define an equivalent "dual problem" which would involve a system of 3 equations.

SOLUTION. The situation here is a little more complicated than Example 2, where all constant terms were positive; here, some effort is required to find a first basic feasible solution.

*Step 1.* We want to pick three components of X to be zero. We cannot pick $M = A = B = 0$, for then $C2 = -.1 < 0$. Anyway, we know $M \geq 0$ and we want to *minimize* M, so we are not surprised that $M = 0$ will not work, Natural choices for this problem are $(A = 0, B = 0, C4 = 0)$, and $(A = 0, B = 0, C6 = 0)$, so that $M = .2$ [the largest constant term in (4.9.15a)]. With $A = 0, B = 0$, and $C4 = 0$, (4.9.15a) becomes

$$-M + C1 \qquad\qquad\qquad = .1$$
$$-M \quad + C2 \qquad\qquad = -.1$$
$$-M \qquad + C3 \qquad\quad = .2$$
$$-M \qquad\qquad\qquad = -.2$$
$$-M \qquad\qquad + C5 \quad = .2$$
$$-M \qquad\qquad\qquad + C6 = -.2.$$

As in Example 2, we would not write this system explicitly, but would apply Gauss Elimination to the M-column of (4.9.15a) and "keep" the fourth row, to obtain

$$
\begin{array}{llll}
.5*A + 2*B + C1 & & -\ C4 & = .3 \\
.1*A & +\ C2 & -\ C4 & = .1 \\
.6*A + 2*B & +\ C3 - C4 & & = .4 \\
M + .3*A + \quad B & & -\ C4 & = .2 \\
.7*A + 2*B & & -\ C4 + C5 & = .4 \\
-.1*A & & -\ C4 & +\ C6 = 0.
\end{array}
$$

(4.9.16)

Thus, a first basic feasible solution, a vertex of S, is ["cover" the A, B, and C4-columns in (4.9.16)]

$$X = (M, A, B, C1, C2, C3, C4, C5, C6)$$
$$= (.2, 0, 0, .3, .1, .4, 0, .4, 0).$$

The objective function F(X) for this vertex has the value

$$Z = F(X) = M = .2.$$

But, using the fourth equation in (4.9.16) we can write F(X) in the equivalent form

(4.9.14b)      $$Z = F(X) = M = -.3*A - B + C4 + .2,$$

and again we see at $A = B = C4 = 0$ that $F(X) = .2$.

*Step 2.* We examine (4.9.14b) and see that we can *reduce* F(X) by choosing $A > 0$ or $B > 0$. We make the arbitrary choice $A > 0$, so we set $B = C4 = 0$ in (4.9.16) and examine the resulting system for a solution with largest positive A, consistent with (4.9.15b). Recall that we do not want to set $M = 0$.

$C1 = 0$ and $A = 3/5$ implies $C5 = -.1/5 < 0.$
$C2 = 0$ and $A = 1$   implies $C1 = -.2 < 0.$
$C3 = 0$ and $A = 2/3$ implies $C1 = -.1/3 < 0.$
$C5 = 0$ and $A = 4/7$ implies (4.9.15b) is satisfied.
$C6 = 0$ and $A = 0$   implies (4.9.15b) is satisfied.

We choose to set $C5 = 0$, for $A = 4/7$ *reduces* F(X) while $A = 0$ does not. We apply Gauss Elimination to the A-column of (4.9.16), and "keep" the fifth row, to obtain

$$
\begin{array}{lll}
4/7 * B + C1 & - \ 2/7 * C4 - \ 5/7 * C5 & = 1/70 \\
- \ 2/7 * B \quad + C2 & - \ 6/7 * C4 - \ 1/7 * C5 & = 3/70 \\
2/7 * B \quad\quad + C3 - \ 1/7 * C4 - \ 6/7 * C5 & = 4/70 \\
M \ + \ 1/7 * B & - \ 4/7 * C4 - \ 3/7 * C5 & = 2/70 \\
A + 20/7 * B & - \ 10/7 * C4 + 10/7 * C5 & = 4/7 \\
2/7 * B & - \ 8/7 * C4 + \ 1/7 * C5 + C6 & = 4/70.
\end{array}
$$

(4.9.17)

Then we "cover" the B-, C4-, and C5-columns, and read-off the next basic feasible solution

$$X = (M, A, B, C1, C2, C3, C4, C5, C6)$$
$$= (2/70, 4/7, 0, 1/70, 3/70, 4/70, 0, 0, 4/70).$$

We use the fifth equation in (4.9.17) to eliminate A from F(X) in (4.9.14b) to obtain

(4.9.14c) $\quad Z = F(X) = -1/7 * B + 4/7 * C4 + 3/7 * C5 + 2/70.$

Also, at $B = C4 = C5 = 0$ we get $F(X) = 2/70$, which equals M in the current basic feasible solution.

*Step 3.* We observe that increasing B will decrease F(X), so we set $C4 = C5 = 0$ in (4.9.17) and examine the resulting system for a solution with largest positive B, consistent with (4.9.15b). We do not consider setting M or A equal zero.

$C1 = 0$ and $B = 1/40$    implies (4.9.15b) is satisfied.
$C2 = 0$ and $B = -3/20$ implies F(X) increased ($B < 0$).
$C3 = 0$ and $B = 4/20$    implies $C1 = -1/10 < 0$.
$C6 = 0$ and $B = 4/20$    implies $C1 = -1/10 < 0$.

Thus, we choose $C1 = C4 = C5 = 0$ in (4.9.17) and solve the resulting system to obtain the next basic feasible solution

$$X = (M, A, B, C1, C2, C3, C4, C5, C6)$$
$$= (1/40, 1/2, 1/40, 0, 1/20, 1/20, 0, 0, 1/20).$$

We use the first equation in (4.9.17) to eliminate B from (4.9.14c) to obtain

(4.9.14d) $\quad F(X) = 1/4 * C1 + 1/2 * C4 + 1/4 * C5 + 1/40.$

*Step 4.* Since C1, C4, and C5 are required to the nonnegative, then the minimum feasible solution is

$$XX = (1/40, 1/2, 1/40, 0, 1/20, 1/20, 0, 0, 1/20).$$

The minimum value of the objective function is indeed

$$F(XX) = 1/40 = MM \text{ (in XX)}.$$

The desired polynomial $P(T) = A * T + B$ is then

$$P(T) = 1/2 * T + 1/40.$$

As we would guess, the line $Y = P(T)$ is the same distance from each of the three specified points. In particular, comparing ordinates, we get

$$P(.2) - .1 = 5/40 - 4/40 = 1/40 \ (= M)$$
$$P(.3) - .2 = 7/40 - 8/40 = -1/40 \ (= -M)$$
$$P(.4) - .2 = 9/40 - 8/40 = 1/40 \ (= M).$$

We have computed the polynomial (4.9.13a) which approximates the specified data "best" in the Chebyshev sense [see (8.1.3)]. Our line is parallel to (and above) the line in Figure 8.1.1.

### EXERCISES

1. Supply the details of Example 2.

2. Supply the details of Example 3.

3. Company A advertises its need for a large number of items of two products, which we name Product No. 1, and Product No. 2. Company B is capable of producing both products, but does not have the capacity to produce all of the required items of either product. Company B wants to offer to supply the combination of products that produces the maximum profit for itself, without purchasing additional machinery. Company B reasons as follows:

   (a) Three machines are involved in the production of each product.

   (b) We have *available* (but do not require that we use all of the time on any particular machine)

600 hours on Machine No. 1,

300 hours on Machine No. 2,

800 hours on Machine No. 3.

(c) To produce one item of Product No. 1 we require

1 hour on Machine No. 1,

1 hour on Machine No. 2,

3 hours on Machine No. 3.

(d) To produce one item of Product No. 2 we require

3 hours on Machine No. 1,

1 hour on Machine No. 2,

1 hour on Machine No. 3.

(e) Our capability is defined as $X(1)$ items of Product No. 1 and $X(2)$ items of Product No. 2, where $X(1)$ and $X(2)$ satisfy

$$X(1) + 3 * X(2) \leq 600$$
$$X(1) + \quad X(2) \leq 300$$
$$3*X(1) + \quad X(2) \leq 800$$
$$X(1) \geq 0, \text{ and } X(2) \geq 0.$$

(f) We make two units (dollars, or thousands of dollars, etc.) of profit on each item of Product No. 1, and one unit of profit on each item of Product No. 2 that we produce. Thus, the objective function to be *maximized* is

$$Z = F(X) = 2 * X(1) + X(2).$$

We have the linear programming problem:

*Find* $(ZZ, XX)$ where $XX = (XX(1), XX(2))$ is in S, $ZZ = F(XX)$, and

$$ZZ = MAX(F(X)), \text{ over } X \in S,$$

where $X = (X(1), X(2))$ varies over the set S defined by the five inequalities in (e).

*Determine* the number XX(1) of items of Product No. 1 and the number XX(2) of items of Product No. 2 that Company B should offer to produce so that its profit is maximized. That is, solve this linear programming problem. First, use the method of Example 1. Then check your solution by using the method of Example 2.

## SUGGESTED READING

1. Birkhoff, G, and S. MacLane, (1953): *A Survey of Modern Algebra.* The MacMillan Company. New York. (Page 300.)

2. Dickson, L. E. (1939): *New First Course in the Theory of Equations.* John Wiley and Sons, Inc. New York. (Page 130.)

3. Milne, W. E. (1949): *Numerical Calculus.* Princeton University Press. Princeton, N. J. (Page 29.)

4. Hildebrand, F. B. (1956): *Introduction to Numerical Analysis.* McGraw-Hill Book Company. New York. (Page 436.)

5. Faddeev, D. K. and V. N. Faddeeva (1963): *Computational Methods of Linear Algebra.* (translated by Robert C. Williams). W. H. Freeman and Co., Publisher. San Francisco and London. (Page 128.)

6. Forsythe, G. E. and C. B. Moler (1967): *Computer Solution of Linear Algebraic Systems.* Prentice-Hall, Inc. Englewood Cliffs, N. J.

6a. ———————. (Page 23.)

7. Todd, J. (Ed.) (1962): *Survey of Numerical Analysis.* McGraw-Hill Book Company. New York. (Page 230.)

8. Gass, S. I. (1964): *Linear Programming* (Second Edition). McGraw-Hill Book Company. New York.

9. Vajda, S. (1961): *Mathematical Programming.* Addison-Wesley Publishing Company, Inc. Reading, Mass.

10. Wilkinson, J. H. (1965): *The Algebraic Eigenvalue Problem.* Clarendon Press. Oxford, England.

# 5 EIGENVALUES AND EIGENVECTORS

## 5.1. MOTIVATION

In this chapter, we discuss two classical methods to compute nontrivial solutions of a *homogeneous* linear system which involves a *parameter* L. See the Power Method for L real in §5.2, L complex in §5.5, and the Jacobi Method in §5.6. Specifically, we consider the linear system

(5.1.1)

$$
\begin{aligned}
(A(1,1)-L)*X(1)+ \quad & A(1,2)*X(2)+\cdots+ \quad && A(1,N)*X(N)=0 \\
A(2,1)*X(1)+(A(2,2)-L)*X(2)+\cdots+ \quad && A(2,N)*X(N)=0 \\
A(3,1)*X(1)+ \quad & A(3,2)*X(2)+\cdots+ \quad && A(3,N)*X(N)=0 \\
& \;\;\vdots && \;\;\vdots && \;\;\vdots \\
A(N,1)*X(1)+ \quad & A(N,2)*X(2)+\cdots+(A(N,N)-L)*X(N)=0
\end{aligned}
$$

and the corresponding matrix equation (the matrix A is real)

$$
\begin{bmatrix}
A(1,1)-L & A(1,2) & A(1,3) & \cdots & A(1,N) \\
A(2,1) & A(2,2)-L & A(2,3) & \cdots & A(2,N) \\
A(3,1) & A(3,2) & A(3,3)-L & \cdots & A(3,N) \\
\vdots & \vdots & \vdots & \vdots & \vdots \\
A(N,1) & A(N,2) & A(N,3) & \cdots & A(N,N)-L
\end{bmatrix}
*
\begin{bmatrix}
X(1) \\ X(2) \\ X(3) \\ \vdots \\ X(N)
\end{bmatrix}
=
\begin{bmatrix}
0 \\ 0 \\ 0 \\ \vdots \\ 0
\end{bmatrix}.
$$

(5.1.2) \qquad $(A - L*I)*X = 0.$

139

For every value of the parameter L, the homogeneous system (5.1.1) always *has* a solution, the trivial solution

$$X = (X(1), X(2), \ldots, X(N)) = (0, 0, \ldots, 0).$$

The homogeneous system has a unique solution if and only if the determinant of the matrix of coefficients is not zero. Thus, (5.1.1) has a *nontrivial* solution if and only if

(5.1.3)   DET(A − L * I) =

$$\begin{vmatrix} A(1, 1) - L & A(1, 2) & A(1, 3) & \cdots & A(1, N) \\ A(2, 1) & A(2, 2) - L & A(2, 3) & \cdots & A(2, N) \\ A(3, 1) & A(3, 2) & A(3, 3) - L & \cdots & A(3, N) \\ \vdots & \vdots & \vdots & & \vdots \\ A(N, 1) & A(N, 2) & A(N, 3) & \cdots & A(N, N) - L \end{vmatrix} = 0.$$

DET(A − L * I) is a real polynomial of degree exactly N in the parameter L

(5.1.4)     CHARP(L) = DET(A − L * I)
                    = $\sum$ C(K) * L ** K, K $\in$ // 0, N //,

called the *characteristic polynomial* of A. The coefficient C(N) = (−1) ** N, and C(0) = DET(A).

The roots of the *characteristic equation*, (5.1.3),

$$\text{CHARP(L)} = 0$$

are real and/or complex numbers denoted by

$$L(1), L(2), L(3), \ldots, L(N),$$

and are called *eigenvalues* (or characteristic values) of A. *Any* nontrivial solution

$$XV(K) = (X(K; 1), X(K; 2), \ldots, X(K; N))$$

of (5.1.1) with L =L(K) is called an *eigenvector* of A corresponding to the eigenvalue L(K).

If the term $-L * X(J)$ in the $J$th equation of (5.1.1) is transposed to the right side of equals, for each $J \in //1, N//$, then we obtain a linear system with corresponding matrix equation

$$
\begin{bmatrix}
A(1,1) & A(1,2) & \cdots & A(1,N) \\
A(2,1) & A(2,2) & \cdots & A(2,N) \\
\vdots & \vdots & & \vdots \\
A(N,1) & A(N,2) & \cdots & A(N,N)
\end{bmatrix}
*
\begin{bmatrix}
X(1) \\
X(2) \\
\vdots \\
X(N)
\end{bmatrix}
=
\begin{bmatrix}
L * X(1) \\
L * X(2) \\
\vdots \\
L * X(N)
\end{bmatrix}
$$

$$
= L *
\begin{bmatrix}
X(1) \\
X(2) \\
\vdots \\
X(N)
\end{bmatrix}.
$$

(5.1.5)  $\qquad A * X = L * X.$

The *characterizing properties* for the eigenvalues and corresponding eigenvectors of any square matrix A (of order N) may now be written, for each $K \in //1, N//$,

$$
\begin{bmatrix}
A(1,1) & A(1,2) & \cdots & A(1,N) \\
A(2,1) & A(2,2) & \cdots & A(2,N) \\
\vdots & \vdots & & \vdots \\
A(N,1) & A(N,2) & \cdots & A(N,N)
\end{bmatrix}
*
\begin{bmatrix}
X(K;1) \\
X(K;2) \\
\vdots \\
X(K;N)
\end{bmatrix}
= L(K) *
\begin{bmatrix}
X(K;1) \\
X(K;2) \\
\vdots \\
X(K;N)
\end{bmatrix}.
$$

(5.1.6)  $\qquad A * XV(K) = L(K) * XV(K).$

As indicated in §4.2, the *set* of eigenvectors of A corresponding to the eigenvalue $L(K)$ form the *null space* of the operator associated with the matrix $(A - L(K) * I)$.

Another geometric interpretation for eigenvalue and eigenvector is based on the relation (5.1.6). We ask for a vector $XV(K)$ that maps (under A) into a constant times itself. See Figure 5.1.1.

If the N eigenvalues of A are distinct, then the rank of $(A - L(K) * I)$ is $N - 1$, and corresponding to each eigenvalue of A there is a one-parameter family of eigenvectors. Sometimes we find it convenient to talk about *the* eigenvector of A corresponding to the eigenvalue $L(K)$. In such a case, we will specify a condition like: (i) eigenvectors are of length unity

$$\text{LENGTH}(XV(K)) = \text{SQRT}\left(\sum X(K;J) ** 2, J \in //1, N//,\right) = 1;$$

or (ii) the $K$th component of $XV(K)$ is unity: $X(K;K) = 1$. If an

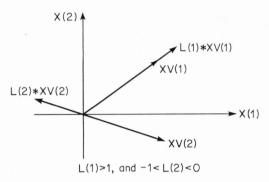

**Figure 5.1.1.**

eigenvalue of A has multiplicity $M > 1$, then there *may* be more than a one-parameter family of eigenvectors of A corresponding to that eigenvalue. See §5.3, below.

Suppose that we have obtained the N eigenvalues of A by finding the roots of the characteristic equation (say by Newton's Method), then we could substitute each eigenvalue for L in (5.1.1) and solve the homogeneous system for a corresponding eigenvector (nontrivial solution). Any set of eigenvectors that correspond to distinct eigenvalues form a *linearly independent* set. In particular, if no two of the eigenvalues

$$L(P), L(Q), L(R)$$

are equal, and if

$$XV(P), XV(Q), XV(R)$$

are corresponding eigenvectors respectively, then the only linear combination of these vectors that equals the zero vector is the trivial combination. That is,

$$Bl * XV(P) + B2 * XV(Q) + B3 * XV(R) = 0$$

implies

$$B1 = B2 = B3 = 0.$$

If a set of nonzero vectors (in the same space) is not linearly independent, then it is *linearly dependent*. The nonzero vectors X1, X2, X3 form a linearly dependent set if

$$B1 * X1 + B2 * X2 + B3 * X3 = 0$$

for some set of constants B1, B2, B3 *not all zero.* If $B1 \neq 0$, we can write

$$X1 = -B2/B1 * X2 - B3/B1 * X3.$$

Thus, every linearly dependent set of vectors contains at least one vector that can be written as a linear combination of the remaining vectors in the set.

If the N eigenvalues of A are *distinct,* then any set of N corresponding eigenvectors form a linearly independent set. These eigenvectors form a *basis* for Euclidean N-space, EN. In particular, every vector X in EN can be written as a linear combination of basis elements. In this case, we say the set of eigenvectors *span the space*; and, if X is any vector in EN, then there is a set of numbers $B(K), K \in //1, N//$, such that

$$X = \sum B(K) * XV(K), K \in //1, N//.$$

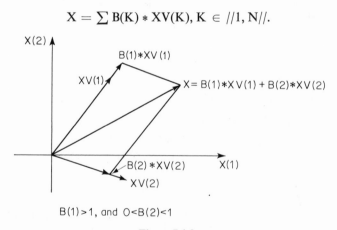

B(1)>1, and 0<B(2)<1

**Figure 5.1.2.**

It is known that real symmetric matrices of order N (even those with repeated eigenvalues) have a set of N eigenvectors which span EN. If A has *fewer* than N linearly independent eigenvectors, then the methods of §5.3 suggest how a set of eigenvectors can be *extended* to define a (canonical) basis for EN.

We consider two essentially different classical methods for computing eigenvalues and corresponding eigenvectors (the Power Method, §5.2, and the Jacobi Method, §5.6). Both methods are iteration processes. The Power Method produces one eigenvalue and an associated eigenvector. A deflation process, presented in §5.4, permits the "removal" of a known eigenvalue and corresponding eigenvector "from" A in the sense that the process defines a new matrix B of order N - 1 which has N - 1 eigenvalues and eigenvectors that are related to the "other" eigenvalues and eigenvectors of A. Thus, one can find a *second* eigenvalue and eigenvector of A by "operating on" an eigenvalue and corresponding eigenvector of B. In §5.5 we indicate how the Power Method can be applied to compute complex eigenvalues of A. The Jacobi Method produces *all* eigenvalues and corresponding eigenvectors of A (a real symmetric matrix).

These two methods were chosen for presentation here because an understanding of them facilitates the study of many "similar" methods presented in more encyclopedic books on eigenvalue problems, like [4]. Also, this explanation of the Power Method involves operations on an arbitrary vector represented as a linear combination of eigenvectors—an important concept in many contexts in numerical analysis, notably in studies concerning stability of numerical methods in differential equations.

### EXERCISES

1. With A the second-order identity matrix, show that the eigenvalues of A are $L = 1, 1$, Show that there is a two-parameter family of eigenvectors of A corresponding to $L = 1$. In particular, the "usual basis" vectors are linearly independent eigenvectors of A. Also, we may write any vector X in the form

$$X = \begin{bmatrix} X1 \\ X2 \end{bmatrix} = X1* \begin{bmatrix} 1 \\ 0 \end{bmatrix} + X2* \begin{bmatrix} 0 \\ 1 \end{bmatrix} = X1*XV(1) + X2*XV(2).$$

2. Show

$$A = \begin{bmatrix} 1 & 1 \\ 0 & 1 \end{bmatrix}$$

has eigenvalues $L = 1, 1$. Show there is only a one-parameter family of eigenvectors of A.

### 5.2. THE POWER METHOD

In this section we describe an iteration process called the Power Method which defines a sequence of estimates to a *real* eigenvalue $L(1)$ of the N*th* order real matrix A. At the same time, the method defines estimates to a corresponding eigenvector $XV(1)$ of A. In §5.5 the Power Method is applied to define estimates to complex eigenvalues.

The method is outlined for three special cases (depending on the relative magnitudes of the eigenvalues of A). Then we consider the General Case where the distribution of the eigenvalues is unknown.

**Case I.**   $|L(1)| > |L(2)| \geq |L(3)| \geq \cdots \geq |L(N)|$,
          where $L(1)$ is "largest," even if $L(1) < 0$.
**Case II.**   $L(1) = L(2) = \cdots = L(P) > |L(P + 1)| \geq \cdots \geq |L(N)|$.
**Case III.**   $|L(1)| = |L(2)| > |L(3)| \geq \cdots \geq |L(N)|$,
          where $L(2) = -L(1)$.

The iteration *converges* for Case I and Case II. In Case III, the iteration *diverges*, but a recognizable pattern appears and we are able to obtain eigenvalues and corresponding eigenvectors. We further assume that the N eigenvalues $L(K)$, $K \in //1, N//$, of A have a set of corresponding eigenvectors

$$XV(1), XV(2), \ldots, XV(N),$$

which span the space EN. Without saying how they were chosen, for the analysis we assume a set $XV(J)$, $J \in //1, N//$, is specified. In particular, for each vector X in EN, there is a set of constants $B(K)$, $K \in //1, N//$, such that

(5.2.1)          $X = \sum B(K) * XV(K), K \in //1, N//.$

Of course, it is not necessary to know the eigenvalues and corresponding eigenvectors in order to *apply* the Power Method.

> *Note.* Real symmetric matrices A have such a set of eigenvectors. When two eigenvalues are equal, we may use one name to denote either eigenvalue, but we *never* use one name to denote two elements of the set of linearly independent eigenvectors.

Eigenvectors are considered in column matrix form (but we will refer to their elements as components) and are characterized by, (5.1.6), for each $K \in //1, N//$,

(5.2.2)          $A * XV(K) = L(K) * XV(K) .$

**Case I.** Suppose that the eigenvalues of A are real and satisfy

(5.2.3)      $|L(1)| > |L(2)| \geq |L(3)| \geq \cdots \geq |L(N)|.$

We outline the *convergent* iteration process for $L(1) > 0$, and then indicate where the outline is changed for $L(1) < 0$.

*Step* 1. Choose a first guess XIT(0) at an eigenvector XV(1) corresponding to L(1). A standard choice is

$$
\text{XIT(0)} = \begin{bmatrix} 1 \\ 1 \\ 1 \\ \vdots \\ 1 \end{bmatrix} = \begin{bmatrix} \text{XIT(0; 1)} \\ \text{XIT(0; 2)} \\ \text{XIT(0; 3)} \\ \vdots \\ \text{XIT(0; N)} \end{bmatrix}.
$$

In theory, the only restriction on the choice of a first guess XIT(0) is that the representation, (5.2.1),

$$\text{XIT(0)} = \sum \text{B(K)} * \text{XV(K)}, \text{K} \in //1, \text{N}//,$$

have the *coefficient* B(1) of XV(1) *not zero*. In practice, even if $B(1) = 0$ in XIT(0), the round-off errors committed when *executing* the iteration will usually produce an iterant [vector, say XIT(1)] with a representation (5.2.1) which *does* involve the eigenvector XV(1).

*Step* 2. Compute

$$A * \text{XIT(0)} = A * \left( \sum \text{B(K)} * \text{XV(K)}, \text{K} \in //1, \text{N}//, \right)$$

[use (5.2.2)]
$$= \sum \text{B(K)} * A * \text{XV(K)}, \text{K} \in //1, \text{N}//,$$
$$= \sum \text{B(K)} * \text{L(K)} * \text{XV(K)}, \text{K} \in //1, \text{N}//,$$
$$\equiv \text{XIT(1)}.$$

*Step* 3. Compute

$$A * \text{XIT(1)} = A * \left( A * \text{XIT(0)} \right) = A ** (2) * \text{XIT(0)}$$
$$= A * \sum \text{B(K)} * \text{L(K)} * \text{XV(K)}, \text{K} \in //1, \text{N}//,$$

[use (5.2.2)]
$$= \sum \text{B(K)} * \text{L(K)} * A * \text{XV(K)}, \text{K} \in //1, \text{N}//,$$
$$= \sum \text{B(K)} * \text{L(K)} ** 2 * \text{XV(K)}, \text{K} \in //1, \text{N}//,$$
$$\equiv \text{XIT(2)}.$$

*Step* 4. [Given the $(M - 1)th$ iterant $XIT(M - 1)$.] Compute

$$A * XIT(M - 1) = A * \big(A * XIT(M - 2)\big) = A ** (M) * XIT(0)$$
$$= A * \sum B(K) * L(K) ** (M - 1) * XV(K), K \in //1, N//,$$
$$= \sum B(K) * L(K) ** (M - 1) * A * XV(K), K \in //1, N//,$$
(5.2.4) $\qquad\qquad = \sum B(K) * L(K) ** M * XV(K), K \in //1, N//,$
$$\equiv XIT(M).$$

*Step* 5. Since the $L(K), K \in //1, N//$, are real and satisfy (5.2.3), when M is large we have from (5.2.4) that

$$XIT(M) = L(1) ** M * \big(B(1) * XV(1)$$
(5.2.5) $\qquad\qquad + \sum B(K) * \big(L(K)/L(1)\big) ** M * XV(K), K \in //2, N//.\big)$
$$= B(1) * L(1) ** M * \big(XV(1) + ORDB\big((L(2)/L(1)\big) ** M)\big)$$
$$\doteq B(1) * L(1) ** M * XV(1).$$

That is, if the components of the iterants are computed as decimal numbers, when M is sufficiently large, then all the terms except the first in the sum defining $XIT(M)$ are insignificant compared to $B(1) * L(1) ** M * XV(1)$. The *convergence* is of the order $ORDB(H ** M)$, with $H = L(2)/L(1)$.

*Step* 6. If the $Jth$ component $XIT(M; J)$ of the estimate $XIT(M)$ is not zero, *write* the normalized vector [the normalizing factor is denoted by $L(1, M)$]

(5.2.6) $\qquad\qquad U = XIT(M)/XIT(M; J) \equiv XIT(M)/L(1, M).$

If M is sufficiently large, so that *computationally* $XIT(M) = B(1) * L(1) ** M * XV(1)$, then *computationally*

(5.2.7) $\qquad\qquad\qquad A * U = L(1) * U.$

Then the $Jth$ *component* of $L(1) * U$ is the eigenvalue $L(1)$, and U [and thus $XIT(M)$] is an eigenvector of A corresponding to $L(1)$.

*Note.* In a computer program that executes the Power Method, we would periodically use (5.2.6) to normalize iterants to a "largest" component to avoid overflow, and at that point in the iteration we would compute $A * U$ and *test* (5.2.7) for convergence (to stop the iteration). It is generally not enough that the normalizing factor $L(1, M)$ be the same for two consecutive tests, but when this happens we test *each* iterant until corresponding components of two consecutive normalized vectors U are unchanged.

If the eigenvalue with largest magnitude is real and *negative*, then after M is large we find corresponding components of successive iterants alternate in sign— unless we normalize each iterant before computing the next vector in the sequence.

In the following example we indicate that the Power Method may converge even when A is not symmetric. Indeed, the eigenvalues of A need not be all real.

**Example.** The polynomial equation

$$(X - 4) * (X - 2) * (X - 1) = X ** 3 - 7 * X ** 2 + 14 * X - 8 = 0$$

is the characteristic equation for the matrix (the *companion matrix* for the equation)

$$A = \begin{bmatrix} 0 & 0 & 8 \\ 1 & 0 & -14 \\ 0 & 1 & 7 \end{bmatrix}.$$

The eigenvalues of A are L = 4, 2, 1. We apply the Power Method with XIT(0) = TRAN[1  1  1], and normalize the iterants at each step to the component with largest magnitude (in this example always the second component).

$$A * XIT(0) = \begin{bmatrix} 0 & 0 & 8 \\ 1 & 0 & -14 \\ 0 & 1 & 7 \end{bmatrix} * \begin{bmatrix} 1 \\ 1 \\ 1 \end{bmatrix} = \begin{bmatrix} 8 \\ -13 \\ 8 \end{bmatrix} \doteq (-13) * \begin{bmatrix} -.615 \\ 1 \\ -.615 \end{bmatrix}$$

$$\equiv L(1, 1) * U(1)$$

so that the first estimate to the eigenvalue L(1) is L(1, 1) = $-13$, and the first estimate to the corresponding eigenvector XV(1) is U(1)=TRAN[$-.615$  1  $-.615$].

$$A * U(1) = \begin{bmatrix} 0 & 0 & 8 \\ 1 & 0 & -14 \\ 0 & 1 & 7 \end{bmatrix} * \begin{bmatrix} -.615 \\ 1 \\ -.615 \end{bmatrix} \doteq \begin{bmatrix} -4.92 \\ 8 \\ -3.30 \end{bmatrix} \doteq (8) * \begin{bmatrix} -.615 \\ 1 \\ -.412 \end{bmatrix}$$

$$\equiv L(1, 2) * U(2).$$

The next three iterants are

$$A * U(2) \doteq \begin{bmatrix} -3.30 \\ 5.15 \\ -1.88 \end{bmatrix} \doteq (5.15) * \begin{bmatrix} -.641 \\ 1 \\ -.365 \end{bmatrix} \equiv L(1, 3) * U(3),$$

$$A * U(3) \doteq \begin{bmatrix} -2.92 \\ 4.47 \\ -1.56 \end{bmatrix} \doteq (4.47) * \begin{bmatrix} -.653 \\ 1 \\ -.349 \end{bmatrix} \equiv L(1, 4) * U(4),$$

$$A * U(4) \doteq \begin{bmatrix} -2.79 \\ 4.23 \\ -1.44 \end{bmatrix} \doteq (4.23) * \begin{bmatrix} -.660 \\ 1 \\ -.340 \end{bmatrix} \equiv L(1, 5) * U(5).$$

It appears that $\text{LIM}(L(1, K)) = 4$, as $K \text{ App} \infty$, and $\text{LIM}(\text{XIT}(K)/L(1, K)) = \text{TRAN}[-2/3 \quad 1 \quad -1/3]$, as $K \text{ App} \infty$. Indeed, $L(1) = 4$ and

$$(A - L(1) * I) * X = \begin{bmatrix} -L(1) & 0 & 8 \\ 1 & -L(1) & -14 \\ 0 & 1 & 7 - L(1) \end{bmatrix} * \begin{bmatrix} X(1) \\ X(2) \\ X(3) \end{bmatrix}$$

$$= \begin{bmatrix} -4 & 0 & 8 \\ 1 & -4 & -14 \\ 0 & 1 & 3 \end{bmatrix} * \begin{bmatrix} X(1) \\ X(2) \\ X(3) \end{bmatrix} = \begin{bmatrix} 0 \\ 0 \\ 0 \end{bmatrix}$$

has $X = \text{TRAN}[-2/3 \quad 1 \quad -1/3]$ as a nontrivial solution [an eigenvector of A corresponding to $L(1) = 4$]. Also, (5.2.2),

$$\begin{bmatrix} 0 & 0 & 8 \\ 1 & 0 & -14 \\ 0 & 1 & 7 \end{bmatrix} * \begin{bmatrix} -2/3 \\ 1 \\ -1/3 \end{bmatrix} = \begin{bmatrix} -8/3 \\ 12/3 \\ -4/3 \end{bmatrix} = (4) * \begin{bmatrix} -2/3 \\ 1 \\ -1/3 \end{bmatrix}.$$

The matrix

$$B = (A - K * I)$$

has eigenvalues $L(1) - K$, $L(2) - K$, ..., $L(N) - K$, where $L(1)$, $L(2)$, ..., $L(N)$, are the eigenvalues of A. Also, an eigenvector of A corresponding to $L(J)$ is also an eigenvector of B corresponding to $L(J) - K$. In the above example, $L(3) = 1$ is the smallest eigenvalue of A, but if we choose $K = 4$, then $L(3) - 4$ is the eigenvalue of B with largest magnitude. In this case, when we find the eigenvalue of B with largest magnitude we know the *smallest* eigenvalue of A. In general, if $L(1)$ is the "largest" eigenvalue of A, and if A has an eigenvalue $L(P)$ with $L(P) \neq L(1)$, then the "largest" eigenvalue of B with $K = L(1)$, call it $LB(1)$, is such that $LB(1) + L(1)$ is an eigenvalue of A—not necessarily the "smallest" eigenvalue of A. If $L(1) > L(2) > \cdots > L(N)$, then the *natural* choice for K to compute $L(1)$ is $K = L(N)$, and to compute $L(N)$ choose $K = L(1)$. Another *good* choice is $K = (L(2) + L(N))/2$ to compute $L(1)$, and $K = (L(1) + L(N-1))/2$ to compute $L(N)$. The reader should execute a few steps of the iteration indicated in the above example for B, first with the "natural" choice $K = 4$ and then with $K = (4 + 2)/2 = 3$. Except for carefully chosen classroom examples, an electronic computer should be used to execute the Power Method.

**Case II.** If the largest eigenvalue of A is of multiplicity P,

$$(5.2.8) \qquad L(1) = L(2) = \cdots = L(P) > |L(P + 1)| \geq \cdots \geq |L(N)|,$$

then the Power Method applied to A gives (5.2.4)

$$XIT(M) = A ** (M) * XIT(0)$$
$$= \sum B(K) * L(1) ** M * XV(K),\ K \in //1, P//,$$
$$+ \sum B(K) * L(K) ** M * XV(K),\ K \in //P + 1, N//.$$

If M is sufficiently large, then computationally (5.2.5)

$$(5.2.9) \qquad XIT(M) = L(1) ** M * \left( \sum B(K) * XV(K),\ K \in //1, P//, \right.$$
$$+ \sum B(K) * (L(K)/L(1)) ** M * XV(K),\ K \in //P + 1, N//, \big)$$
$$= L(1) ** M * \left( \sum B(K) * XV(K),\ K \in //1, P//, \right.$$
$$+ ORDB\big((L(P + 1)/L(1)) ** M\big)\big)$$
$$\doteq L(1) ** M * \sum B(K) * XV(K),\ K \in //1, P//.$$

Also, when $XIT(M)$ is normalized, (5.2.6.), the normalized vector U is (computationally) an eigenvector of A corresponding to $L(1)$, (5.2.7). Thus, the Power Method *converges* for Case II, and we use the same test for convergence that we use in Case I. Sometimes a set of P linearly independent eigenvectors of A corresponding to $L(1)$ can be found by applying the Power Method with a variety of first guesses $XIT(0)$.

**Case III.** If the eigenvalues of A are real and satisfy

$$(5.2.10) \qquad\qquad L(1) = -L(2) > |L(3)| \geq \cdots \geq |L(N)|,$$

then the Power Method applied to A gives (5.2.4)

$$XIT(2 * M) = A ** (2 * M) * XIT(0)$$
$$= B(1) * L(1) ** (2 * M) * XV(1) + B(2) * L(2) ** (2 * M) * XV(2)$$
$$+ \sum B(K) * L(K) ** (2 * M) * XV(K), K \in //3, N//,$$
$$= L(1) ** (2 * M) * \big(B(1) * XV(1) + B(2) * XV(2)\big)$$
$$+ \sum B(K) * L(K) ** (2 * M) * XV(K), K \in //3, N//,$$

and

$$XIT(2 * M + 1) = A ** (2 * M + 1) * XIT(0)$$
$$= L(1) ** (2 * M + 1) * \big(B(1) * XV(1) - B(2) * XV(2)\big)$$
$$+ \sum B(K) * L(K) ** (2 * M + 1) * XV(K), K \in //3, N//.$$

If M is sufficiently large, then *computationally* (5.2.5)

(5.2.11a)     $XIT(2 * M) = L(1) ** (2 * M) * \big(B(1) * XV(1) + B(2) * XV(2)$
$$+ ORDB\big((L(3)/L(1)) ** (2 * M)\big)\big)$$
$$\doteq L(1) ** (2 * M) * \big(B(1) * XV(1) + B(2) * XV(2)\big)$$

and

(5.2.11b)     $XIT(2 * M + 1) \doteq L(1) ** (2 * M + 1) * \big(B(1) * XV(1)$
$$- B(2) * XV(2)\big).$$

Thus, if $XIT(2 * M)$, or $XIT(2 * M + 1)$, is normalized to the J*th* component, (5.2.6), then the J*th* component of $A * (A * U)$ equals $L(1) ** 2$. Also, $L(1)$ is the positive square root of $L(1) ** 2$, and $L(2) = -L(1)$.

*Note.* Our criterion for deciding that M *is* sufficiently large (so we can stop the iteration): Periodically, normalize an iterant (5.2.6) and compute the J*th* component of $A * (A * U)$ to define a sequence of estimates to $L(1) ** 2$, We stop the iteration when this sequence "converges" to $L(1) ** 2$, and U is the "same" as the vector $A * (A * U)$ when normalized. In practice, if it does not converge, then we look for complex eigenvalues.

Eigenvectors $XV(1)$ and $XV(2)$, corresponding to $L(1)$ and $L(2)$ respectively, are obtained in the following way. After M is sufficiently large, so that computationally (5.2.11a, b) hold, then

(5.2.12a)          $XIT(2 * M + 1) + L(1) * XIT(2 * M)$
$$\doteq 2 * B(1) * L(1) ** (2 * M + 1) * XV(1)$$

is an eigenvector of A corresponding to L(1), and

$$(5.2.12b) \qquad XIT(2 * M + 1) - L(1) * XIT(2 * M)$$
$$\doteq 2 * B(2) * \left(-L(1)\right) ** (2 * M + 1) * XV(2)$$

is an eigenvector of A corresponding to L(2). The iteration *diverges,* but we are able to examine *consecutive* iterants [maybe XIT(2 * M + 1) and XIT (2 * M + 2)], recognize a pattern, use either iterant to find L(1) and L(2), and add the second iterant to L(1) times the first iterant to obtain an eigenvector of A corresponding to L(1), etc.

**General Case.** Suppose the Power Method is applied to a real matrix A where the eigenvalues are known to be real but the distribution of the eigenvalues of A is unknown. Denote the generated sequence by

$$(5.2.13) \qquad XIT(1), XIT(2), XIT(3), \ldots, XIT(M), \ldots.$$

If A has a largest eigenvalue of multiplicity P, then the sequence converges to an eigenvector corresponding to the largest eigenvalue of A: for M sufficiently large, (5.2.9),

$$(5.2.14) \qquad XIT(M) \doteq L(1) ** M * \sum B(K) * XV(K), K \in //1, P//.$$

This is Case I for P = 1, and Case II for P > 1. *Otherwise,* the generated sequence does not converge to an eigenvector of A, but does converge to a *recognizable* linear combination of eigenvectors corresponding to those eigenvalues satisfying [compare Case III, (5.2.10)]

$$(5.2.15) \qquad |L(1)| = |L(2)| = \cdots$$
$$= |L(P + Q)| > |L(P + Q + 1)| \geq \cdots \geq |L(N)|,$$

where L(1) = L(2) = $\cdots$ = L(P) and L(P + 1) = $\cdots$ = L(P + Q) = −L(1). That is, for M sufficiently large, [compare (5.2.11a, b)], *computationally*

$$(5.2.16a) \qquad XIT(2 * M) \doteq L(1) ** (2 * M) * \left(\sum B(K) * XV(K), K \in //1, P//, \right.$$
$$\left. + \sum B(K) * XV(K), K \in //P + 1, P + Q//,\right)$$

and

$$(5.2.16b) \qquad XIT(2 * M + 1) \doteq L(1) ** (2 * M + 1)$$
$$* \left(\sum B(K) * XV(K), K \in //1, P//, \right.$$
$$\left. - \sum B(K) * XV(K), K \in //P + 1, P + Q//,\right).$$

If we normalize $XIT(2 * M)$, or $XIT(2 * M + 1)$, to its $Jth$ component, (5.2.6),

$$U = XIT(2 * M)/L(1, 2 * M),$$

or

$$U = XIT(2 * M + 1)/L(1, 2 * M + 1),$$

then the $Jth$ component of $A * (A * U)$ equals $L(1) ** 2$. Thus, $L(1)$ is the positive square root of $L(1) ** 2$, and $L(K) = L(1)$ for each $K \in //2, P//$. Also, $L(K) = -L(1)$ for each $K \in //P + 1, P + Q//$. We use the same criterion for stopping the iteration that we used in Case III. Eigenvectors of $A$ corresponding to $L(1)$ and $L(P + 1) = -L(1)$ may be obtained by [compare (5.2.12a, b)]

(5.2.17a)     $XIT(2 * M + 1) + L(1) * XIT(2 * M)$

$\doteq 2 * L(1) ** (2 * M + 1) * \sum B(K) * XV(K), K \in //1, P//,$

an eigenvector of $A$ corresponding to $L(1)$, and

(5.2.17b)     $XIT(2 * M + 1) - L(1) * XIT(2 * M)$

$\doteq 2 * \big(-L(1)\big) ** (2 * M + 1) * \sum B(K) * XV(K), K \in //P + 1, P + Q//,$

an eigenvector of $A$ corresponding to $L(P + 1) = -L(1)$. Again, it is only required that we use *consecutive* iterants. The term "first iterant" replaces $XIT(2 * M)$, and "second iterant" replaces $XIT(2 * M + 1)$ in the above analysis.

SUMMARY FOR THE GENERAL CASE

We apply the Power Method to a matrix $A$ whose eigenvalues are not known to us. After a few steps in the iteration, we test for convergence as if we had Case I; that is, normalize an iterant (5.2.6) and ask (5.2.7)

$$A * U = L(1, M) * U ?$$

Even if the normalizing factor $L(1, M)$ is not changing, we would continue the iteration and test each subsequent iterant until we found corresponding components of U from consecutive tests to be equal. If the computed elements of the sequence (5.2.13) do not pass the Case I test, then we apply the Case III test. That is, normalize an iterant (5.2.6) and compute the $Jth$ component of $A * (A * U)$. Thus we generate a sequence of these

J*th* components. If they converge to a number $T > 0$. then we proceed as if $L(1) = SQRT(T)$, and use (5.2.17a, b). If this sequence of J*th* components of $A * (A * U)$ does not converge, then we test for complex eigenvalues (§5.5).

If $P > 1$ in (5.2.14), or if $P > 1$ and/or $Q > 1$ in (5.2.16a, b), and if one first guess XIT(0) has led to $L(1)$ and an XV(1), then *another* first guess XIT(0) will lead to a sequence (5.2.13) which leads to (5.2.14) or (5.2.17a, b)—possibly another eigenvector of A corresponding to $L(1)$.

Deflation methods like that discussed in §5.4 may be used to determine if a given eigenvalue has multiplicity $P > 1$. Deflation methods may also be used with the Power Method to determine eigenvalues of A which are neither largest nor smallest in magnitude.

A method for computing complex eigenvalues by the Power Method is considered in §5.5.

The reader is referred to the texts listed in Suggested Reading at the end of the chapter for more comprehensive discussions of these and other methods for computing eigenvalues and eigenvectors of matrices.

**EXERCISE**

1. With

$$A = \begin{bmatrix} 1 & 1 \\ 0 & 1 \end{bmatrix}, \quad \text{and} \quad XIT(0) = \begin{bmatrix} 1 \\ 1 \end{bmatrix},$$

use the Power Method to show that when normalized to the first component the sequence of estimates to the eigenvector converges to $XV(1) = TRAN [1 \quad 0]$ like $1/N$ converges to zero as N App $\infty$.

**5.3. THE JORDAN CANONICAL FORM. SIMILAR MATRICES**

In §5.2 we saw how the Power Method can be applied to any real matrix A that has a real largest eigenvalue $L(1)$ satisfying (5.2.8) [or two real largest eigenvalues $L(1)$ and $L(P + 1) = -L(1)$ satisfying (5.2.15)] to obtain $L(1)$ and a corresponding vector U [or U and V] such that *computationally*

(5.3.1a)                          $A * U = L(1) * U.$

(5.3.1b)          $[Or, A * U = L(1) * U, \text{ and } A * V = -L(1) * V].$

The Power Method can also be used to find the smallest eigenvalue of A.

In this section, before considering (§5.4) methods for computing other eigenvalues and eigenvectors of A, we present some relations between any square (real or complex) matrix A and its eigenvalues and eigenvectors. Specifically, we briefly discuss the Jordan Canonical Form of A, (5.3.10), which involves the eigenvalues of A explicitly. The Jordan Canonical Transformation INV(S) * A * S transforms A into its Jordan Canonical Form LL. The matrix S involves linearly independent eigenvectors of A explicitly, and possibly involves some other vectors which are related to these eigenvectors.

First, we consider (5.3.5), an important special case of the Jordan Canonical Form of A.

It can be shown that if the N*th* order matrix A is real and symmetric, or if the eigenvalues of A (not necessarily symmetric) are real and distinct, then there exist N linearly independent eigenvectors of A:

(5.3.2)          $A * XV(K) = L(K) * XV(K), \text{ for each } K \in //1, N//,$

and

(5.3.3)     $\sum B(K) * XV(K), K \in //1, N//, = 0$ only if all the $B(K) = 0.$

In particular, if a matrix S is defined by

(5.3.4)          $S = [XV(1) \quad XV(2) \quad XV(3) \quad \cdots \quad XV(N)],$

where the columns of S are the eigenvectors of A corresponding to $L(1)$, $L(2), \ldots, L(N)$, then

(5.3.5)          $A * S = S * LL, \text{ where}$

$$LL = \begin{bmatrix} L(1) & 0 & 0 & \cdots & 0 \\ 0 & L(2) & 0 & \cdots & 0 \\ 0 & 0 & L(3) & \cdots & 0 \\ \vdots & \vdots & \vdots & & \vdots \\ 0 & 0 & 0 & \cdots & L(N) \end{bmatrix}.$$

Since the columns of S are linearly independent, $DET(S) \neq 0$, $INV(S)$ exists, and

(5.3.6)                    $INV(S) * A * S = LL.$

The matrix LL is *similar* to the matrix A.

> *Note.* The matrix P is *similar* to the matrix Q if there exists a nonsingular matrix T such that $P = INV(T) * Q * T$. Also, Q is similar to P since $Q = T * P * INV(T) = INV(INV(T)) * P * INV(T)$. In the first case, we say P is obtained from Q by a *similarity transformation*. The eigenvalues of similar matrices are equal. For, if $DET(T) \neq 0$ and $P = INV(T) * Q * T$, then
>
> $$DET(P - L * I) = DET(INV(T) * Q * T - L * I)$$
> $$= DET(INV(T) * Q * T - L * INV(T) * T)$$
> $$= DET(INV(T) * (Q - L * I) * T)$$
> $$= DET(INV(T)) * DET(Q - L * I) * DET(T)$$
>
> and
>
> (5.3.7)    $DET(P - L * I) = 0$ if and only if $DET(Q - L * I) = 0.$

Thus, if A is real and symmetric, or if the eigenvalues of A are real and distinct, then A is similar to a diagonal matrix LL whose diagonal elements are the eigenvalues of A. And LL is obtained from A by the similarity transformation (5.3.6) where the columns of S are N linearly independent eigenvectors of A. For this special case, LL in (5.3.5) is the Jordan Canonical Form of A, and the similarity transformation (5.3.6) is a Jordan Canonical Transformation. Many methods have been devised to find LL and S for this important case. In §5.6 we discuss one of these, the Jacobi Method.

More generally, let A be an arbitrary N*th* order matrix. The *minimal polynomial* of A is defined to be the monic polynomial

$$MINP(X) = X ** K + \sum A(J) * X ** J, J \in //0, K - 1//,$$

such that $MINP(A) = 0$ and if $F(X)$ is any polynomial with the property $F(A) = 0$, then $MINP(X)$ is a factor of $F(X)$; i.e., $MINP(A)$ is the zero matrix, and $MINP(X)$ divides every monic polynomial $F(X)$ with the property $F(A) = 0$. The matrix A is known (Cayley-Hamilton Theorem) to satisfy its characteristic equation. Thus the minimal polynomial of A divides the characteristic polynomial of A. All the *distinct* eigenvalues of A are zeros of the minimal polynomial of A, and all the zeros of the minimal polynomial of A are eigenvalues of A.

Thus, if $L(1)$, $L(2)$, ..., $L(P)$ are the distinct eigenvalues of the N*th* order matrix A, then the minimal polynomial of A is

$$(5.3.8) \quad \text{MINP(X)} = (X - L(1)) ** \text{EM}(1) * (X - L(2)) ** \text{EM}(2)$$
$$* \cdots * (X - L(P)) ** \text{EM(P)},$$

where $K = \text{EM}(1) + \text{EM}(2) + \cdots + \text{EM(P)}$ is the degree of MINP(X). The factors $(X - L(J)) ** \text{EM(J)}$ are called *elementary divisors* of A. The characteristic polynomial of A is (5.1.4)

$$(5.3.9) \quad \text{CHARP(X)} = \pm (X - L(1)) ** \text{EC}(1) * (X - L(2)) ** \text{EC}(2)$$
$$* \cdots * (X - L(P)) ** \text{EC(P)},$$

where $N = \sum \text{EC(J)}$, $J \in //1, P//$, and each $\text{EC(J)} \geq \text{EM(J)}$. Clearly, if A has only distinct eigenvalues, then $\text{EM(J)} = \text{EC(J)} = 1$ for each $J \in //1, N//$, and $\text{MINP(X)} = \pm \text{CHARP(X)}$. It can be shown that if A is real and symmetric then $\text{EM(J)} = 1$, $J \in //1, P//$, and the elementary divisors are linear.

Equation (5.3.6) has the following *generalization*: If A is any N*th* order matrix (real or complex) with distinct eigenvalues $L(1)$, $L(2)$, ..., $L(P)$ and minimal polynomial (5.3.8), then there exists a nonsingular matrix S such that

$$(5.3.10) \quad \text{INV(S)} * A * S = \text{LL}, \text{ where}$$

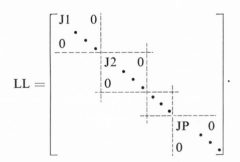

The matrix LL is called the *Jordan Canonical Form* of A, and the similarity transformation used to define LL is a *Jordan Canonical Transformation*. The *Jordan Canonical Box* J1 is an $\text{EM}(1)by\text{EM}(1)$ matrix with all diagonal elements equal $L(1)$, unity *immediately above* the diagonal elements, and all other elements of J1 are zero.

$$(5.3.11) \quad J1 = \begin{bmatrix} L(1) & 1 & 0 & \cdots & 0 & 0 \\ 0 & L(1) & 1 & \cdots & 0 & 0 \\ 0 & 0 & L(1) & \cdots & 0 & 0 \\ \vdots & \vdots & \vdots & & \vdots & \vdots \\ 0 & 0 & 0 & \cdots & L(1) & 1 \\ 0 & 0 & 0 & \cdots & 0 & L(1) \end{bmatrix},$$

an EM(1)*by*EM(1) matrix. In the *block* of LL containing J1, the three dots on the diagonal of LL after J1 indicate that there may be other Jordan Canonical Boxes involving $L(1)$ with order less than or equal to EM(1). The Jordan Canonical Boxes are oriented in LL so that all diagonal elements of each Jordan Canonical Box (eigenvalues of A) are the diagonal elements of LL. The elements of LL *not* in some Jordan Canonical Box are zero. The Jordan Canonical Form of A is unique *up to* the *order* in which the Jordan Canonical Boxes *appear* on the diagonal of LL. The presence of M Jordan Canonical Boxes involving $L(1)$ in LL implies the existence of M linearly independent eigenvectors of A corresponding to $L(1)$.

**Example 1.** If the minimal polynomial of an 8*th* order matrix A is

$$\text{MINP(X)} = (X - L(1)) ** 3 * (X - L(2)),$$

[EM(1) = 3, EM(2) = 1], and the characteristic polynomial of A is

$$\text{CHARP(X)} = (X - L(1)) ** 6 * (X - L(2)) ** 2,$$

[EC(1) = 6, EC(2) = 2], then the Jordan Canonical Form of A, (5.3.10), *could* have the form

$$(5.3.12) \quad LL = \begin{bmatrix} L(1) & 1 & 0 & 0 & 0 & 0 & 0 & 0 \\ 0 & L(1) & 1 & 0 & 0 & 0 & 0 & 0 \\ 0 & 0 & L(1) & 0 & 0 & 0 & 0 & 0 \\ 0 & 0 & 0 & L(1) & 1 & 0 & 0 & 0 \\ 0 & 0 & 0 & 0 & L(1) & 0 & 0 & 0 \\ 0 & 0 & 0 & 0 & 0 & L(1) & 0 & 0 \\ 0 & 0 & 0 & 0 & 0 & 0 & L(2) & 0 \\ 0 & 0 & 0 & 0 & 0 & 0 & 0 & L(2) \end{bmatrix}.$$

Clearly, if the elementary divisors of A are *linear,* then LL is a *diagonal* matrix. That is, (5.3.10) becomes (5.3.5).
We can write the equation (5.3.10) in the form

(5.3.13)                    $A * S = S * LL$

with the matrix S written as in (5.3.4)

(5.3.14)           $S = [U(1) \quad U(2) \quad U(3) \quad \cdots \quad U(N)].$

If LL and J1 have the forms (5.3.10) and (5.3.11) respectively, then the first EM(1) columns of S are defined by

(5.3.15a)               $A * U(1) = L(1) * U(1),$

and

(5.3.15b)     $A * U(K) = L(1) * U(K) + U(K - 1),$ for each $K \in //2, EM(1)//.$

*Note* 1. There are $EM(1) = 3$ columns of S which correspond to J1, but of these vectors only U(1) is an eigenvector of A corresponding to L(1).
*Note* 2. If L(1) and U(1) are known (say, from an application of the Power Method to A), then U(2) can be found by solving

$$A * U(2) = L(1) * U(2) + U(1).$$

Then U(3) can be found, etc.

If there is another Jordan Canonical Box in LL that involves L(1), then there will be another column of S which is also an eigenvector of A corresponding to L(1). This vector with U(1) forms a linearly independent set. If there are M Jordan Canonical Boxes in LL that involve L(1), then precisely M columns of S form a linearly independent set of eigenvectors of A corresponding to L(1).
In an entirely analogous way we define the columns of S that correspond to Jordan Canonical Boxes of LL that involve other eigenvalues of A.

**Example 2.** If a matrix A has the Jordan Canonical Form given in (5.3.12), one might *obtain* the columns of S involved in the Jordan Canonical Transformation (5.3.10) which defines LL as follows: [See Exercise 4.]

1. Find L(1) and three linearly independent eigenvectors of A corresponding to L(1), say XV(1), XV(2), and XV(3). Write U(1), U(4), and U(6) as linear combinations of these eigenvectors. For example, write

$$U(1) = C(1) * XV(1) + C(2) * XV(2) + C(3) * XV(3).$$

2. Find L(2) and two linearly independent eigenvectors of A corresponding to L(2). Call these eigenvectors U(7) and U(8).

3. Compute the coefficients in the eigenvectors U(1), U(4), and U(6) so that they are linearly independent, *and* so that U(2), U(3), and U(5) exist as solutions of

$$A * U(2) = L(1) * U(2) + U(1)$$
$$A * U(3) = L(1) * U(3) + U(2)$$
$$A * U(5) = L(1) * U(5) + U(4).$$

## EXERCISES

1. Write explicitly the eight matrix equations equivalent to

$$A * S = S * LL$$

for LL given in (5.3.12). Compare these with (5.3.15a, b), and step (3) in Example 2. Write corresponding formulas when unity is moved *immediately below* the diagonal in each Jordan Box.

2. Verify that the following vectors are eigenvectors of A. That is, compute A * U(1), etc.

$$A = \begin{bmatrix} 0 & 0 & 8 \\ 1 & 0 & -14 \\ 0 & 1 & 7 \end{bmatrix}, \quad U(1) = \begin{bmatrix} -2/3 \\ 1 \\ -1/3 \end{bmatrix}, \quad U(2) = \begin{bmatrix} 4 \\ -5 \\ 1 \end{bmatrix},$$

$$U(3) = \begin{bmatrix} 8/3 \\ -2 \\ 1/3 \end{bmatrix}.$$

Form S and verify that A * S = S * LL. Verify that INV(S) * A * S = LL.

3. Discuss the feasibility of the following methods to determine (compute) the minimal polynomial of a given matrix A. See references listed in Suggested Reading for other methods.

(a) Suppose the distinct eigenvalues of A are known, call them L(1), L(2), ..., L(P). Compute the matrices, for each K ∈ //1, P//,

$$(A - L(K) * I), \text{ and } (A - L(K) * I) ** (J) \text{ for each } J \in //2, N - P//.$$

Choose *sets* of exponents $E(K) \geq 1$, for each $K \in //1, P//$, such that

$$\sum E(K), K \in //1, P//, \leq N.$$

For each such set of P exponents $E(K)$, *test*

$$\text{PROD}((A - L(K) * I) ** E(K)), K \in //1, P//, = 0?$$

Find, in the finite set of such choices, the set of exponents $E(K), K \in //1, P//$, that "pass" the test *and* have

$$\sum E(K), K \in //1, P//, = \text{minimum}.$$

With this "best" set of exponents $E(K), K \in //1, P//$, we have

$$\text{MINP}(X) = \text{PROD}((X - L(K)) ** E(K)), K \in //1, P//.$$

(b) Compute the N matrices $A ** (J), J \in //1, N//$. Write the $N ** 2$ linear equations defined by equating corresponding elements in the (sum) matrix on the left and the zero matrix on the right in

$$\sum B(J) * A ** (J), J \in //0, N//, = 0.$$

Find a nontrivial solution $(B(N), B(N - 1), \ldots, B(1), B(0))$ of the linear system with *each*

$$B(N - Q) = 0, Q \in //0, M//,$$

for M as large as possible. If no solution has $B(N) = 0$, then $\text{MINP}(X) = \pm \text{CHARP}(X)$. If $B(N) = 0$ and $M \geq 0$, then the minimal polynomial of A is

$$\text{MINP}(X) = \left(\sum B(J) * X ** J, J \in //0, N - M - 1//,\right)/B(N - M - 1).$$

4. Show by methods (a) and (b) of Exercise 3 that the minimal polynomial of A is

$$\text{MINP}(X) = (X - 1) ** 2,$$

where

$$A = \begin{bmatrix} 1 & 1 & 0 \\ 0 & 1 & 0 \\ 0 & 0 & 1 \end{bmatrix}.$$

Clearly, the choice $S = I$ satisfies (5.3.13). Find another matrix S by applying the method of Example 2 with eigenvectors $XV(1) = TRAN[2\ 0\ 1]$ and $XV(2) = TRAN\ [1\ 0\ 2]$. That is, set $U(1) = C(1) * XV(1) + C(2) * XV(2)$ in the first equation in step (3), and find that $U(2)$ exists if $C(1) = -2 * C(2)$, etc.

## 5.4. DEFLATION

The purpose of this section is to present an elementary example of an important class of *deflation* processes that are useful when the following questions arise.

Suppose that one eigenvalue of the N*th* order matrix A and a corresponding eigenvector are known; for example, suppose that the largest eigenvalue $L(1)$ and a corresponding eigenvector $XV(1)$ have been obtained by the Power Method.

**Question 1.** How can we determine the multiplicity of $L(1)$?

**Question 2.** If the multiplicity of $L(1)$ is unity, how can we obtain (by the Power Method) the second largest eigenvalue $L(2)$, and a corresponding eigenvector $XV(2)$?

**Question 3.** If the multiplicity of $L(1)$ is greater than unity, is there another eigenvector of A corresponding to $L(1)$? If not, how do we proceed to find the other columns of S [involved in the Jordan Canonical Transformation (5.3.10)] that correspond to $L(1)$?

If we have the characteristic polynomial of A, (5.1.4),

$$CHARP(L) = DET(A - L * I),$$

then we can use synthetic division to obtain a *reduced* (in degree) polynomial $P1(L) = CHARP(L) / (L - L(1))$ and compute $P1(L(1))$. If $P1(L(1)) = 0$, then the multiplicity of $L(1)$ is at least 2, etc. If $P1(L(1)) \neq 0$, then the multiplicity of $L(1)$ is unity. We can apply methods like those in Chapter 3 to obtain a zero of P1(L), etc. Having computed the eigenvalues of A, the corresponding eigenvectors of A are obtained by solving the appropriate linear system (5.1.2). More generally, the columns of S in the Jordan Canonical Transformation (5.3.10) are obtained by solving the appropriate linear system (5.3.15a, b).

Similarly, deflation processes are used to obtain from A a *reduced* (in order) matrix B by "removing" from A *certain* eigenvalues and corresponding eigenvectors of A. The eigenvalues of B are the *other* eigenvalues of A, and eigenvectors of B lead to corresponding eigenvectors of A. The Power Method is frequently used to find an eigenvalue and a corresponding eigenvector of B, and a deflation process is applied to reduce B, etc.

Deflation methods are particularly useful when N is large, when only a few eigenvalues and corresponding eigenvectors are required, and when those eigenvalues required are distinct and large relative to the other eigenvalues of A.

The reader is referred to [1a], [2a], [3a], and [4] for descriptions of this and other processes designed to answer some of the above questions. Note particularly the *Method of Exhaustion* where the order of the reduced matrices is always the order of A but the eigenvalue being "removed" is replaced by zero.

Let L(1) and XV(1) = TRAN[U1   U2   U3   $\cdots$   UN] denote an eigenvalue and a corresponding eigenvector of A, where XV(1) is normalized so that U1 = 1. Define

$$
(5.4.1) \qquad T = \begin{bmatrix} 1 & 0 & 0 & \cdots & 0 \\ U2 & 1 & 0 & \cdots & 0 \\ U3 & 0 & 1 & \cdots & 0 \\ \vdots & \vdots & \vdots & & \vdots \\ UN & 0 & 0 & \cdots & 1 \end{bmatrix}
$$

so that

$$
INV(T) = \begin{bmatrix} 1 & 0 & 0 & \cdots & 0 \\ -U2 & 1 & 0 & \cdots & 0 \\ -U3 & 0 & 1 & \cdots & 0 \\ \vdots & \vdots & \vdots & & \vdots \\ -UN & 0 & 0 & \cdots & 1 \end{bmatrix}.
$$

Since the eigenvalues of similar matrices are equal [recall (5.3.7)], then the matrix

(5.4.2)  $INV(T) * A * T$

$$
= \begin{bmatrix}
L(1) & A(1,2) & A(1,3) & \cdots & A(1,N) \\
0 & A(2,2) - U2 * A(1,2) & A(2,3) - U2 * A(1,3) & \cdots & A(2,N) - U2 * A(1,N) \\
0 & A(3,2) - U3 * A(1,2) & A(3,3) - U3 * A(1,3) & \cdots & A(3,N) - U3 * A(1,N) \\
\vdots & \vdots & \vdots & & \vdots \\
0 & A(N,2) - UN * A(1,2) & A(N,3) - UN * A(1,3) & \cdots & A(N,N) - UN * A(1,N)
\end{bmatrix}
$$

$$
= \begin{bmatrix}
L(1) & A(1,2) & A(1,3) & \cdots & A(1,N) \\
0 & & & & \\
0 & & & B & \\
\vdots & & & & \\
0 & & & &
\end{bmatrix}
$$

has the *same eigenvalues* that A has. Thus the other eigenvalues of A, [L(2), ..., L(N)], are the N − 1 eigenvalues of B. If an eigenvalue L(2) of B and a corresponding eigenvector V = TRAN[V2  V3  $\cdots$  VN] are found (say, by applying the Power Method to B), then an eigenvector of INV(T) * A * T corresponding to L(2) is defined by

(5.4.3)  $(INV(T) * A * T) * \begin{bmatrix} V1 \\ V \end{bmatrix}$

$$
= \begin{bmatrix}
L(1) & A(1,2) & A(1,3) & \cdots & A(1,N) \\
0 & & & & \\
0 & & & B & \\
\vdots & & & & \\
0 & & & &
\end{bmatrix} * \begin{bmatrix} V1 \\ V \end{bmatrix}
$$

$$
= \begin{bmatrix}
L(1) * V1 + A(1,2) * V2 + A(1,3) * V3 + \cdots + A(1,N) * VN \\
B * V
\end{bmatrix}
$$

$$
= L(2) * \begin{bmatrix} V1 \\ V \end{bmatrix}.
$$

That is,

$$
L(1) * V1 + A(1,2) * V2 + A(1,3) * V3 + \cdots
$$
$$
+ A(1,N) * VN = L(2) * V1
$$

and

$$B * V = L(2) * V.$$

Thus, if $L(1) \neq L(2)$,

(5.4.4)     $V1 = (A(1, 2) * V2 + A(1, 3) * V3 + \cdots + A(1, N) * VN) / (L(2) - L(1))$.

And, since

$$(INV(T) * A * T) * \begin{bmatrix} V1 \\ V \end{bmatrix} = L(2) * \begin{bmatrix} V1 \\ V \end{bmatrix},$$

when both sides of this matrix equation are multiplied on the left by T we get

(5.4.5)     $$A * T * \begin{bmatrix} V1 \\ V \end{bmatrix} = L(2) * T * \begin{bmatrix} V1 \\ V \end{bmatrix}.$$

Thus, an eigenvector of A corresponding to $L(2)$ $[\neq L(1)]$ is given by

(5.4.6)     $$XV(2) = T * \begin{bmatrix} V1 \\ V \end{bmatrix} = \begin{bmatrix} V1 \\ U2 * V1 + V2 \\ U3 * V1 + V3 \\ \vdots \\ UN * V1 + VN \end{bmatrix}.$$

The reduced matrix B in (5.4.2) is said to be obtained by a *deflation on* A *with* $L(1)$ and $XV(1)$.

*Before* applying the Power Method to B one could determine if $L(1)$ had multiplicity greater than unity by computing $DET(B - L(1) * I)$, say by Crout Reduction.

If the multiplicity of $L(1)$ is unity, then we can expect the Power Method applied to B to yield an eigenvalue $L(2)$ *different* from $L(1)$ and a corresponding eigenvector V. Then (5.4.4) and (5.4.6) may be applied to obtain an eigenvector $XV(2)$ of A corresponding to $L(2)$. Then a matrix C of order $N - 2$ may be obtained by a deflation on B with $L(2)$ and V, etc. See the example below.

If the multiplicity of $L(1)$ is greater than unity, then we could *try* other first guesses $XIT(0)$ in the Power Method. If an eigenvector $XV(2)$ of A corresponding to $L(1)$ is found where $XV(2)$ is not a constant times $XV(1)$, then a matrix C of order $N - 2$ may be obtained by a deflation on B with $L(1)$ and the $(N - 1)$-vector V defined by $(5.4.6)$ with the known $XV(2)$ and $XV(1)$.

If the multiplicity of $L(1)$ is greater than unity, and if we can find *no* new linearly independent eigenvectors of A corresponding to $L(1)$, then we may seek other columns of S in $(5.3.10)$ that correspond to $L(1)$ by seeking a solution $U(2)$ of $(5.3.15b)$

$$(5.4.7) \qquad A * U(2) = L(1) * U(2) + XV(1).$$

Then $U(2)$ is *not* an eigenvector of A, and the deflation process described here cannot be applied using $U(2)$.

*Note.* In our discussion of the Power Method we assumed A had N linearly independent eigenvectors so that the LL matrix in $(5.3.10)$ is diagonal, like LL in $(5.3.5)$. For a discussion of the Power Method to obtain $L(1)$, $XV(1)$, and $U(2)$ in $(5.4.7)$, see [2b].

**Example.** In the example of §5.2, we saw that

$$A = \begin{bmatrix} 0 & 0 & 8 \\ 1 & 0 & -14 \\ 0 & 1 & 7 \end{bmatrix}$$

has eigenvalues $L(1) = 4$, $L(2) = 2$, and $L(3) = 1$. Also, an eigenvector of A corresponding to $L(1)$ is $XV(1) = TRAN[-2/3 \quad 1 \quad -1/3]$. First, we execute a deflation on A with $L(1)$ and $XV(1)$. With $XV(1)$ normalized to the first component, $(5.4.1)$ then becomes

$$T = \begin{bmatrix} 1 & 0 & 0 \\ -3/2 & 1 & 0 \\ 1/2 & 0 & 1 \end{bmatrix}$$

and $(5.4.2)$ becomes

$$INV(T) * A * T = \begin{bmatrix} 4 & 0 & 8 \\ 0 & 0 & -2 \\ 0 & 1 & 3 \end{bmatrix}, \text{ where } B = \begin{bmatrix} 0 & -2 \\ 1 & 3 \end{bmatrix}.$$

Since

$$DET(B - L(1) * I) = \begin{vmatrix} -4 & -2 \\ 1 & -1 \end{vmatrix} = 6 \neq 0,$$

then $L(1) = 4$ has multiplicity unity. The largest eigenvalue of B is $L(2) = 2$, and an eigenvector of B corresponding to $L(2)$ is $V = TRAN[1 \quad -1]$. Thus, using (5.4.4).

$$V1 = \big(0 * (1) + 8 * (-1)\big)/(2 - 4) = 4,$$

and an eigenvector of $INV(T) * A * T$ corresponding to $L(2) = 2$ is

$$\begin{bmatrix} V1 \\ V \end{bmatrix} = \begin{bmatrix} 4 \\ 1 \\ -1 \end{bmatrix}.$$

Using (5.4.6),

$$XV(2) = T * \begin{bmatrix} V1 \\ V \end{bmatrix} = \begin{bmatrix} 4 \\ -5 \\ 1 \end{bmatrix}$$

is an eigenvector of A corresponding to $L(2) = 2$. Now we execute a deflation on B with $L(2)$ and V. Here

$$T = \begin{bmatrix} 1 & 0 \\ -1 & 1 \end{bmatrix}, \text{ and } INV(T) * B * T = \begin{bmatrix} 2 & -2 \\ 0 & 1 \end{bmatrix}.$$

The reduced matrix C is $1\,by\,1$, and $C = [1]$. The eigenvalue of C is $L(3) = 1$, and a corresponding eigenvector of C is $W = [1]$. An eigenvector of $INV(T) * B * T$ corresponding to $L(3) = 1$ is

$$\begin{bmatrix} W1 \\ W \end{bmatrix} = \begin{bmatrix} (-2) * (1)/(1 - 2) \\ 1 \end{bmatrix} = \begin{bmatrix} 2 \\ 1 \end{bmatrix},$$

and an eigenvector of B corresponding to $L(3) = 1$ is

$$T * \begin{bmatrix} W1 \\ W \end{bmatrix} = \begin{bmatrix} 2 \\ -1 \end{bmatrix} = \begin{bmatrix} V2 \\ V3 \end{bmatrix}.$$

An eigenvector of $INV(T) * A * T$ corresponding to $L(3) = 1$ is

$$
\begin{bmatrix} V1 \\ V2 \\ V3 \end{bmatrix} = \begin{bmatrix} \big(0*(2) + 8*(-1)\big)/(1-4) \\ 2 \\ -1 \end{bmatrix} = \begin{bmatrix} 8/3 \\ 2 \\ -1 \end{bmatrix}.
$$

Thus, an eigenvector of A corresponding to $L(3) = 1$ is

$$
XV(3) = T * \begin{bmatrix} V1 \\ V2 \\ V3 \end{bmatrix} = \begin{bmatrix} 1 & 0 & 0 \\ -3/2 & 1 & 0 \\ 1/2 & 0 & 1 \end{bmatrix} * \begin{bmatrix} 8/3 \\ 2 \\ -1 \end{bmatrix} = \begin{bmatrix} 8/3 \\ -2 \\ 1/3 \end{bmatrix}.
$$

Finally, S in the Jordan Canonical Transformation (5.3.6) is

$$
S = [XV(1)\ \ XV(2)\ \ XV(3)] = \begin{bmatrix} -2/3 & 4 & 8/3 \\ 1 & -5 & -2 \\ -1/3 & 1 & 1/3 \end{bmatrix},
$$

and the Jordan Canonical Form of A is

$$
LL = INV(S) * A * S = \begin{bmatrix} 4 & 0 & 0 \\ 0 & 2 & 0 \\ 0 & 0 & 1 \end{bmatrix}.
$$

The reader should supply the details for this example, and verify $A * S = S * LL$.

## 5.5. THE POWER METHOD FOR COMPLEX EIGENVALUES

In §5.2 we applied the Power Method with first guess $XIT(0)$ to any real matrix A with only real eigenvalues, and generated a sequence of vectors (5.2.13)

(5.5.1)          $XIT(1), XIT(2), XIT(3), \ldots, XIT(M), \ldots$

The sequence *either* converges to an eigenvector of A, (5.2.14), *or* diverges where a recognizable linear combination of two consecutive iterants is (computationally) an eigenvector of A, (5.2.17a, b). In the latter case, the coefficients of the linear combination involve the corresponding eigenvalue explicitly. We are able to determine the necessary eigenvalue by normalizing (5.2.6) either iterant to get U, and find L(1) ** 2 to be the Jth component of A * (A * U), etc.

In this section, we consider another important case where the Power Method does not define a sequence of vectors that converge directly to an eigenvector of A, but does generate a *recognizable* linear combination of eigenvectors. The divergence mentioned above is detected by noting that after M is sufficiently large,

$$XIT(M + 2) = L(1) ** 2 * XIT(M).$$

In the case now to be considered, the divergence is characterized by more radical (and, when computing, apparently random) variations in magnitude and sign of components of iterants. Here, we give a brief description of the method and refer the reader to [2c] for a discussion of the error.

Let L(1) and L(2) be conjugate complex numbers that are eigenvalues of A. Suppose that they are related to the other eigenvalues of A by

(5.5.2)          $|L(1)| = |L(2)| > |L(3)| \geq \cdots \geq |L(N)|.$

Suppose that the first guess XIT(0) in an application of the Power Method to A is such that elements of the sequence (5.5.1) are defined by [compare with (5.2.4)]

(5.5.3)     $XIT(M) \equiv A ** (M) * XIT(0)$

$= \sum C(K) * L(K) ** M * XV(K), K \in // 1, N //,$

where C(1) and C(2) are nonzero conjugate complex numbers. Then, when M is sufficiently large, the eigenvalues L(1) and L(2) are solutions of

(5.5.4)          $X ** 2 + P * X + Q = 0,$

where P and Q are defined by

(5.5.5)
$A(M + 2) + P * A(M + 1) + Q * A(M) = 0$
$B(M + 2) + P * B(M + 1) + Q * B(M) = 0.$

The A(M + 2), A(M + 1), and A(M) are corresponding (Jth) components of XIT(M + 2), XIT(M + 1), and XIT(M) respectively. The B(M + 2), B(M + 1), and B(M) are *another* set of corresponding components of these vectors. We may choose any two sets of corresponding components of any three *consecutive* iterants after XIT(M). We also assume that the chosen components satisfy

$$A(M + 1) * B(M) - A(M) * B(M + 1) \neq 0.$$

Specifically,

$$P = (-A(M + 2) * B(M) + A(M) * A(M + 2))/$$

(5.5.6)     $$(A(M + 1) * B(M) - A(M) * B(M + 1))$$

$$Q = (-A(M + 1) * B(M + 2) + A(M + 2) * B(M + 1))/$$

$$(A(M + 1) * B(M) - A(M) * B(M + 1)).$$

*Note.* XIT(M) may be normalized, say to its first component, but XIT(M + 1) and XIT(M + 2) are not normalized.

If A(M), A(M + 1), and A(M + 2) are the J*th* components of XIT(M), XIT(M + 1), and XIT(M + 2) respectively, and B(M), B(M + 1), and B(M + 2) are the J*th* components of XIT(M + 1), XIT(M + 2), and XIT (M + 3), then (5.5.5) is usually written

(5.5.7)     $$A(M + 2) + P * A(M + 1) + Q * A(M) = 0$$

$$A(M + 3) + P * A(M + 2) + Q * A(M + 1) = 0$$

and (5.5.6) takes the form

$$P = (-A(M + 2) * A(M + 1) + A(M) * A(M + 3)/$$

(5.5.8)     $$(A(M + 1) ** 2 - A(M) * A(M + 2))$$

$$Q = (-A(M + 1) * A(M + 3) + A(M + 2) ** 2)/$$

$$(A(M + 1) ** 2 - A(M) * A(M + 2)).$$

When L(1) and L(2) have been computed as roots of (5.5.4), then we have (computationally)

$$U1 = XIT(M + 1) - L(2) * XIT(M)$$

is an eigenvector of A corresponding to L(1), and

$$U2 = XIT(M + 1) - L(1) * XIT(M)$$

is an eigenvector of A corresponding to L(2).

### 5.6. THE JACOBI METHOD

In this section we outline a classical iteration method which is useful when *all* eigenvalues of a real symmetric matrix are required. A set of corresponding eigenvectors of A are obtainable as a function of the transformations involved in the iteration. We chose the Jacobi Method because it is easy to code and because an understanding of the Jacobi Method is important for an understanding of other methods.

In §5.3 we saw that if A is any N*th* order real and symmetric matrix, then there exists a nonsingular matrix (5.3.4)

$$(5.6.1) \qquad S = [XV(1) \quad XV(2) \quad XV(3) \quad \cdots \quad XV(N)]$$

(the columns of S are eigenvectors of A) which can be used to define a similarity transformation (5.3.6)

$$(5.6.2) \qquad INV(S) * A * S = LL,$$

where LL is a diagonal matrix with diagonal elements the eigenvalues of A.

The *Jacobi Method* described here is an iteration process which defines a sequence [A(0) ≡ A]

$$A(1), A(2), A(3), \cdots, A(M), \cdots$$

of estimates to LL of (5.6.2). Each element of the sequence is obtained from its predecessor by a similarity transformation

$$A(1) = INV(R(1)) * A * R(1)$$
$$A(2) = INV(R(2)) * A(1) * R(2)$$

(5.6.3)          ⋮

$$A(M) = INV(R(M)) * A(M - 1) * R(M)$$

⋮

where the matrices R(K), K ∈ // 1, ∞ //, are chosen so that each matrix A(K) is more nearly diagonal (LL) than was A(K − 1).

If we write

$$A(2) = INV(R(2)) * A(1) * R(2)$$
$$= INV(R(2)) * INV(R(1)) * A * R(1) * R(2)$$
$$= INV(R(1) * R(2)) * A * (R(1) * R(2))$$
$$= INV(S(2)) * A * S(2),$$

and in general

(5.6.4)   A(M) = INV(R(1) ∗ R(2) ∗ ⋯ ∗ R(M)) ∗ A
  ∗ (R(1) ∗ R(2) ∗ ⋯ ∗ R(M))
  = INV(S(M)) ∗ A ∗ S(M),

it can be shown that when the R(K) are defined as indicated below, then

(5.6.5)   LIM(A(M)) = LL, as M App ∞, and
  LIM(S(M)) = S, as M App ∞.

That is, using the Jacobi Method we can compute (at least theoretically) (i) an A(M) (similar to A) as nearly diagonal as we please, and (ii) an S(M) whose K*th* column is a "good" estimate to an eigenvector of A corresponding to the "eigenvalue" in the K*th* row and K*th* column of A(M).

Each matrix R(K) involved in (5.6.3) is associated with a particular *element* of the matrix A(K − 1), so we use the name R(K; I, J) to indicate that the (I, J)*th* element of A(K − 1) is the "key" element associated with R(K). Here, we assume I < J. We write R(K; I, J)(P, Q) for the element in the P*th* row and Q*th* column of R(K; I, J), and define R(K; I, J) by

(5.6.6)

$$R(K; I, J) = \begin{cases} R(K; I, J)(I, I) = R(K; I, J)(J, J) = COS(T) \\ R(K; I, J)(I, J) = -R(K; I, J)(J, I) = -SIN(T) \\ R(K; I, J)(P, P) = +1, \text{ for } P \neq I, P \neq J \\ R(K; I, J)(P, Q) = 0 \text{ otherwise.} \end{cases}$$

For example, with CT = COS(T), and ST = SIN(T)

$$R(K; 2, 5) = \begin{bmatrix} 1 & 0 & 0 & 0 & 0 & 0 & \cdots & 0 \\ 0 & CT & 0 & 0 & -ST & 0 & & \\ 0 & 0 & 1 & 0 & 0 & 0 & & \\ 0 & 0 & 0 & 1 & 0 & 0 & & \\ 0 & ST & 0 & 0 & CT & 0 & & \\ 0 & 0 & 0 & 0 & 0 & 1 & & \\ \vdots & & & & & & \ddots & \\ 0 & & & & & & & 1 \end{bmatrix}.$$

The matrix $R(K; I, J)$ is *orthogonal* since $TRAN(R(K; I, J)) = INV(R(K; I, J))$. Also, $R(K; I, J)$ is called a *rotation* matrix, since $Y = R(K; I, J) * X$ corresponds to a change of coordinates: a rotation of axes (by the angle T) in the $(I, J)$ coordinate plane. With $R(K; I, J)$ defined as in (5.6.6), consider the similarity transformation

(5.6.7) $$C = TRAN(R(K; I, J)) * A * R(K; I, J) .$$

The only elements of C which are *potentially* different from corresponding elements of A are those in the I*th* and J*th* rows and columns of C. With $CT = COS(T)$, $ST = SIN(T)$, $A = TRAN(A)$, and $I < J$, the elements of C in (5.6.7) are

$$C(P, Q) = A(P, Q), \text{ for } P \neq I, P \neq J, Q \neq I, Q \neq J.$$
$$C(P, I) = C(I, P) = CT * A(P, I) + ST * A(P, J),$$
$$\text{for } P \neq I, P \neq J.$$
$$C(P, J) = C(J, P) = -ST * A(P, I) + CT * A(P, J),$$
$$\text{for } P \neq I, P \neq J.$$

(5.6.8) $$C(I, I) = CT ** 2 * A(I, I) + 2 * CT * ST * A(I, J)$$
$$+ ST ** 2 * A(J, J).$$
$$C(J, J) = ST ** 2 * A(I, I) - 2 * CT * ST * A(I, J)$$
$$+ CT ** 2 * A(J, J).$$
$$C(I, J) = C(J, I) = (CT ** 2 - ST ** 2) * A(I, J)$$
$$+ CT * ST * (A(J, J) - A(I, I)).$$

We say that C in (5.6.7) is obtained from A by a *rotation about* $A(I, J)$. The sum of the squares of elements of A, written $SSQ(A)$, *equals* the sum of the squares of elements of C.

(5.6.9) $$SSQ(A) \equiv \sum\sum A(P, Q) ** 2, P \in //1, N//, Q \in //1, N//,$$
$$= SSQ(C).$$

The sum of the squares of the off-diagonal elements of C, written $SSQOD(C)$, *minus* the sum of the squares of the off-diagonal elements of A is

(5.6.10) $$SSQOD(C) - SSQOD(A) = 2 * (C(I, J) ** 2 - A(I, J) ** 2).$$

If $CT = COS(T)$ and $ST = SIN(T)$ are chosen so that $C(I, J)$, (5.6.8), is zero, then $SSQOD(C)$ is less than $SSQOD(A)$ by $2 * A(I, J) ** 2$.

Since

(5.6.11)    $C(I, J) = C(J, I) = A(I, J) * COS (2 * T)$
$+ .5 * (A(J, J) - A(I, I)) * SIN(2 * T),$

then a natural choice for T so that $C(I, J) = 0$ is defined by

(5.6.12)    $TAN(2 * T) = 2 * A(I, J)/(A(I, I) - A(J, J)) \equiv X,$    $|T| \le \pi/4.$

The *Jacobi Method requires* the choice of I and J in $R(K) = R(K; I, J)$ of (5.6.3) and (5.6.6) so that the elements of $A(K - 1)$ satisfy

$$|A(K - 1)(I, J)| \ge |A(K - 1)(P, Q)|, \text{ for } I < J, P \ne Q,$$

*and* with T given by (5.6.12) where $A(K - 1)(I, J)$ replaces $A(I, J)$, etc. $SIN(T)$ and $COS(T)$ are chosen so that the *maximal off-diagonal elements* $A(K - 1)(I, J)$ *and* $A(K - 1)(J, I)$ *of* $A(K - 1)$ *are annihilated.*

One variation of the Jacobi Method is the *serial method* where we define the sequence $R(K) = R(K; I, J)$, $K \in // 1, \infty //$, with I and J chosen in some serial order, say $(I, J)$ equal $(1, 2), (1, 3), \ldots, (1, N)$, $(2, 3), \ldots, (2, N), \ldots, (N - 1, N)$, $(1, 2), \ldots$, etc., and if some $A(I, J)$ under consideration is zero, then the next element in the sequence is considered for annihilation. Another variation is the *threshold method*, where elements for annihilation are considered in some serial order, but an annihilation is executed only if the element being considered is greater in absolute value than a preassigned number (the threshold). When the magnitudes of all off-diagonal elements are less than the threshold, the threshold is reduced in steps until *all* the magnitudes of off-diagonal elements are less than a specified acceptable upper bound for magnitudes of off-diagonal elements in the final (almost diagonal) form.

In Example 3 of §2.2 we discussed the problem of computing for (5.6.12)

$$T = .5 * ARCTAN(X).$$

In practice, we do not compute T and then compute $SIN(T)$ and $COS(T)$. We *usually* compute an estimate to one function, say $ST1 \doteq SIN(T)$, and then compute an estimate $CT1 \doteq COS(T)$ so that ST1 and CT1 are *compatible*

$$ST1 ** 2 + CT1 ** 2 = 1.$$

Even if ST1 and CT1 are not computed so that $C(I, J) = 0$, *it is most important that* ST1 *and* CT1 *be compatible in each of the matrices* $R(K)$ in (5.6.3).

Now, we present one method for *computing* compatible estimates to $SIN(T)$ and $COS(T)$ involved in (5.6.6) so that $C(I, J) \doteq 0$, (5.6.11). It is supposed that the threshold method is being used, and if at some point in the iteration we find $|X| > .5$. then *after* a rotation to get $C(I, J)$ we consider $C(I, J)$ for annihilation before proceeding.

If $A(I, I) = A(J, J)$ we might choose $SIN(T)$ and $COS(T)$ from a table of values of sine and cosine where $T \doteq 20$ degrees, and where $SIN(T)$ and $COS(T)$ are as compatible as possible to the number of significant digits being used in the calculation. If in (5.6.12) we have $|X| > .5$, then we could choose a compatible pair $(SIN(T), COS(T))$ where $T \doteq 13$ degrees. If in (5.6.12) we have $|X| \le .5$, then we could compute $SIN(T)$ and $COS(T)$ by

(5.6.13)
$$SIN(T) = 2 * Y/(1 + Y ** 2)$$
$$COS(T) = (1 - Y ** 2)/(1 + Y ** 2),$$

where

(5.6.14)　　$Y = (.25) * X + ( - .078125) * X ** 3 + (.044921875) * X ** 5$
　　　　　　$+ ( - .031066894531) * X ** 7$
　　　　　　$+ (.023536682128) * X ** 9$
　　　　　　$+ ( - .018833637237) * X ** (11)$
　　　　　　$+ (.015630662441) * X ** (13) + \cdots.$

Note that $SIN(T)$ and $COS(T)$ in (5.6.13) *are compatible* even if Y in (5.6.14) is in error.

The expression for Y in (5.6.14) is derived by the following considerations. From (5.6.12)

(5.6.15)　　　　　　　$T = .5 * ARCTAN(X).$

Define

(5.6.16)　　　　　　　$Y \equiv TAN(T/2)$

so that

(5.6.17) $$Z \equiv \text{TAN}(T) = 2 * Y/(1 - Y ** 2),$$

and

(5.6.18) $$X = \text{TAN}(2 * T) = 2 * Z/(1 - Z ** 2),$$

hence the choice (5.6.13). From (5.6.15) and (5.6.16), we need

(5.6.19) $$Y = \text{TAN}(.25 * \text{ARCTAN}(X)).$$

*Instead* of computing Y from (5.6.19) using subroutines we write, from (5.6.17),

$$Y = (-1 \pm \text{SQRT}(1 + Z))/Z.$$

We write $\text{SQRT}(1 + Z)$ as a binomial series to obtain

$$Y = 1/Z * (-1 + \sum \text{BINCO}(.5, K) * Z ** (2 * K), K \in //0, \infty//,)$$
$$= \sum \text{BINCO}(.5, K) * Z ** (2 * K - 1), K \in //1, \infty//.$$

From (5.6.18),

$$Z = \sum \text{BINCO}(.5, K) * X ** (2 * K - 1), K \in //1, \infty//.$$

We substitute this value for Z into the last form for Y to obtain (5.6.14).


### EXERCISES

1. Consider an arbitrary matrix A of order 6. With $CT = \text{COS}(T)$ and $ST = \text{SIN}(T)$, use (5.6.6) to write explicitly the *6th* order matrix $R(K; 2.4)$. Compute (5.6.7)

$$C = \text{TRAN}(R(K; 2, 4)) * A * R(K; 2, 4).$$

Use your calculation to verify (5.6.8).

**2.** For

$$A = \begin{bmatrix} 1 & 0 & 1 \\ 0 & 1 & 0 \\ 1 & 0 & -1 \end{bmatrix}$$

use (5.6.12) to find T to annihilate $A(3, 1)$ and $A(1, 3)$. With this value of $T[= \pi/8]$, form $R(1; 1, 3)$ and compute the rotation about $A(1, 3)$. Check (5.6.9) and (5.6.10).

*Note.* In this classroom example, we get a diagonal form (the Jordan Canonical Form of A), but in practice even elements previously made zero by a rotation may be changed. Check that the columns of $R(1; 1, 3)$ are eigenvectors of A.

*Hint.* For this exercise use, $CT ** 2 - ST ** 2 = 2 * ST * CT = 1/SQRT (2)$.

## SUGGESTED READING

1. Bodewig, E. (1959): *Matrix Calculus*. Interscience Publishers, Inc. New York.

1a. _____ . (Page 357.)

2. Faddeev, D. K. and V. N, Faddeeva, (1963): *Computational Methods of Linear Algebra* (translated by Robert C. Williams). W. H. Freeman and Co., Publishers. San Francisco and London.

2a. _____ . (Page 332.)

2b. _____ . (Page 300.)

2c. _____ . (Page 297.)

3. Householder, A. S. (1964): *The Theory of Matrices in Numerical Analysis*. Blaisdell Publishing Co. New York.

3a. _____ . (Page 168.)

4. Wilkinson, J. H. (1965): *The Algebraic Eigenvalue Problem*. Clarendon Press. Oxford.

# 6  FINITE DIFFERENCES

### 6.1. MOTIVATION

Finite differences are useful in many contexts in numerical analysis. Motivated by the applications suggested in this chapter, we shall find finite differences useful (i) in Chapter 7, when describing the coefficients of various representations of polynomial estimates to functions, (ii) in Chapters 9 and 10, when we operate on (differentiate and integrate) expressions that involve finite differences, and (iii) in Chapters 11 and 12, when we apply operators that involve finite differences to compute estimates to solutions of differential equations. In most of these applications finite differences are used because they *simplify notations* and (sometimes) suggest applications for the expressions that involve them.

In this chapter we first give the definition, notation, and a brief discussion of the finite differences used in the chapters mentioned above. The remainder of this chapter consists of *applications* of finite differences to tables of functions and to polynomials—*intended to suggest*: (i) how errors are propagated in tables and how they may be detected; (ii) how one might deduce some of the characterizing properties of functions that contain the entries (number pairs) in the table as a finite subset; and (iii) how one might pick (influenced by *estimates* of truncation error in §7.4) sets of characterizing properties for piecewise polynomial estimates to the tabulated functions.

*Note.* It is so essential that §6.2 be read with a pencil that we sprinkle exercises throughout the text of that section.

178

## 6.2. DEFINITIONS AND NOTATION

A finite difference is a *linear operator* defined on finite subsets of functions. (Finite differences may also be applied to functions.)

The term *operator* is associated with functions

$$L: DOM \rightarrow RNG,$$

where DOM is a set *other than* a set of real or complex numbers. For example, an MbyN real matrix may be considered an operator which maps DOM (a set of N-tuples) into RNG (a set of M-tuples). The differentiation operator, DER ** (1), and the definite integral operator, $\int$, over $T \in (A, B)$, map $F(X) = SIN(X)$ into

$$DER ** (1)F(X) = COS(X),$$

$$\int F(T), \text{ over } T \in (A, B), = -COS(B) + COS(A).$$

The indefinite integral operator, $\int$, maps $F(X) = SIN(X)$ into

$$\int F(X) = -COS(X) + C,$$

where C is an arbitrary constant, so that the element of RNG is a set of functions.

An operator with RNG a set of numbers (real or complex) is called a *functional*. Since a finite difference applied to a polynomial gives a polynomial, we call them operators.

Notice that an operator is simply *written before* the object being operated on—without any operation symbol separating them.

An operator, L, may have the property

$$L(A1 * F(X)) = A1 * L(F(X)),$$

where A1 is a constant. When no confusion is possible, we may write LF(X) for L(F(X)), as we did above with $L \equiv DER ** (1)$.

An operator, L, is *linear* if when L is defined on $F(X)$, on $G(X)$, and on a linear combination of $F(X)$ and $G(X)$, say $A1 * F(X) + B1 * G(X)$ where A1 and B1 are *any* constants, then

$$L(A1 * F(X) + B1 * G(X)) = A1 * LF(X) + B1 * LG(X).$$

The operators, DER $**$ (1) and $\int$, over T $\in$ (A, B), above, are linear.[1]

The *sum* of linear operators (S $\equiv$ A1 $*$ L1 $+$ B1 $*$ L2) is defined by

$$S(F(X)) = (A1 * L1 + B1 * L2)F(X) \equiv A1 * L1(F(X)) + B1 * L2(F(X)).$$

Two operators, L1 and L2, are *equal* if $L1(F(X)) = L2(F(X))$ for every F(X) for which L1 and L2 are defined, and we write L1 = L2.

The *identity* operator, denoted by I, is characterized by

$$I(F(X)) \equiv 1 * F(X) = F(X).$$

The *product* of two operators, L1 and L2, is defined by

$$(L1)(L2)(F(X)) = L1(L2(F(X))),$$

read: L2 operating on F(X) *followed by* L1. In particular, we write

$$L ** (2)F(X) = L(LF(X)), \; L ** (3)F(X) = L(L(LF(X))), \text{ etc.}$$

If L2 operating on $F(X)$ followed by L1 has the effect of leaving $F(X)$ *unchanged*

$$L1(L2(F(X))) \equiv 1 * F(X) = F(X),$$

we write

$$(L1)(L2) = I,$$

and call L1 a *left inverse* of L2 and call L2 a *right inverse* of L1. If

$$(L1)(L2) = (L2)(L1) = I,$$

then L1 is called a *proper inverse* of L2, and we write

---

[1]The indefinite integral operator, $\int$, is linear in the sense that if A1 $\neq$ 0, or B1 $\neq$ 0, then the *set* of functions that results from

$$A1 * \int F(X) + B1 * \int G(X) \equiv A1 * (FF(X) + C1) + B1 * (GG(X) + C2)$$

is the same as the *set* of functions that results from

$$\int (A1 * F(X) + B1 * G(X)) \equiv (A1 * FF(X) + B1 * GG(X)) + C3,$$

where C1, C2, and C3 are arbitrary constants.

$$L1 = INV(L2), \text{ and } L2 = INV(L1).$$

*Note.* Unless explicitly stated to the contrary, inverses considered in this text are proper inverses.

The finite difference operators considered in this chapter are linear and single-valued and map DOM (a set of subsets of tables of functions) into RNG (usually a set of real numbers). A typical table [finite subset of the function $F(X)$] involved in DOM is

$$(X(K), F(X(K))), \quad K \in //A, B//.$$

We frequently write $F(X(K)) = F(K)$, and assume $X(K) < X(K + 1)$. The *set* of first elements $X(K)$ of number pairs in DOM is called the *grid* on which $F(X)$ is tabulated.

Two important cases are considered: (i) the $X(K)$, $K \in //A, B//$, are only required to be ordered so that $X(K) < X(K + 1)$; and (ii) the $X(K)$, $K \in //A, B//$, are *equally spaced* in the sense that $X(K + 1) = X(K) + H$ for a constant $H > 0$. In the first case we say the *nonuniform grid* consists of $B - A + 1$ distinct points, and in the latter case we have a *uniform* or *regular* or *equally spaced grid* with a *mesh* of length H.

**Exercise 1.** Construct a table of $F(X) = X ** 3$ for the uniform grid $X(K) = K$, $K \in //0, 10//$. Compare the first three columns of Table 6.3.2, below.

One finite difference operator that permits the domain, DOM, to involve tables of functions at *nonuniform grids* is the *divided difference operator*

(6.2.1) $$[ \quad , \quad ]: DOM \rightarrow RNG.$$

When DOM involves only one table of *one* function, F, we then write[2]

(6.2.2a) $$[ \quad , \quad ]F: DOM \rightarrow RNG.$$

In this case, a typical element of DOM is (a pair of distinct elements of F)

(6.2.2b) $$(X(P), F(X(P)); X(Q), F(X(Q))) \equiv (X(P), F(P); X(Q), F(Q)),$$

and the corresponding element of RNG is (a real number) defined by

(6.2.2c) $$[X(P), X(Q)]F = (F(Q) - F(P)) / (X(Q) - X(P)).$$

[2]In some texts this is written f[ , ].

As usual, except for emphasis, we will refer only to formulas corresponding to (6.2.2c). We call [X(P), X(Q)]F in (6.2.2c) the *first divided difference of* F *at* X(P), X(Q).

The first divided difference operator is *linear* in the (tabulated) functions involved in the domain DOM. That is, if the functions F and G, and any linear combination of them, A1 ∗ F + B1 ∗ G, are involved in DOM, then

$$[X(P), X(Q)](A1 * F + B1 * G) \equiv ((A1 * F(Q) + B1 * G(Q))$$
$$- (A1 * F(P) + B1 * G(P)))/(X(Q) - X(P))$$
$$= A1 * (F(Q) - F(P))/(X(Q) - X(P))$$
$$+ B1 * (G(Q) - G(P))/(X(Q) - X(P))$$
$$= A1 * [X(P), X(Q)]F + B1 * [X(P), X(Q)]G.$$

The first divided difference operator is *symmetric* in the sense that

$$(6.2.2d) \quad [X(P), X(Q)]F = (F(Q) - F(P)) / (X(Q) - X(P))$$
$$= (F(P) - F(Q))/(X(P) - X(Q))$$
$$= [X(Q), X(P)]F.$$

That is, the *value* of the first divided difference is *not changed* if the order in which the X's appear in the symbol is reversed.

**Exercise 2.** Use the table constructed in Exercise 1 and demonstrate property (6.2.2d) for various choices of P, Q with P ≠ Q.

**Exercise 3.** With G(X) = X ∗∗ 2 and F(X) = X ∗∗ 3 construct a table of A ∗ F(X) + B ∗ G(X) for X(K) = K, K ∈ //0, 10//. With this table, for various choices for P, Q, check the the linearity of [ , ].

The second divided difference operator is also defined for functions tabulated on nonuniform grids. Here

$$(6.2.3a) \qquad\qquad [ \quad , \quad , \quad ]F: DOM \rightarrow RNG,$$

where a typical element of DOM is (three elements of F)

$$(6.2.3b) \qquad (X(P), F(P); X(Q), F(Q); X(R), F(R)),$$

and the corresponding element in RNG is

(6.2.3c)  $[X(P), X(Q), X(R)]F$

$\equiv ([X(Q), X(R)]F - [X(P), X(Q)]F) / (X(R) - X(P))$

$= ((F(R) - F(Q)) / (X(R) - X(Q))$

$- (F(Q) - F(P)) / (X(Q) - X(P))) / (X(R) - X(P)).$

We call $[X(P), X(Q), X(R)]F$ the *second divided difference of* F *at* X(P), $X(Q), X(R)$. Note that the denominator is the difference of the X's which do *not* appear in *both* first divided differences in the numerator. Since we can write

(6.2.3d)  $[X(P), X(Q), X(R)]F$

$= F(P) / ((X(P) - X(Q)) * (X(P) - X(R)))$

$+ F(Q) / ((X(Q) - X(P)) * (X(Q) - X(R)))$

$+ F(R) / ((X(R) - X(P)) * (X(R) - X(Q))),$

and an interchange of two elements in the symbol $[X(P), X(Q), X(R)]F$ only results in the interchange of two terms on the right of (6.2.3d), then corresponding to (6.2.2d) we have

(6.2.3e)  $[X(P), X(Q), X(R)]F = [X(P), X(R), X(Q)]F$

$= [X(R), X(P), X(Q)]F = \cdots.$

That is, the value of the second divided difference of F is independent of the order in which the grid points appear in the symbol. Thus

(6.2.3f)  $[X(P), X(Q), X(R)]F$

$= ([X(Q), X(R)]F - [X(P), X(Q)]F) / (X(R) - X(P))$

$= ([X(R), X(Q)]F - [X(P), X(R)]F) / (X(Q) - X(P))$

$=$ etc.

In general, the N*th divided difference of* $F(X)$ *at* the $N + 1$ distinct grid points $X(P), X(Q), X(R), \ldots, X(S), X(T)$, is

(6.2.4a)  $[X(P), X(Q), X(R), \ldots, X(S), X(T)]F$

$= ([X(Q), X(R), \ldots, X(S), X(T)]F$

$- [X(P), X(Q). \ldots, X(S)]F) / (X(T) - X(P)),$

which may be written[3] in the symmetric form

(6.2.4b)    $[X(P), \ldots, X(T)]F$

$$= F(P) / ((X(P) - X(Q)) * (X(P) - X(R)) * \cdots * (X(P) - X(T)))$$
$$+ F(Q) / ((X(Q) - X(P)) * (X(Q) - X(R)) * \cdots * (X(Q) - X(T)))$$
$$+ \cdots + F(T) / ((X(T) - X(P)) * (X(T) - X(Q))$$
$$* \cdots * (X(T) - X(S))).$$

Again, interchanging any two elements of the symbol $[X(P), X(Q), X(R), \ldots, X(S), X(T)]F$ only interchanges the position of two terms in the sum (6.2.4b) so that

(6.2.4c)    $[X(P), X(Q), X(R), \ldots, X(S), X(T)]F$

$$= [X(Q), X(P), X(R), \ldots, X(S), X(T)]F = \text{etc.}$$

And

(6.2.4d)    $[X(P), X(Q), X(R), \ldots, X(S), X(T)]F$

$$= ([X(P), X(R), \ldots, X(S), X(T)]F$$
$$- [X(Q), X(P), \ldots, X(S)]F) / (X(T) - X(Q)) = \text{etc.}$$

That is, the Nth divided difference of $F(X)$ at any $N + 1$ distinct grid points is the difference of *any* two $(N - 1)th$ divided differences of $F(X)$ at N of the $N + 1$ grid points, but having only $N - 1$ of the grid points in common, *divided by* the difference of the two grid points *not* used in *both* $(N - 1)th$ differences.

    The following schematic diagram, or *difference table*, is often useful when discussing (or computing by hand) differences of $F(X)$.

**Table 6.2.1**

Each entry (difference) in the table is obtained as follows: *divide* the entry

---

[3]The proof is by induction. See [1a].

below and to the left minus the entry above and to the left *by* the grid point corresponding to $F(X)$ at the end of the lower diagonal minus the grid point corresponding to $F(X)$ at the end of the upper diagonal. For example,

$$[X(1), X(2), X(3)]F = ([X(2), X(3)]F - [X(1), X(2)]F) \,/\, (X(3) - X(1)),$$

and

$$[X(0), X(1), X(2), X(3)]F$$
$$= ([X(1), X(2), X(3)]F - [X(0), X(1), X(2)]F)/(X(3) - X(0)).$$

**Exercise 4.** For the table of Exercise 1, construct a difference table corresponding to Table 6.2.1.

In view of (6.2.4d), we could have formed a difference table to compute $[X(0), X(4)]F$, $[X(0), X(1), X(4)]F$, $[X(0), X(1), X(2), X(4)]F$, etc., as indicated in Table 6.2.2.

**Table 6.2.2**

| X(0) | F(0) | | | | |
|------|------|---|---|---|---|
| X(1) | F(1) | [X(0), X(1)]F | | | |
| X(2) | F(2) | [X(0), X(2)]F | [X(0), X(1), X(2)]F | | |
| X(3) | F(3) | [X(0), X(3)]F | [X(0), X(1), X(3)]F | [X(0), X(1), X(2), X(3)]F | |
| X(4) | F(4) | [X(0), X(4)]F | [X(0), X(1), X(4)]F | [X(0), X(1), X(2), X(4)]F | |

Then,

$$[X(0), X(1), X(4)]F = ([X(0), X(4)]F - [X(0), X(1)]F)/(X(4) - X(1)), \text{ etc.}$$

**Exercise 5.** For the table of Exercise 1, construct a difference table corresponding to Table 6.2.2. Write a computer program to compute and print the entries in Table 6.2.2.

*Hint.* The first printed line might be $X(0)$, $F(0)$ with the second printed line $X(1)$, $F(1)$, $[X(0), X(1)]F$, etc.

The remaining operators considered in this section are defined on sets involving functions tabulated at *equally spaced* grid points, e.g.,

$$X(K) \equiv X(0) + K * H, K \in //0, N//, \quad H > 0.$$

Probably the most used finite difference operator is the *forward difference*

$$\Delta: \text{DOM} \to \text{RNG}.$$

If the domain DOM involves only one tabulated function, say $F(X)$, then we write

(6.2.5a) $$\Delta F: \text{DOM} \to \text{RNG},$$

where a typical element of DOM is

(6.2.5b) $$(X(K), F(X(K)); X(K + 1), F(X(K + 1)))$$
$$\equiv (X(K), F(K); X(K + 1), F(K + 1)),$$

and the corresponding element of RNG is

(6.2.5c) $$\Delta F(X(K)) = \Delta F(K) \equiv F(K + 1) - F(K).$$

The number $\Delta F(K)$ in (6.2.5c) is called the *first forward difference of* F *at* $X(K)$. And, $\Delta$ is *linear*, since

$$\Delta(A * F + B * G)(K) = (A * F + B * G)(K + 1) - (A * F + B * G)(K)$$
$$= (A * F(K + 1) + B * G(K + 1))$$
$$- (A * F(K) + B * G(K))$$
$$= A * (F(K + 1) - F(K)) + B * (G(K + 1) - G(K))$$
$$= A * \Delta F(K) + B * \Delta G(K).$$

Also, $\Delta F$ is related to $[ \quad , \quad ]F$ by

(6.2.5d) $$\Delta F(K) = (F(K + 1) - F(K)) * (X(K + 1) - X(K))/$$
$$(X(K + 1) - X(K))$$
$$= H * [X(K), X(K + 1)]F.$$

*Note.* We assume that the reader is now sufficiently familiar with operator notation and terminology, like that used in (6.2.5a) and (6.2.5b), so that we may henceforth abbreviate definitions of operators by describing a typical element of the range RNG for each operator. That is, to define $\Delta$ we would give (6.2.5c) and assume that the reader "understood" (6.2.5a, b).

The *second forward difference of* F *at* X(K) is

$$\Delta ** (2)F(K) \equiv \Delta(\Delta F(K)) \equiv \Delta F(K + 1) - \Delta F(K)$$
$$= F(K + 2) - 2 * F(K + 1) + F(K).$$

Also,

$$\Delta ** (2)F(K) = 2 * H ** 2 * [X(K), X(K + 1), X(K + 2)]F.$$

The R*th forward difference of* F *at* X(K) is

(6.2.6a)  $\Delta ** (R)F(K) \equiv \Delta(\Delta ** (R - 1)F(K))$
$$= \Delta ** (R - 1)F(K + 1) - \Delta ** (R - 1)F(K)$$
$$= F(K + R) - BINCO(R, 1) * F(K + R - 1)$$
$$+ BINCO(R, 2) * F(K + R - 2)$$
$$- \cdots + (- 1) ** (R - 1) * BINCO(R, 1) * F(K + 1)$$
$$+ (- 1) ** R * F(K).$$

And,

(6.2.6b)  $\Delta ** (R)F(K)$
$$= (R!) * H ** R * [X(K), X(K + 1), \ldots, X(K + R)]F.$$

Corresponding to Table 6.2.1 we have the table of forward differences, Table 6.2.3.

**Table 6.2.3**

**Exercise 6.** For the table of Exercise 1, construct a difference table corresponding to Table 6.2.3.

**Exercise 7.** Use your tables from Exercises 4 and 6 to check property (6.2.6b) for various choices of R.

One may be able to detect an error committed when *computing* differences by applying the following *test*. Using the notation of Table 6.2.3,

$$(6.2.7a) \quad \sum \Delta F(K), K \in // \, 0, M//, = (F(1) - F(0)) + (F(2) - F(1))$$
$$+ \cdots + (F(M + 1) - F(M))$$
$$= F(M + 1) - F(0),$$

and, in general,

$$(6.2.7b) \quad \sum \Delta ** (R + 1)F(K), K \in // \, 0, M//,$$
$$= \Delta ** (R)F(M + 1) - \Delta ** (R)F(0).$$

That is, the sum of the entries in any column of differences should equal the difference between the last and first entries of the preceding column.

Two other frequently used finite difference operators defined on *equally spaced grids* are the backward difference operator, $\nabla$, and the central difference operator, $\delta$.

The *first backward difference of* F *at* X(K) is

$$(6.2.8a) \quad \nabla F(K) \equiv F(K) - F(K - 1) = \Delta F(K - 1).$$

Also [compare (6.2.6a)],

$$(6.2.8b) \quad \nabla ** (R)F(K) = \nabla(\nabla ** (R - 1)F(K))$$
$$= \nabla ** (R - 1)F(K) - \nabla ** (R - 1)F(K - 1)$$
$$= F(K) - BINCO(R, 1) * F(K - 1)$$
$$+ BINCO(R, 2) * F(K - 2) - \cdots$$
$$+ (- 1) ** (R - 1) * BINCO(R, 1) * F(K - R + 1)$$
$$+ (- 1) ** R * F(K - R)$$
$$= \Delta ** (R)F(K - R).$$

A table of backward differences is indicated in Table 6.2.4.

**Table 6.2.4**

$$\vdots$$

| X(K − 3) | F(K − 3) | | | |
| X(K − 2) | F(K − 2) | ∇F(K − 2) | | |
| X(K − 1) | F(K − 1) | ∇F(K − 1) | ∇ ** (2)F(K − 1) | |
| X(K) | F(K) | ∇F(K) | ∇ ** (2)F(K) | ∇ ** (3)F(K) |

$$\vdots$$

**Exercise 8.** Using the table of Exercise 1, construct a difference table corresponding to Table 6.2.4. Use your table of Exercise 6 to check property (6.2.8b).

The *central difference* operator, $\delta$, is defined at elements of an equally spaced grid $X(K) = X(0) + K * H$, $K \in // - N, N //$, $H > 0$, *and* at the mid-points

$$X(.5) = X(0) + .5 * H,$$
$$X(1.5) = X(1) + .5 * H, \ldots,$$
$$X(K + .5) = X(K) + .5 * H, \text{ etc.}$$

of the intervals determined by the grid points. The *first central difference of* F *at* $X(K)$ is

$$\delta F(X(K)) = \delta F(K) \equiv F(X(K) + .5 * H) - F(X(K) - .5 * H)$$
$$= F(K + .5) - F(K - .5) = \Delta F(K - .5)$$

which is the difference of values of $F(X)$ at points *other than* the tabulated points $(X(K), F(K))$, $K \in // - N, N //$. Also, the first central difference of F at the intermediate point $X(K + .5)$

$$\delta F(K + .5) \equiv F(K + 1) - F(K) = \Delta F(K)$$

is defined in terms of $F(X)$ at tabulated points. The *second central difference of* F *at* $X(K)$ is

$$\delta ** (2)F(K) = \delta(\delta F(K)) \equiv \delta F(K + .5) - \delta F(K - .5)$$
$$= F(K + 1) - 2 * F(K) + F(K - 1) = \Delta ** (2)F(K - 1),$$

while

$$\delta ** (2)F(K + .5) \equiv \delta F(K + 1) - \delta F(K)$$
$$= F(K + 1.5) - 2 * F(K + .5) + F(K - .5)$$
$$= \Delta ** (2)F(K - .5).$$

In general,

(6.2.9a)  $\delta ** (2 * M)F(K)$

$\equiv \delta ** (2 * M - 1)F(K + .5) - \delta ** (2 * M - 1)F(K - .5)$

$= F(K + M) - BINCO(2 * M, 1) * F(K + M - 1) + \cdots$

$+ (-1) ** (2 * M - 1) * BINCO(2 * M, 1) * F(K - M + 1)$

$+ (-1) ** (2 * M) * F(K - M)$

$= \Delta ** (2 * M)F(K - M),$

and

(6.2.9b)  $\delta ** (2 * M + 1)F(K + .5) = \Delta ** (2 * M + 1)F(K - M),$

while *even* central difference at $X(K + .5)$ and *odd* central differences at $X(K)$ do not involve the tabulated points $(X(K), F(K))$, $K \in // - N, N//$.

**Exercise 9.** Using the table of Exercise 1, construct a difference table including the central differences indicated in Table 6.2.5.

Some relations between $\Delta$, $\nabla$, and $\delta$ are indicated in Table 6.2.5.

**Table 6.2.5**

$\vdots$

| X(-2) | F(-2) | | |
|---|---|---|---|
| X(-1) | F(-1) | $\Delta F(-2) = \nabla F(-1) = \delta F(-1.5)$ | $\Delta **(2)F(-2) = \nabla **(2)F(0) = \delta **(2)F(-1)$ |
| X(0) | F(0) | $\Delta F(-1) = \nabla F(0) = \delta F(-.5)$ | $\Delta **(2)F(-1) = \nabla **(2)F(1) = \delta **(2)F(0)$ |
| X(1) | F(1) | $\Delta F(0) = \nabla F(1) = \delta F(.5)$ | $\Delta **(2)F(0) = \nabla **(2)F(2) = \delta **(2)F(1)$ |
| X(2) | F(2) | $\Delta F(1) = \nabla F(2) = \delta F(1.5)$ | |

$\vdots$

**Exercise 10.** Use your tables from Exercises 6, 8, and 9 to verify the relations indicated in Table 6.2.5.

Two operators that are essentially different[4] from the finite difference operators discussed thus far are the *averaging operator*, $\mu$, and the *shifting operator,* E, defined by

(6.2.10)  $\mu F(X(K)) = \mu F(K) \equiv .5 * (F(K + .5) + F(K - .5)),$

(6.2.11a)  $E F(X(K)) = E F(K) \equiv F(K + 1),$

and

[4]In §6.4 we shall see that $\Delta$ applied to a polynomial of degree N generates a polynomial of degree N-1, (the reader can easily show that $\nabla$ and $\delta$ have this property), while the operators $\mu$ and E do *not* reduce the degree of a polynomial.

(6.2.11b)     $E ** (R)F(K) \equiv E(E ** (R - 1)F(K)) = \cdots = F(K + R).$

The operator $\mu$ is frequently used to *simplify the representation* of expressions that are averages of expressions involving differences. For example, write (7.3.32a) as (7.3.32b).

The operator E is useful when examining relationships between operators. Let INV(E) denote the inverse operator that satisfies

$$(INV(E))(E)F(K) \equiv INV(E)(E(F(K))) = INV(E)(F(K + 1)) = F(K)$$

and

$$(E)(INV(E))F(K) \equiv E(INV(E)F(K)) = F(K).$$

Thus

$$INV(E)F(K) \equiv F(K - 1).$$

Let $E ** (1/2)$ be the operator that when followed by *itself* gives E. Thus, define

$$E ** (1/2)F(K) \equiv F(K + .5).$$

Similarly, define

$$E ** (- 1/2)F(K) \equiv F(K - .5).$$

Now we can write

$$\Delta = E - I, \nabla = I - INV(E), \delta = E ** (1/2) - E ** (-1/2), \text{ and}$$
$$\mu = .5 * (E ** (1/2) + E ** (-1/2)).$$

Also,

$$E = I + \Delta, \ E = INV(I - \nabla),$$
$$E ** (1/2) = (I + .25 * \delta ** 2) ** (1/2) + .5 * \delta,$$
$$\mu = (I + .25 * \delta ** 2) ** (1/2).$$

These and other useful representations for the operator $E ** S$, where S is any real number, and $E ** S$ as applied to *polynomials*, are discussed in [1b].

## EXERCISES[5]

**11.** Check that $\nabla$, $\delta$, $\mu$, and E are linear.

**12.** Verify for a specific example (e.g., your table of Exercise 1) that $\Delta = E - I$, $\nabla = I - INV(E)$, $E = INV(I - \nabla)$, etc.

**13.** Select from your table of Exercise 1 entries $(X(K), F(K))$, $K = 0, 1, 3, 4, 8, 10$. For these six number-pairs listed in any convenient order, construct a difference table corresponding to Table 6.2.1. Is this table (F) such that (6.2.6b) applies? If not, why not?

**14.** Select a few nontrivial formulas in Exercises 3 through 7 of §7.3, that involve these operators, and *rewrite* the formulas in the one-line notation of this text.

### 6.3. PROPAGATION OF ERROR IN DIFFERENCE TABLES

In this section we use the forward difference operator, $\Delta$. The reader should formulate similar remarks with examples for the difference operators $[\ldots]$, $\nabla$, and $\delta$.

Consider the function and its differences indicated in Table 6.3.1, where an error of E is committed when $(X(0), F(0) + E)$ is recorded instead of $(X(0), F(0))$.

**Table 6.3.1**

| K | X(K) | F(K) | $\Delta F$ | $\Delta ** (2)F$ | $\Delta ** (3)F$ |
|---|------|------|------------|------------------|------------------|
| ⋮ | ⋮ | ⋮ | ⋮ | ⋮ | ⋮ |
| -3 | X(-3) | F(-3) | | | |
| -2 | X(-2) | F(-2) | $\Delta F(-3)$ | $\Delta ** (2)F(-3)$ | $\Delta ** (3)F(-4)$ |
| -1 | X(-1) | F(-1) | $\Delta F(-2)$ | $\Delta ** (2)F(-2) + E$ | $\Delta ** (3)F(-3)$ |
| 0 | X(0) | F(0) + E | $\Delta F(-1) + E$ | $\Delta ** (2)F(-1) - 2 * E$ | $\Delta ** (3)F(-3) + E$ |
| 1 | X(1) | F(1) | $\Delta F(0) - E$ | $\Delta ** (2)F(0) + E$ | $\Delta ** (3)F(-2) - 3 * E$ |
| 2 | X(2) | F(2) | $\Delta F(1)$ | $\Delta ** (2)F(1)$ | $\Delta ** (3)F(-1) + 3 * E$ |
| 3 | X(3) | F(3) | $\Delta F(2)$ | | $\Delta ** (3)F(0) - E$ |
| ⋮ | ⋮ | ⋮ | ⋮ | ⋮ | $\Delta ** (3)F(1)$ |
| | | | | ⋮ | ⋮ |

[5]Exercises 1 through 10 appear in text.

The propagated error[1] in elements of the column headed by $\Delta **(M)F$ are E times signed binomial coefficients arranged symmetric to the row of the table containing the erroneous element $(X(0), F(0) + E)$. They are the the terms of the expansion of $E * (1 - 1) ** M$ using the binomial theorem.

**Example.** Consider $F(X) = X ** 3$ tabulated at $X(K) = K$, $K \in //1, 11//$, as in Table 6.3.2.

**Table 6.3.2**

| K | X(K) | F(K) | $\Delta F$ | $\Delta **(2)F$ | $\Delta **(3)F$ | $\Delta **(4)F$ |
|---|------|------|-----|------|------|------|
| 1 | 1 | 1 | | | | |
| 2 | 2 | 8 | 7 | 12 | | |
| 3 | 3 | 27 | 19 | 18 | 6 | 0 |
| 4 | 4 | 64 | 37 | 24 | 6 | 0 |
| 5 | 5 | 125 | 61 | 30 | 6 | 0 |
| 6 | 6 | 216 | 91 | 36 | 6 | 0 |
| 7 | 7 | 343 | 127 | 42 | 6 | 0 |
| 8 | 8 | 512 | 169 | 48 | 6 | 0 |
| 9 | 9 | 729 | 217 | 54 | 6 | 0 |
| 10 | 10 | 1000 | 271 | 60 | 6 | |
| 11 | 11 | 1331 | 331 | | | |

If an error of unity is made in computing F(6), and differences are computed as indicated in Table 6.3.3, then the pattern of Table 6.3.1 appears (compare Table 6.3.2).

**Table 6.3.3**

| K | X(K) | F(K) | $\Delta F$ | $\Delta **(2)F$ | $\Delta **(3)F$ | $\Delta **(4)F$ | $\Delta **(5)F$ |
|---|------|------|-----|------|------|------|------|
| 1 | 1 | 1 | | | | | |
| 2 | 2 | 8 | 7 | 12 | | | |
| 3 | 3 | 27 | 19 | 18 | 6 | 0 | |
| 4 | 4 | 64 | 37 | 24 | 6 | 1 | 1 |
| 5 | 5 | 125 | 61 | 31 | 7 | -4 | -5 |
| 6 | 6 | 217 | 92 | 34 | 3 | 6 | 10 |
| 7 | 7 | 343 | 126 | 43 | 9 | -4 | -10 |
| 8 | 8 | 512 | 169 | 48 | 5 | 1 | 5 |
| 9 | 9 | 729 | 217 | 54 | 6 | 0 | 1 |
| 10 | 10 | 1000 | 271 | 60 | 6 | | |
| 11 | 11 | 1331 | 331 | | | | |

If we know that the fourth and higher differences are supposed to be zero (see §6.4), we can locate the error by recalling the symmetry in Table 6.3.1.

[1]Equations (6.2.7a, b) may be used in a test to detect errors committed when computing differences. Here, we assume that no computing errors are committed.

An indication of how round-off errors *could*[2] be propagated in a difference table is given in Table 6.3.4.

**Table 6.3.4**

| K | X(K) | F(K) | $\Delta$F | $\Delta **$ (2)F | $\Delta **$ (3)F |
|---|------|------|-----------|------------------|------------------|
| 0 | X(0) | F(0) − E | | | |
| 1 | X(1) | F(1) + E | $\Delta$F(0) + 2 * E | | |
| | | | $\Delta$F(1) − 2 * E | $\Delta **$ (2)F(0) − 4 * E | |
| 2 | X(2) | F(2) − E | $\Delta$F(2) + 2 * E | $\Delta **$ (2)F(1) + 4 * E | $\Delta **$ (3)F(0) + 8 * E |
| 3 | X(3) | F(3) + E | | | |

The propagated error in elements of the column headed by $\Delta **$ (M)F is $\pm$ E * 2 ** M. Usually the rounding error, E, is not a constant as indicated in Table 6.3.4. In an entry, $(X(K), F(K) + E(K))$, where the last digit retained is in the 10 ** $(- P)$ position, we assume $|E(K)| \leq .5 * 10 ** (-P)$. We then expect that the propagated error in $\Delta **$ (M)F(K) due to rounding the F(K) will not exceed 2 ** $(M − 1) * 10 ** (-P)$. This *bound* on the error due to rounding the F(K) is *probably conservative*, and probably serves as a conservative bound on the round-off error in the $\Delta **$ (M)F(K) even if some rounding of data is experienced when computing the differences.

### 6.4. DIFFERENCES OF A POLYNOMIAL. APPLICATIONS

Some of the most important applications of finite differences are motivated by the following two theorems. For this presentation grids are uniform and the difference operator is $\Delta$. After recalling relations between $\Delta$ and other finite difference operators given in §6.2, the reader should be able to formulate corresponding theorems involving other differences. Can you state similar theorems involving nonuniform grids?

**Theorem 1.** (Fundamental Theorem of Difference Calculus)

H1: N any positive integer.

H2: A(N), A(N − 1), . . . , A(0), are real numbers with A(N)≠0.

H3: X, H are real, and H > 0.

H4: $P(N; X) = \sum A(K) * X ** K$, K ∈ //0, N//.

H5: $\Delta P(N; X) \equiv P(N; X + H) − P(N; X)$, and for K ∈ //1, N //,

$\Delta **$ (K + 1)P(N; X) $\equiv \Delta **$ (K)P(N; X + H) − $\Delta **$ (K)P(N; X).

C1: $\Delta **$ (N)P(N; X) = A(N) * H ** N * N!        (6.4.1a)

C2: $\Delta **$ (N + 1)P(N; X) = 0.        (6.4.1b)

---

[2]The coeffecients of E in the F(K) column are chosen so that errors will not cancel.

*Proof.* The proof is by induction on N. If $N = 1$,

$$\Delta P(1; X) = P(1; X + H) - P(1; X)$$
$$= A(1) * (X + H) + A(0) - (A(1) * X + A(0))$$
$$= A(1) * H = A(1) * H ** 1 * 1!$$

and since $\Delta P(1; X)$ is a constant,

$$\Delta ** (2)P(1; X) = \Delta(\Delta P(1; X)) = 0.$$

If the conclusions, C1 and C2, hold for $N = K$ then

(6.4.2a)      $\Delta ** (K)P(K; X) = A(K) * H ** K * K!$

(6.4.2b)      $\Delta ** (K + 1)P(K; X) = 0.$

It will be sufficient to show that

(6.4.3)      $\Delta P(K + 1; X) = A(K + 1) * H * (K + 1) * X ** K$
$$+ PP(K - 1; X),$$

where $PP(K - 1; X)$ is a polynomial of degree $K - 1$. For then

$$\Delta ** (K + 1)P(K + 1; X)$$
$$= A(K + 1) * H * (K + 1) * \Delta ** (K)(X ** K) + \Delta ** (K)PP(K - 1; X),$$

and by (6.4.2a, b)

$$\Delta ** (K)(X ** K) = H ** K * K!, \text{ and } \Delta ** (K)PP(K - 1; X) = 0,$$

so that

$$\Delta ** (K + 1)P(K + 1; X) = A(K + 1) * H ** (K + 1) * (K + 1)!,$$

and

$$\Delta ** (K + 2)P(K + 1; X) = 0,$$

and the induction is complete. We now establish (6.4.3):

$$\Delta P(K + 1; X) = P(K + 1; X + H) - P(K + 1; X)$$
$$= A(K + 1) * ((X + H) ** (K + 1) - X ** (K + 1))$$
$$+ A(K) * ((X + H) ** K - X ** K)$$
$$+ A(K - 1) * ((X + H) ** (K - 1) - X ** (K - 1))$$
$$+ \cdots + A(1) * ((X + H) - X) + (A(0) - A(0))$$
$$= A(K + 1) * (X ** (K + 1) + (K + 1) * H * X ** K$$
$$+ BINCO(K + 1, 2) * H ** 2 * X ** (K - 1)$$
$$+ \cdots + H ** (K + 1) - X ** (K + 1))$$
$$+ A(K) * (X ** K + K * H * X ** (K - 1)$$
$$+ BINCO(K, 2) * H ** 2 * X ** (K - 2)$$
$$+ \cdots + H ** K - X ** K) + \cdots + A(1) * H$$
$$= A(K + 1) * (K + 1) * H * X ** K$$
$$+ (A(K + 1) * BINCO(K + 1, 2) * H ** 2$$
$$+ A(K) * BINCO(K, 1) * H) * X ** (K - 1)$$
$$+ \cdots + (A(K + 1) * H ** (K + 1)$$
$$+ A(K) * H ** K + \cdots + A(1) * H)$$
$$= A(K + 1) * (K + 1) * H * X ** K + PP(K - 1; X).$$

We can *not* conclude that if the N$th$ difference of $F(X)$ on a specified equally spaced grid is constant that the function, $F(X)$, is a polynomial of degree N. For example, let $F(X) = X + SIN(X)$, and tabulate $F(X(K))$ at $X(K) = K * \pi$, $K \in //0, N//$. Here $\Delta F(X(K)) = \pi$ for each K.

However, we *can* state that there exists precisely one polynomial of degree N that agrees with $F(X)$ at those specified consecutive grid points which were used to compute the constant N$th$ differences.

**Theorem 2.**

H1: N any positive integer. R and S any integers with $S \geq R + N$.

H2: $F(X)$ is tabulated at the equally spaced grid points $X(K)$, $K \in // R, S //$.

H3: $\Delta ** (N)F(X(K)) = $ (constant) $\neq 0$, $K \in // R, S - N //$.

C1: There exists a polynomial, $P(N; X)$, of degree N satisfying

(6.4.4) $\qquad P(N; X(K)) = F(X(K))$, $K \in // R, S //$.

C2: The polynomial in C1 is unique.

*Proof.* 1. We shall see in §7.2 that $N + 1$ distinct points, $X(K)$, $K \in //R$,

$R + N//$, determine *uniquely* the $N + 1$ coefficients in[1]

$$P(N; X) = \sum A(K) * X ** K, \quad K \in //0, N //,$$

so that $P(N; X(K)) = F(X(K)), K \in // R, R + N //$. So the theorem is true if $S = R + N$. Now we outline a proof for $S = R + N + T$ by induction on $T$.

2. By (1) and (6.4.1a),

$$\Delta ** (N)F(X(R)) = \Delta ** (N)P(N; X(R)) = A(N) * H ** N * N!,$$

which is also the nonzero constant given in hypothesis H3. Thus $A(N) \neq 0$, and $A(N)$ has the same value in every polynomial of degree $N$ defined as in (1) using any $N + 1$ consecutive points from $X(K), K \in //R, S//$.

3. The unique polynomial of degree $N$, $PP(N; X)$, having $Nth$ difference $A(N) * H ** N * N!$ and agreeing with $F(X)$ at $X(K), K \in //R + 1, R + N + 1//$, has only $N$ independent parameters $AA(N - 1), AA(N - 2), \ldots, AA(1), AA(0)$, which are determined by the conditions

$$PP(N; X(K)) = F(X(K)), K \in // R + 1, R + N //.$$

Thus,

$$PP(N, X) = P(N; X), \text{ and } P(N; X(K)) = F(X(K)), K \in // R, R + N + 1//.$$

4. If $P(N; X)$ defined in (1) satisfies $P(N; X(K)) = F(X(K)), K \in // R, R + N + T//$, where $T$ is any positive integer satisfying $R + N + T < S$, then we repeat the argument in (3): Let $PP(N; X)$ be characterized by

$$PP(N; X(K)) = F(X(K)), K \in // R + T + 1, R + N + T + 1//,$$

where $AA(N) = A(N)$ and $AA(N - 1), \ldots, AA(0)$ are determined by

$$PP(N; X(K)) = F(X(K)), K \in //R + T + 1, R + N + T //,$$

so that $PP(N; X) = P(N, X)$, and

$$P(N; X(K)) = F(X(K)), K \in // R, R + N + T + 1//.$$

---

[1]See §6.5 for other representations of the general polynomial of degree $N$. Of course, each representation involves $N + 1$ parameters. In each form for $P(N; X)$ considered here, only *one* parameter is involved in $\Delta ** (N)P(N; X(R))$.

5. Thus, the argument in (4) may be repeated until $R + N + T + 1 = S$.

In practice, the degree of success experienced in applications of these theorems depends to a large extent on the ingenuity (and luck) of the person applying them. The following examples are presented as illustrations of how these theorems might be applied to solve *three fundamental problems* in numerical analysis:

Suppose a function $F(X)$ is so complicated (expensive to evaluate) that our budget will permit us to compute $F(X)$ at only $N + 1$ points[2] $X(K)$, $K \in //0, N//$. Or, suppose we have a table of $F(X), \{(X(K), F(X(K)))$ $|K \in //0, N//\}$, where the entries have been obtained by an experiment which would be prohibitively expensive to set-up again to obtain the pair $(XX, F(XX))$ which is not in the table.

**Problem 1.** Find a function, $P(X)$ (here assumed to be a polynomial or set of polynomials), characterized by

(6.4.5) $\qquad F(X(K)) = P(X(K)) + E(K), K \in //0, N//,$

where each $|E(K)|$ is less than some specified bound on the error permissible in the representation of $F(X(K))$ by $P(X(K))$. If $E(K) = 0$, $K \in //0, N//$, then $P(X)$ is an *interpolation function*. See §7.1.

An important example of Problem 1 is that of finding a function, $P(X)$, inexpensive to evaluate, that can be stored in a computer and evaluated by the computer at specified points to define elements of a given table. Thus one can avoid the problem of storing the individual entries of the table and providing a table look-up routine.

**Problem 2.** Find a function, $P(X)$, (a polynomial or set of polynomials) characterized by

(6.4.6) $\qquad F(X) = P(X) + E(X), \quad |E(X)| < G(X)$ *on the interval of interest,*

where $G(X)$ is some specified bound on the truncation error of $P(X)$ on the interval of interest.

**Problem 3.** Find a solution of Problem 2 with the additional property that the result of applying a linear operator, L, to $P(X)$ is usable as an estimate to $LF(X)$. That is, so that

(6.4.7) $\qquad |LE(X)| = |L(F(X) - P(X))| = |LF(X) - LP(X)|$

is less than a specified bound (function) on the interval of interest.

[2]In §7.4 we shall see how a judicious choice of grid $X(K), K \in //0, N//$, can affect the quality of a numerical solution to these problems.

Problem 1 asks for a method of *storing a table* in a computer.

Problem 2 asks for much more than does Problem 1. In (6.4.6), $E(X)$ must be small *throughout an interval*, and not just small at the $X(K)$, $K \in //0, N//$. If $E(X(K)) = 0, K \in //0, N//$, then $P(X)$ is an interpolation function that defines usable estimates to $F(X)$ at points not in the given table. Least-square polynomials (see Chapter 8), generally with some $E(X(K)) \neq 0$, are sometimes used to solve a Problem 2. Linear programming methods are often used to solve Problem 1 with some $E(K) \neq 0$.

Possibly even more severe restrictions are put on the desired $P(X)$ in Problem 3, since $|E(X)|$ could be uniformly small and $|LE(X)|$ could be large at some points in the interval of interest. For example, let L be derivative.

We saw in Chapter 2 how a function, $F(X)$, can be estimated in the neighborhood of one point by Taylor Polynomials, where the coefficients of the polynomials involve derivatives of $F(X)$ at the point. Clearly, if these derivatives are available at enough points in the interval of interest, then one could probably solve the above problems by defining a finite set of Taylor Polynomials (each is used on a specified subinterval) covering the whole interval of interest. See Exercise 8 in §2.2.

Usually the necessary derivatives are *not* available, so that we may not use Taylor Polynomials to solve these problems.

*We use polynomials whose coefficients are defined in terms of available information, usually the tabulated points* $(X(K), F(X(K)))$, $K \in //0, N//$. Chapter 7 is presented as a discussion of various representations of polynomial parts of $P(X)$ characterized by (6.4.5.) with each $E(K) = 0$. Also, $E(X)$ of (6.4.6) is discussed in §7.4. In Chapter 8 we consider Problem 2 with some $E(X(K)) \neq 0$. Chapter 9 and Chapter 10 are discussions of Problem 3 where the operator L is differentiation and integration respectively.

The following examples are intended as a guide: (i) to determine subsets of a table that can be estimated in the sense of (6.4.5) by one polynomial; (ii) to determine the appropriate degree for each polynomial; and (iii) to determine an appropriate set of characterizing properties for each polynomial.

**Example 1.** Discuss the table of forward differences for

$$F(X) = \begin{cases} X ** 3, & X \leq 0 \\ X ** 2, 0 \leq X \leq 6 \\ -X + 42, & X \geq 6 \end{cases}$$

at $X(K) = K, K \in //-5, 10//$. See Table 6.4.1.

Table 6.4.1

| X(K) | F(K) | ΔF | Δ**(2)F | Δ**(3)F | Δ**(4)F | Δ**(5)F | Δ**(6)F |
|------|------|------|---------|---------|---------|---------|---------|
| −5 | −125 |  |  |  |  |  |  |
|  |  | 61 |  |  |  |  |  |
| −4 | −64 |  | −24 |  |  |  |  |
|  |  | 37 |  | 6 |  |  |  |
| −3 | −27 |  | −18 |  | 0 |  |  |
|  |  | 19 |  | 6 |  | 0 |  |
| −2 | −8 |  | −12 |  | 0 |  | 0 |
|  |  | 7 |  | 6 |  | 0 |  |
| −1 | −1 |  | −6 |  | 0 |  | −4 |
|  |  | 1 |  | 6 |  | −4 |  |
| 0 | 0 |  | 0 |  | −4 |  | 6 |
|  |  | 1 |  | 2 |  | 2 |  |
| 1 | 1 |  | 2 |  | −2 |  | 0 |
|  |  | 3 |  | 0 |  | 2 |  |
| 2 | 4 |  | 2 |  | 0 |  | −2 |
|  |  | 5 |  | 0 |  | 0 |  |
| 3 | 9 |  | 2 |  | 0 |  | 0 |
|  |  | 7 |  | 0 |  | 0 |  |
| 4 | 16 |  | 2 |  | 0 |  | −14 |
|  |  | 9 |  | −14 |  | −14 |  |
| 5 | 25 |  | 2 |  | −14 |  | 54 |
|  |  | 11 |  | 12 |  | 40 |  |
| 6 | 36 |  | −12 |  | 26 |  | −78 |
|  |  | −1 |  | 0 |  | −38 |  |
| 7 | 35 |  | 0 |  | −12 |  | 50 |
|  |  | −1 |  | 0 |  | 12 |  |
| 8 | 34 |  | 0 |  | 0 |  |  |
|  |  | −1 |  |  |  |  |  |
| 9 | 33 |  | 0 |  |  |  |  |
|  |  | −1 |  |  |  |  |  |
| 10 | 32 |  |  |  |  |  |  |

Since

$$\Delta ** (3)F(K) = 6, \ K \in //-5, \ -2//,$$

Theorem 2 implies there is a polynomial of degree 3 that agrees with F(X) *at* X(K), K ∈ //−5, 1//, but F(X) is *not* a cubic polynomial on −5 ≤ X ≤ 1. Since

$$\Delta ** (2)F(K) = 2, \ K \in //0, \ 4//,$$

there is a polynomial of degree 2 that agrees with F(X) *at* X(K), K ∈ //0, 6//, and here F(X) *is* a quadratic polynomial on 0 ≤ X ≤ 6. And, since

$$\Delta F(K) = -1, \ K \in //6, \ 9//,$$

there is a linear polynomial which agrees with F(X) at X(K), K ∈ //6, 10//. Again, it *happens* that F(X) *is* a linear polynomial on 6 ≤ X ≤ 10. Of course, the table would *look* the same if F(X) consisted of a set of line segments connecting consecutive points listed in the table.

It is important to notice (see Table 6.4.1) that even though F(X) consists entirely of polynomial segments, differences of F(X) may not become and remain uniformly small. If the table contains as many as N + 2 grid points where F(X) is a polynomial of degree N, then one (N + 1)*th* difference will be zero, but higher differences using N + 2 of these points [with points where F(X) is not that polynomial,] will probably be quite large—the growth is projected in a manner somewhat like the propagation of error in Table 6.3.1, but in this case symmetric about the row of the table near where F(X) changes from one polynomial to another. Thus, it is important to recognize groups of *low* order differences that are approximately constant. This is also important because we prefer to work with low degree polynomials (preferably N < 5).

**Example 2.** Discuss the difference table for $F(X) = SIN(X)$ at $X(K) = 2 * K$ degrees, $K \in //-2, 9//$. See Table 6.4.2.

**Table 6.4.2**

| K | X(K) (degrees) | X(K) (radians) | F(K) | ΔF | Δ**(2)F | Δ**(3)F |
|---|---|---|---|---|---|---|
| −2 | −4 | −.06981 | −.06976 | | | |
| | | | | .03486 | | |
| −1 | −2 | −.03491 | −.03490 | | .00004 | |
| | | | | .03490 | | −.00004 |
| 0 | 0 | 0 | 0 | | 0 | −.00004 |
| | | | | .03490 | | |
| 1 | 2 | .03491 | .03490 | | −.00004 | −.00005 |
| | | | | .03486 | | −.00004 |
| 2 | 4 | .06981 | .06976 | | −.00009 | |
| | | | | .03477 | | −.00003 |
| 3 | 6 | .10472 | .10453 | | −.00013 | −.00006 |
| | | | | .03464 | | |
| 4 | 8 | .13963 | .13917 | | −.00016 | −.00003 |
| | | | | .03448 | | |
| 5 | 10 | .17453 | .17365 | | −.00022 | −.00003 |
| | | | | .03426 | | −.00004 |
| 6 | 12 | .20944 | .20791 | | −.00025 | |
| | | | | .03401 | | −.00005 |
| 7 | 14 | .24435 | .24192 | | −.00029 | |
| | | | | .03372 | | |
| 8 | 16 | .27925 | .27564 | | −.00034 | |
| | | | | .03338 | | |
| 9 | 18 | .31416 | .30902 | | | |

Since

$$\Delta F(K) \doteq .03490, \quad K \in //-2, 1//,$$

we expect (motivated by Theorem 2) that some linear polynomial, call it $P(1; X)$, will give a close estimate to $F(X)$ at $X(K)$, $K \in //-2, 2//$. Experience and some luck are often helpful when picking a set of characterizing properties for the estimating polynomial. Here, we want to pick *two* of the five tabulated points[3] involved, call them $(A, F(A))$ and $(B, F(B))$, and define $P(1; X)$ so that

$$P(1; A) = F(A) \text{ and } P(1; B) = F(B).$$

The symmetry of these five points about $(X(0), F(0)) = (0, 0)$ suggests that we pick $A = X(-1)$ and $B = X(1)$, or $A = X(-2)$ and $B = X(2)$. Either choice defines a line through $(X(0), F(0))$. A sketch of $SIN(X)$ indicates that $A = X(-2)$, $B = X(2)$ is the better choice to minimize the maximum error on the interval $[-5 \text{ deg.}, +5 \text{ deg.}]$. Since

$$\Delta ** (2)F(K) \doteq -.00025, \quad K \in //3, 7//,$$

and

$$\Delta ** (3)F(K) \doteq -.00005, \quad K \in //3, 6//,$$

we expect that some polynomial of degree 2, call it $P(2; X)$, will give a close estimate to $F(X)$ at $X(K)$, $K \in //3, 9//$. The choice of *three* of these points to characterize $P(2; X)$ is influenced by the following rule of thumb.[4]

---

[3]We might have used the method of *least-squares*, see Chapter 8, to define a linear polynomial *using* all five points.

[4]As with most rules of thumb, there are exceptions. It may be that minimizing the maximum value of $|E(X)|$ in (6.4.6) is more important than convenience of representation of $P(N; X)$. In that case, we should like to pick the Chebyshev Abscissas, (7.4.14), as grid points. See Example 3, below, and Example 4 of §7.4.

*Rule of Thumb.* Pick equally spaced grid points [so that we may use the several convenient representations, discussed in Chapter 7, of interpolation polynomials whose coefficients involve differences of F(X)], and do not pick all the points from a small segment of the interval of interest.

Thus, we might define P(2; X) so that

$$P\big(2; X(K)\big) = F\big(X(K)\big), K \in //4, 2, 8//.$$

Since

$$\Delta ** (3)F(K) \doteq -.00005, K \in //{-}1, 6//,$$

we might define a polynomial of degree 3, call it P(3; X), so that

$$P\big(3; X(K)\big) = F\big(X(K)\big), K \in //0, 3, 9//,$$

and use P(3; X) to estimate F(X) *throughout* the interval [−4 deg., 18 deg.].

**Example 3.** Suppose a set of characterizing properties for an interpolation polynomial, P(N; X), has been picked, say

(6.4.8)        $$P\big(N; X(K)\big) = F\big(X(K)\big), K \in //R, M, R + N * M//.$$

In §7.4, it is shown, (7.4.12), that

$$E(N; X) = F(X) - P(N; X)$$
$$= \big(X - X(R)\big) * \big(X - X(R + M)\big) * \cdots * \big(X - X(R + N * M)\big)$$
$$* DER ** (N + 1)F(Z)/(N + 1)!,$$

for some Z in the smallest interval containing X, X(R), X(R + M), . . . , and X(R + N * M), and by (7.4.17), we may write

$$E(N; X) = \big(X - X(R)\big) * \cdots * \big(X - X(R + N * M)\big)$$
$$* [X(R), X(R + M), . . . , X(R + N * M), X]F.$$

If the (N + 1)*th* divided difference of F(X) does not change much for X in the interval of interest, we *may* be able to use the estimate

(6.4.9)        $$E(N; X) \doteq \big(X - X(R)\big) * \cdots * \big(X - X(R + N * M)\big)$$
$$* [X(R), . . . , X(R + N * M), X(R + N * M + M)]F$$
$$= \big(X - X(R)\big) * \cdots * \big(X - X(R + N * M)\big)$$
$$* \Delta ** (N + 1)F(R)/$$
$$\big((X(R + M) - X(R)) ** (N + 1) * (N + 1)!\big).$$

In that case, we have an estimate of the truncation error of the estimate P(N; X) at all elements of the table as well as at intermediate points X not tabulated. In practice, we are sometimes able to use estimates like (6.4.9) to pick an N and a subset X(R), X(R + M), . . . , X(R + N * M), of the given grid X(K), K ∈ //N1, N2//, so that P(N; X) characterized by (6.4.8) solves Problem 1 or Problem 2 in the sense that (6.4.9) implies that the E(K) in Problem 1, or the E(X) in Problem 2, is less than a specified bound. [Compare the "three basic problems" in §2.2 where only one quantity was unspecified.]

### 6.5. SOME REPRESENTATIONS OF A POLYNOMIAL

In §6.4, we considered the general polynomial of degree N represented in the form

(6.5.1)     $P(N; X) = \sum A(K) * X ** K$, $K \in //0, N //$, where $A(N) \neq 0$.

In this section we indicate that $P(N; X)$ could be written in infinitely many equivalent forms. We illustrate a few of the more important ones. The reader is already familiar with the representation

(6.5.2)     $P(N; X) = A(N) * (X - X(1)) * (X - X(2)) * \cdots$
$$* (X - X(N - 1)) * (X - X(N))$$
[sometimes written: $PN(X) = AN * (X - X1) * (X - X2) * \cdots$
$$* (X - XNM1) * (X - XN)],$$

where $X(K)$, $K \in //1, N//$, (real or complex numbers) are the zeros of $P(N; X)$. Here, the parameters are $A(N)$, and $X(K)$, $K \in //1, N //$.

The *factorial function*, $FAC(N; X)$, defined by

(6.5.3a)     $FAC(N; X) \equiv X * (X - 1) * \cdots * (X - N + 1)$,
$$FAC(0; X) \equiv 1,$$

is a *polynomial*[1] of degree N in X. If X is the integer N, we write

(6.5.3b)     $FAC(N; X) = FAC(N; N) = N * (N - 1) * \cdots * 2 * 1 = N!$,
$$FAC(0; 0) = 1 = 0!.$$

The *binomial coefficient function*, $BINCO(X, N)$, is defined by

(6.5.4)     $BINCO(X, N) \equiv FAC(N; X) / N!$,
$$BINCO(X, 0) \equiv 1$$

for any nonnegative integer N and real number X. For any polynomial, $P(N; X)$, represented in the form (6.5.1), we may write [with constants $B(K)$, $C(K)$, $K \in //0, N//$,]

---

[1]If N is not required to be a nonnegative integer, we write $FAC(N, X) = \Gamma(X + 1)/\Gamma(X - N + 1)$, where the *gamma function*, $\Gamma(X)$, satisfies $\Gamma(N + 1) = N!$. See [3]. In computing, the form (6.5.3a) is preferred.

(6.5.5)          $P(N; X) = \sum B(K) * FAC(K; X), K \in // 0, N //,$

and

(6.5.6)     $P(N; X) = \sum C(K) * BINCO(X, K), K \in //0, N //,$

where $C(K) = B(K) * K!$.

**Example 1.** Write $P(X) = 2 * X ** 4 - 10 * X ** 2 + 8$ in the forms (6.5.2), (6.5.5) and (6.5.6). The zeros of $P(X)$ are $1, -1, 2,$ and $-2$, thus

$$P(X) = 2 * (X ** 2 - 1) * (X ** 2 - 4)$$
$$= 2 * (X - 1) * (X + 1) * (X - 2) * (X + 2).$$

Since

$$FAC(4; X) = X * (X - 1) * (X - 2) * (X - 3)$$
$$= X ** 4 - 6 * X ** 3 + 11 * X ** 2 - 6 * X$$
$$FAC(3; X) = X * (X - 1) * (X - 2) = X ** 3 - 3 * X ** 2 + 2 * X$$
$$FAC(2; X) = X * (X - 1) = X ** 2 - X$$
$$FAC(1; X) = X, \text{ and } FAC(0, X) \equiv 1,$$

then

$$P(X) - 2 * FAC(4; X) = 12 * X ** 3 - 32 * X ** 2 + 12 * X + 8$$
$$P(X) - 2 * FAC(4; X) - 12 * FAC(3; X) = 4 * X ** 2 - 12 * X + 8$$
$$P(X) - 2 * FAC(4; X) - 12 * FAC(3; X) - 4 * FAC(2; X) = -8 * X + 8$$
$$P(X) - 2 * FAC(4; X) - 12 * FAC(3; X) - 4 * FAC(2; X)$$
$$+ 8 * FAC(1; X) - 8 * FAC(0; X) = 0$$

so that

$$P(X) = 2 * FAC(4; X) + 12 * FAC(3; X) + 4 * FAC(2; X)$$
$$- 8 * FAC(1; X) + 8 * FAC(0; X).$$

Since

$$FAC(K; X) = BINCO(X, K) * K!,$$

then

$$P(X) = 2 * 4! * BINCO(X, 4) + 12 * 3! * BINCO(X, 3)$$
$$+ 4 * 2! * BINCO(X, 2) - 8 * 1! * BINCO(X, 1)$$
$$+ 8 * 0! * BINCO(X, 0).$$

The method of Example 1 can be applied to represent $P(N; X)$, (6.5.1), in the form

(6.5.7)          $P(N; X) = \sum B(K) * PP(K; X), K \in //0, N //,$

where $PP(K; X)$ is any polynomial of degree *exactly* K. Sometimes the nature of the problem whose solution is to involve $P(N; X)$ will suggest a particular family $PP(K; X)$, $K \in //0, N//$.

**Example 2.** Let $X(J)$, $J \in //0, N//$, be $N + 1$ distinct real numbers. In Chapter 7, we use the form (6.5.7) with

$$PP(K; X) \equiv (X - X(0)) * (X - X(1)) * \cdots * (X - X(K - 1)), \text{ for each}$$
$$K \in //1, N//,$$
$$\equiv 1, \text{ for } K = 0$$

in (7.3.2) to obtain (7.3.3), (7.3.4), and (7.3.8).

*Note.* (7.3.4) may be written in the form (6.5.5): $B(K) = \Delta ** (K)F(0)/K!.$

We use

$$PP(K; X) \equiv (X - X(N)) * (X - X(N - 1)) * \cdots * (X - X(N - K + 1)),$$
$$\text{for each } K \in //1, N//,$$
$$\equiv 1, \text{ for } K = 0$$

in (7.3.5) to obtain (7.3.6) and (7.3.7).

### EXERCISES

**1.** Select a few nontrivial formulas from Exercises 3 through 7 of §7.3 that involve the binomial coefficient function BINCO, etc., and *rewrite* these formulas in the one-line notation of this text.

**2.** Show for specific values of K that

(6.5.8)      $BINCO(S + K - 1, K) = (- 1) ** K * BINCO(- S, K).$

### SUGGESTED READING

1. Hildebrand, F.B. (1956): *Introduction to Numerical Analysis*. McGraw-Hill Book Company. New York.

1a. _____ . (Page 39.)

1b. _____ . (Page 131.)

2. Kunz, K.S. (1957): *Numerical Analysis*. McGraw-Hill Book Company. New York.

3. *Handbook of Mathematical Functions with Formulas, Graphs, and Mathematical Tables*. (1964): National Bureau of Standards Applied Mathematics Series 55. (Page 255.)

# 7 INTERPOLATION

## 7.1 MOTIVATION

This chapter is presented as an introduction to interpolation functions. Rational and some nonalgebraic interpolation functions are important in many contexts in numerical analysis. However, in this elementary text we direct most of our attention to a few classical forms for *interpolation polynomials*. We discuss their characterization, construction, representations, evaluation, and the associated truncation error when they are considered an estimate to a function, F(X), on an interval. We shall see that this truncation error depends on the choice of a set of characterizing properties for the interpolation polynomial. The least-square polynomials considered in Chapter 8 are generally not interpolation polynomials.

An *interpolation function* is a function, P(X), that involves a set of parameters where the parameters are defined by a specified set of conditions imposed on P(X). Typical conditions are: P(X) has a prescribed value at $X = X1$; $P'(X)$ has a prescribed value at $X = X1$; $\int P(T)$, over $T \in (A, B)$, has a prescribed value. We usually assume a *form* for P(X) that is *linear* in the parameters, and pick characterizing properties that when applied to P(X) define a linear system in the unknown parameters (the type of system that we solve best).

A *typical form* for an interpolation function is

(7.1.1)     $P(X) = \sum A(K) * U(K, X), K \in //0, N//,$

where the functions U(K, X) are *chosen*—the choice usually depends on the job P(X) is expected to do. For example, if P(X) is to be used as an estimate to a function that is known to be periodic,[1] then one might pick

$$U(0, X) \equiv 1, U(1, X) = SIN(X), U(2, X) = COS(X),$$
$$U(3, X) = SIN(2 * X), U(4, X) = COS(2 * X),$$
$$U(5, X) = SIN(3 * X), \text{etc.}$$

If the function is known to have N*th* forward difference, $\Delta ** (N)F(X)$, approximately constant in the interval of interest (see §6.4 and §6.5), then one would probably pick each U(K, X) = PP(K, X), a polynomial of degree exactly K, so that P(X) will be an *interpolation polynomial*.

If (7.1.1) is an interpolation polynomial and if all of the parameters are determined by conditions that P(X) agree with F(X) at specified points, then P(X) is called a *Lagrange Interpolation Polynomial*.

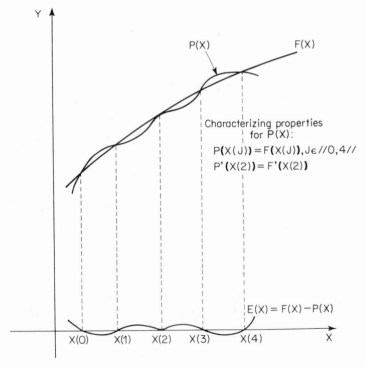

**Figure 7.1.1**

[1] Suppose that a change of variables has been executed to make the period equal $2 * \pi$.

Most of this chapter is devoted to a discussion of characterization, construction, representations (recall §6.5), etc., of Lagrange Interpolation Polynomials.

Other interpolation polynomials considered here are those characterized by (7.3.14), (7.3.22b), (7.7.27b), (7.3.29), and (7.4.24b).

Two useful estimating polynomials (not derived as interpolation polynomials) are obtained by computing the arithmetic mean of interpolation polynomials. See Stirling's Formula, (7.3.32), and Bessel's Formula (7.3.33).

## 7.2 EXISTENCE OF LAGRANGE INTERPOLATION POLYNOMIALS

Let the interpolation polynomial

$$(7.2.1) \qquad P(N; X) = \sum A(K) * X ** K, \, K \in //0, N//,$$

be characterized by the $N + 1$ conditions

$$(7.2.2) \qquad P(N; X(J)) = F(X(J)), \, J \in //0, N//,$$

where the $X(J), J \in //0, N//,$ are distinct and the $F(X(J))$ are given. This is *the Lagrange Interpolation Polynomial*. The coefficients in (7.2.1) are then defined by the linear system (compare Example 2 on page 93)

$$P(N; X(J)) = \sum X(J) ** K * A(K), \, K \in //0, N//,$$
$$= F(X(J)), \text{ for each } J \in //0, N//,$$

or by the matrix equation

$$(7.2.3) \qquad
\begin{bmatrix}
1 & X(0) & X(0) ** 2 & \cdots & X(0) ** N \\
1 & X(1) & X(1) ** 2 & \cdots & X(1) ** N \\
1 & X(2) & X(2) ** 2 & \cdots & X(2) ** N \\
\vdots & \vdots & \vdots & & \vdots \\
1 & X(N) & X(N) ** 2 & \cdots & X(N) ** N
\end{bmatrix}
*
\begin{bmatrix}
A(0) \\
A(1) \\
A(2) \\
\vdots \\
A(N)
\end{bmatrix}
=
\begin{bmatrix}
F(X(0)) \\
F(X(1)) \\
F(X(2)) \\
\vdots \\
F(X(N))
\end{bmatrix}.
$$

The determinant of the matrix of coefficients in (7.2.3) is the Vandermonde Determinant and is known (see [1]) to have the value

$$PROD\,(X(I) - X(J)), I, J \in //0, N//, \text{ and } I > J,$$
$$\equiv (X(1) - X(0)) * (X(2) - X(0)) * \cdots * (X(N) - X(0))$$
$$* (X(2) - X(1)) * \cdots * (X(N) - X(1))$$
$$* (X(3) - X(2)) * \cdots * (X(N) - X(N - 1)),$$

which is not zero since the X(J) are distinct. Thus (7.2.3) *has* a *unique* solution, and the Lagrange Interpolation Polynomial (7.2.1) characterized by (7.2.2) exists and is unique.

A programmer chooses to evaluate P(N; X) in the form

$$P(N; X) = (\cdots(((A(N) * X + A(N - 1)) * X + A(N - 2)) * X$$
$$+ A(N - 3))\cdots) * X + A(0)$$

instead of evaluating P(N; X) by repeatedly raising X to the appropriate powers, etc. By this he is able to reduce both computing time and the number of storage cells used for that problem.

Similarly, we find it convenient to have several *representations* for the (unique) Lagrange Interpolation Polynomial. Criteria that characterize one representation as more convenient than another should involve: (i) the cost of determining the unkown coefficients of the form; (ii) availability of computing aids (tables of functions, computers, etc.); and (iii) the cost of evaluating the form (one or many times).

We conclude this section with a brief discussion of several forms for P(N; X), the Lagrange Interpolation Polynomial. These will be discussed in more detail in subsequent sections of this and other chapters.

The representation (7.2.1) for P(N; X) is obtained by expanding the determinant in

(7.2.4)

$$\begin{vmatrix} P(N;X) & 1 & X & X**2 & \cdots & X**N \\ F(X(0)) & 1 & X(0) & X(0)**2 & \cdots & X(0)**N \\ F(X(1)) & 1 & X(1) & X(1)**2 & \cdots & X(1)**N \\ \vdots & \vdots & \vdots & \vdots & & \vdots \\ F(X(N)) & 1 & X(N) & X(N)**2 & \cdots & X(N)**N \end{vmatrix} = 0$$

by the first row. The coefficients A(K) are those obtained by solving (7.2.3) by Cramer's Rule, and this method requires the evaluation of $N + 2$ determinants of order $N + 1$—usually much too expensive to be practical.

Upon expanding (7.2.4) by the first column we obtain

$$(7.2.5) \qquad P(N; X) = \sum F(X(K)) * LC(N, K; X), K \in //0, N//,$$

where the LC(N, K; X) are polynomials of degree N, called the *Lagrange Coefficients* for the grid X(J), J $\in$ //0, N//, characterized for each K $\in$ //0, N//, by the $N + 1$ conditions (which depend only on the grid used)

$$(7.2.6) \qquad \begin{aligned} &LC(N, K; X(J)) = 0 \text{ for } J \in //0, N//, \text{ and } \quad J \neq K, \\ &LC(N, K; X(K)) = 1. \end{aligned}$$

In §7.3 we shall discuss a general procedure for constructing polynomials like (7.2.5). Here, the polynomials LC(N, K; X) are easy to define, but to *compute* P(N; XX) we must evalute each of the $N + 1$ polynomials LC(N, K; X), K $\in$ //0, N//, at X = XX.

We will find, see §7.3, that the coefficients of Lagrange Interpolation Polynomials represented in the forms

$$(7.2.7) \qquad P(N; X)$$
$$= A(0) + A(1) * (X - X(0))$$
$$+ A(2) * (X - X(0)) * (X - X(1)) + \cdots$$
$$+ A(N) * (X - X(0)) * (X - X(1)) * \cdots * (X - X(N - 1)),$$

and

$$(7.2.8) \qquad P(N; X)$$
$$= B(0) + B(1) * (X - X(N))$$
$$+ B(2) * (X - X(N)) * (X - X(N - 1)) + \cdots$$
$$+ B(N) * (X - X(N)) * (X - X(N - 1)) * \cdots * (X - X(1))$$

are particularly easy to compute when the X(J) are uniformly spaced: X(J) = X(0) + J * H, J $\in$ //0, N//, and H > 0.

A delightful property of Lagrange Interpolation Polynomials represented in the form (7.2.7) is that

(7.2.9)     $P(N + 1; X) = P(N; X) + A(N + 1) * (X - X(0))$

$* (X - X(1)) * \cdots * (X - X(N)),$

using $X(J) = X(0) + J * H$, $J \in //0, N + 1//$. Compare (7.3.3), below.

Similarly, if $P(N; X)$ is represented in the form (7.2.8) using $X(J) = X(0) + J * H$, $J \in //0, N//$, and $PP(X)$ is the Lagrange Interpolation Polynomial of degree $N + 1$ in the form (7.2.8) using $X(J) = X(0) + J * H$, $J \in //0, N//$, and $X(-1) = X(0) - H$, then

(7.2.10)     $PP(X) = P(N; X) + B(N + 1) * (X - X(N))$

$* (X - X(N - 1)) * \cdots * (X - X(1)) * (X - X(0)),$

where $B(N + 1)$ is a simple function of the $B(K)$, $K \in //0, N//$, used in $P(N; X)$ and $F(X(-1))$. Compare (7.3.7) and the remark following it.

Clearly, $P(N; X)$ in (7.2.9) or (7.2.10) could be *any* representation of the Lagrange Interpolation Polynomial using $X(J) = X(0) + J * H$, $J \in //0, N//$.


## 7.3 CONSTRUCTION OF INTERPOLATION POLYNOMIALS

The practicing numerical analyst, when presented a *new* problem stated in the jargon of the field in which the proposer works, usually works with the proposer to *restate* the problem as a system of mathematical equations (and/or inequalities) which characterize the solution of the original problem.

As exercises in the construction of functions from a set of characterizing properties we develop four representations of the Lagrange Interpolation Polynomial,[1] and we obtain a few other interpolation polynomials.

The Lagrange Interpolation Polynomial, $P(N; X)$, characterized by

(7.3.1)
$$X(K) = X(0) + K * H, K \in //0, N//, \quad H > 0$$
$$P(N; X(K)) = F(X(K)), K \in //0, N//,$$

may be written in the form

(7.3.2)     $P(N; X)$

$= A(0) + A(1) * (X - X(0))$

$+ A(2) * (X - X(0)) * (X - X(1)) + \cdots$

$+ A(N) * (X - X(0)) * (X - X(1)) * \cdots * (X - X(N - 1)),$

---

[1]See the Exercises at the end of this section for other representations of the Lagrange Interpolation Polynomial.

where the $N + 1$ coefficients $A(K)$ are to be determined so that the conditions (7.3.1) are satisfied. We usually write $F(K)$ for $F(X(K))$.

The choice of the *form* (7.3.2) is convenient for several reasons. The matrix of coefficients in the matrix equation corresponding to (7.2.3), obtained by requiring that the conditions (7.3.1) be satisfied for the form (7.3.2), is in lower-triangular form. The solution of the system (equivalent to a back-substitution in the Gauss Elimination Process) may be written

$$A(K) = \Delta ** (K)F(0)/(K! * H ** K), K \in //0, N//,$$

so that (7.3.2) becomes

(7.3.3)  $P(N; X) = F(0) + \Delta F(0) * (X - X(0))/H$
$+ \Delta ** (2)F(0) * (X - X(0)) * (X - X(1))/(2 * H ** 2)$
$+ \cdots + \Delta ** (N)F(0) * (X - X(0))$
$* (X - X(1)) * \cdots * (X - X(N - 1))/$
$(N! * H ** N).$

This form of the Lagrange Interpolation Polynomial is called *Newton's Forward Difference Formula* at $X(0)$. Also (7.3.3) is important because it has the property (7.2.9), which is often applied when the degree of the interpolation polynomial is increased by adding grid points $X(N + 1) = X(N) + H$, etc. The saving is particularly dramatic when we have available a table of forward differences of the function and we are evaluating the polynomial for a particular value of X.

Under the change of variable

$$S = (X - X(0))/H, \text{ or } X = X(0) + H * S,$$

Newton's Forward Difference Formula may be written in the more familar form

(7.3.4)  $P(N; X) = P(N; X(0) + H * S)$
$= F(0) + \Delta F(0) * S + \Delta ** (2)F(0) * S * (S - 1)/2!$
$+ \cdots + \Delta ** (N)F(0) * S * (S - 1)$
$* (S - 2) * \cdots * (S - N + 1)/N!$
$= F(0) + BINCO(S, 1) * \Delta F(0)$
$+ BINCO(S, 2) * \Delta ** (2)F(0) + \cdots$
$+ BINCO(S, N) * \Delta ** (N)F(0)$
$= \sum BINCO(S, K) * \Delta ** (K)F(0), K \in //0, N//.$

This representation of P(N; X) is particularly useful when X(−1) ≤ X ≤ X (1), so that −1 ≤ S ≤ 1; then the use of existing tables of the binomial coefficient function may simplify calculations on a desk computer. See §7.5, below.

Another important form for the Lagrange Interpolation Polynomial, P(N; X), characterized by (7.3.1) is

(7.3.5)    P(N; X)

= B(0) + B(1) ∗ (X − X(N))

+ B(2) ∗ (X − X(N)) ∗ (X − X(N − 1)) + ⋯

+ B(N) ∗ (X − X(N)) ∗ (X − X(N − 1)) ∗ ⋯ ∗ (X − X(1)).

The corresponding matrix of coefficients in (7.2.3) is *upper-triangular*, and solution of the system gives

B(K) = ∇ ∗∗ (K)F(N)/(K! ∗ H ∗∗ K), K ∈ //0, N//,

so that (7.3.5) becomes

(7.3.6)    P(N; X) = F(N) + ∇F(N) ∗ (X − X(N))/H

+ ∇ ∗∗ (2)F(N) ∗ (X − X(N))

∗ (X − X(N − 1))/(2 ∗ H ∗∗ 2) + ⋯

+ ∇ ∗∗ (N)F(N) ∗ (X − X(N)) ∗ (X − X(N − 1))

∗ ⋯ ∗ (X − X(1))/(N! ∗ H ∗∗ N).

This is *Newton's Backward Difference Formula* at X(N). Under the change of variable

S = (X − X(N))/H, or X = X(N) + H ∗ S,

(7.3.6) may be written

(7.3.7)    P(N; X) = P(N; X(N) + H ∗ S)

= F(N) + ∇F(N) ∗ S + ∇ ∗∗ (2)F(N) ∗ S ∗ (S − 1)/2!

+ ⋯ + ∇ ∗∗ (N)F(N) ∗ S ∗ (S − 1)

∗ ⋯ ∗ (S − N + 1)/N!

= Σ (−1) ∗∗ K ∗ BINCO(−S, K)

∗ ∇ ∗∗ (K)F(N), K ∈ //0, N//.

For $X(-1) \leq X \leq X(1)$, $-1 \leq S \leq 1$, so tables of BINCO(S, K) may be used. And, since (7.3.6) has the property (7.2.10), where

$$B(N + 1) = \nabla ** (N + 1)(F(N)/((N + 1)! * H ** (N + 1)),$$

[B(N + 1) involves F(−1) explicitly] then Newton's Backward Difference Formula is useful when we want to increase the degree of the Lagrange Interpolation Polynomial by introducting new grid points $X(-1) = X(0) - H$, etc.

In particular, Newton's Forward Difference Formula, (7.3.4), is usually used when we wish to interpolate values of F(X) near the *beginning* of a table, or to extend the table by extrapolation (backwards) from the first entry (X(0), F(0)). Also, Newton's Backward Difference Formula, (7.3.7), is used when we wish to interpolate values of F(X) near the *end* of a table, or to extend the table by extrapolation (forward) from the last entry (X(N), F(N)).

SUMMARY

The forms (7.3.2) and (7.3.5) were *chosen* because the associated linear system [that results when we apply the conditions (7.3.1)] is already in the form (4.4.4) that requires only back-substitution for its solution. The elements of the matrix of coefficients of this linear system are powers of H, and the elements of the column of constants are values of F(X) at the grid points. Thus it is clear that the coefficients A(K) and B(K) can be expressed as functions of H and differences of F(X). That they are such simple functions is pleasant.

The formulas (7.3.4) and (7.3.7) hold only for uniform grids, but the advantage of choosing the form (7.3.2) to simplify the problem of determining the coefficients A(K) did not depend on choosing a uniform grid—indeed, the grid points need *not* be ordered so that $X(0) < X(1) < \cdots < X(N)$. If we choose the form (7.3.2) and any N + 1 distinct points X(J), $J \in //0, N//$, and solve the (triangular) linear system that results when we apply the conditions (7.2.2) to P(N; X), we get

$$A(K) = [X(0), X(1), \cdots, X(K)]F,$$

and the Lagrange Interpolation Polynomial characterized by (7.2.2) can be written

(7.3.8)     $P(N; X) = F(0) + [X(0), X(1)]F * (X - X(0))$
$+ [X(0), X(1), X(2)]F * (X - X(0)) * (X - X(1)) + \cdots$
$+ [X(0), X(1), \cdots, X(N)]F * (X - X(0))$
$* (X - X(1)) * \cdots * (X - X(N - 1)).$

This is called *Newton's Fundamental Formula*, or *Newton's Divided Difference Formula*.

The remainder of this section consists of illustrations of a *general* method for *constructing polynomials* from a set of characterizing properties, like (7.2.2), which is essentially different from methods that require solution of linear systems or expansion of determinants, e. g., (7.2.3) or (7.2.4).

We have seen, (7.2.5) and (7.2.6), that the Lagrange Interpolation Polynomial can be written in the form

(7.3.9)     $P(N; X) = \sum F(X(K)) * LC(N, K; X), K \in //0, N//,$

where the Lagrange Coefficients, LC(N, K; X), are polynomials of degree N characterized by: for each $K \in //0, N//,$

(7.3.10)     $LC(N, K; X(J)) = 0$ for $J \in //0, N//,$ and $J \neq K,$
$LC(N, K; X(K)) = 1.$

We will *construct* the LC(N, K; X) using (7.3.10) and well-known elementary properties of polynomials.

Since LC(N, K; X) is a polynomial of degree N with zeros X(0), X(1), $\cdots, X(K - 1), X(K + 1), \cdots, X(N)$, then there exists a constant AK such that

$LC(N, K; X) = AK * (X - X(0)) * \cdots * (X - X(K - 1))$
$* (X - X(K + 1)) * \cdots * (X - X(N))$
$\equiv AK * PROD (X - X(J)), J \in //0, N//,$ and $J \neq K,$

and then, after applying the last condition of (7.3.10) to this form to determine AK,

(7.3.11)   $LC(N, K; X) = ((X - X(0)) * \cdots * (X - X(K - 1))$
$* (X - X(K + 1)) * \cdots * (X - X(N)))/$
$((X(K) - X(0)) * \cdots * (X(K) - X(K - 1))$
$* (X(K) - X(K + 1)) * \cdots * (X(K) - X(N)))$

(7.3.12) $\quad \equiv (\text{PROD}(X - X(J)), J \in //0, N//, \text{and } J \neq K, )/$
$\quad\quad (\text{PROD}(X(K) - X(J)), J \in //0, N //, \text{and } J \neq K,).$

This last form will be useful in §7.5.

Examination of the form (7.3.11) reveals the following three important properties of the Lagrange Coefficients: (i) the LC(N, K; X) depend only the variable point X and the grid X(J), J $\in //0, N//$; (ii) the LC(N, K; X) are dimensionless quantities, e.g., if the unit for X is inches, then (in.) ** N appears in the numerator and the denominator of (7.3.11), and they cancel; (iii) the form (7.3.11) is invariant under the change of variable

$$X = A + H * S,$$

for then

(7.3.13) $\quad$ LC(N, K; X) = PROD(S − S(J)), J $\in //0, N//$, and J $\neq$ K, /
$\quad\quad (\text{PROD}(S(K) − S(J)), J \in //0, N//, \text{and } J \neq K,).$

That is, the Lagrange Coefficients, LC(N, K; X), depend only on the *relative* positions of the points involved, and the *forms* (7.3.11) and (7.3.12) are invariant under a change of coordinate of the form X = A + H * S, i.e., under a translation and/or change of scale.

As a second illustration of this method for constructing polynomials from a set of characterizing properties, we consider the following problem: Find the polynomial P(N + 1; X) of degree N + 1, *or less*, characterized by

$\quad$ X(J), J $\in //0, N//$, are N + 1 distinct grid points

(7.3.14) $\quad$ P(N + 1; X(K)) = F(X(K)) $\equiv$ F(K), K $\in //0, N//$,

$\quad$ P'(N + 1; X(0)) = F'(X(0)) $\equiv$ F'(0).

We choose the form

(7.3.15) $\quad$ P(N + 1; X) = $\sum$ F(K) * A(K, X), K $\in //0, N//$,
$\quad\quad$ + F'(0) * B(0, X),

where the coefficients A(K, X), K $\in //0, N//$, and B(0, X) are polynomials of degree N + 1, *or less*, characterized by

(7.3.16a) $\quad$ A(K, X(J)) = 0, J $\in //0, N//$, and J $\neq$ K,

(7.3.16b) $\quad$ A(K, X(K)) = 1,

(7.3.16c)       $B(0, X(J)) = 0, J \in //0, N//,$

(7.3.16d)       $DER(A(K, X(0))) = 0, K \in //0, N//,$

(7.3.16e)       $DER(B(0, X(0))) = 1.$

By (7.3.16c) we must have

$$B(0, X) = B0 * (X - X(0)) * (X - X(1)) * \cdots * (X - X(N)),$$

and upon applying (7.3.16e) to this form to determine the constant B0 we get

(7.3.17)       $B(0, X) = (PROD(X - X(J)), J \in //0, N//,)/$
$$(PROD(X(0) - X(J)), J \in //1, N//,).$$

If $K \neq 0$, then by (7.3.16a) and (7.3.16d) we must have

$$
\begin{aligned}
A(K, X) &= AK * (X - X(0)) ** 2 * (X - X(1)) * \cdots \\
&\quad * (X - X(K - 1)) * (X - X(K + 1)) * \cdots \\
&\quad * (X - X(N)) \\
&= AK * (X - X(0)) \\
&\quad * (PROD(X - X(J)), J \in //0, N//, \text{ and } J \neq K,),
\end{aligned}
$$

and applying (7.3.16b) to this form to determine the constant AK we get

(7.3.18)       $A(K, X)$
$$= (X - X(0)) * (PROD(X - X(J)), J \in //0, N//, \text{ and } J \neq K,)/$$
$$((X(K) - X(0)) * (PROD(X(K) - X(J)), J \in //0, N//, \text{ and } J \neq K,)).$$

If $K = 0$, then (7.3.16a) and the assumption that $A(0, X)$ may be a polynomial of degree $N + 1$ imply

$$A(0, X) = A0 * (A * X + B) * (X - X(1)) * \cdots * (X - X(N)).$$

If we require that

(7.3.19)                $A * X(0) + B = 1,$

then (7.3.16b) determines A0 so that

(7.3.20)     $A(0, X) = (A * X + B) * (PROD(X - X(J)), J \in //1, N//,)/$
$(PROD(X(0) - X(J)), J \in //1, N//,).$

The condition (7.3.16d) with $K = 0$ applied to (7.3.20) gives

(7.3.21)     $A = - \sum (1/(X(0) - X(J))), J \in //1, N//,$

which with (7.3.19) determines (7.3.20) uniquely.

Thus the unique polynomial of degree $N + 1$, or less, characterized by (7.3.14), and represented in the form (7.3.15), has coefficients represented by (7.3.17), (7.3.18), and (7.3.20) where A and B in (7.3.20) are determined by (7.3.21) and (7.3.19).

This method for constructing polynomials can be used to obtain the *Hermite Polynomial*

(7.3.22a)     $P(2 * N + 1; X) = \sum F(K) * HH(K, X), K \in //0, N//,$
$+ \sum F'(K) * H(K, X), K \in //0, N//,$

which is a polynomial of degree $2 * N + 1$, *or less*, characterized by

$X(J), J \in //0, N//$, are $N + 1$ distinct grid points
(7.3.22b)     $P(2 * N + 1; X(K)) = F(X(K)) \equiv F(K), K \in //0, N//,$
$P'(2 * N + 1; X(K)) = F'(X(K)) \equiv F'(K), K \in //0, N//.$

The coefficients $HH(K, X), H(K, X), K \in //0, N//$, are polynomials of degree $2 * N + 1$, *or less*, characterized by: for each $K \in //0, N//$,

(7.3.23a)     $HH(K, X(J)) = 0, J \in //0, N//,$ and $J \neq K,$
(7.3.23b)     $HH(K, X(K)) = 1,$
(7.3.23c)     $H(K, X(J)) = 0, J \in //0, N//,$
(7.3.23d)     $HH'(K, X(J)) = 0, J \in //0, N//,$
(7.3.23e)     $H'(K, X(J)) = 0, J \in //0, N//,$ and $J \neq K,$
(7.3.23f)     $H'(K, X(K)) = 1.$

Parroting the analysis given above to determine the coefficients of the form (7.3.15) characterized by (7.3.16), we see: conditions (7.3.23c), (7.3.23e), and (7.3.23f) define

(7.3.24)     H(K, X)

$$= (X - X(K)) * (PROD(X - X(J)), J \in //0, N//, \text{ and } J \neq K,) ** 2/$$
$$\big(PROD(X(K) - X(J)), J \in //0, N//, \text{ and } J \neq K,\big) ** 2,$$

and conditions (7.3.23a), (7.3.23b), and (7.3.23d) define

(7.3.25)     HH(K, X)

$$= (AK * X + BK) * (PROD(X - X(J)), J \in //0, N//, \text{ and } J \neq K, ) ** 2/$$
$$\big(PROD(X(K) - X(J)), J \in //0, N//, \text{ and } J \neq K, \big) ** 2,$$

where

(7.3.26)
$$AK = -2 \sum 1/(X(K) - X(J)), J \in //0, N//, \text{ and } J \neq K,$$
$$BK = 1 - AK * X(K).$$

This method for constructing polynomials can be used for such forms as

(7.3.27a)     $P(9, X) = \sum F(K) * A(K, X), K \in //0, 4//,$
$$+ \sum F'(K) * B(K, X), K \in //0, 2//,$$
$$+ \sum F''(K) * C(K, X), K \in //1, 2//,$$

characterized by

(7.3.27b)
$$X(J), J \in //0, 4//, \text{ are distinct grid points}$$
$$P(9, X(K)) = F(K), K \in //0, 4//,$$
$$P'(9, X(K)) = F'(K), K \in //0, 2//,$$
$$P''(9, X(K)) = F''(K), K \in //1, 2//,$$

if terms involving $F(X(J))$ and $F'(X(J))$ are included when $F''(X(J))$ is involved in (7.3.27a). Similarly, forms involving higher derivatives may be used.
    In particular, the form

(7.3.28)     $P(2, X) = F(1) * A1(X) + F'(1) * B1(X) + F''(1) * C1(X),$

where it is required that

(7.3.29)
$$P(2, X(1)) = F(X(1)) \equiv F(1)$$
$$P'(2, X(1)) = F'(X(1)) \equiv F'(1)$$
$$P''(2, X(1)) = F''(X(1)) \equiv F''(1),$$

has coefficients characterized by

$$A1\,(X(1)) = 1, \quad A1'\,(X(1)) = 0, \quad A1''\,(X(1)) = 0$$
$$B1\,(X(1)) = 0, \quad B1'\,(X(1)) = 1, \quad B1''\,(X(1)) = 0$$
$$C1\,(X(1)) = 0, \quad C1'\,(X(1)) = 0, \quad C1''\,(X(1)) = 1,$$

which lead, by the above method, to the polynomials of degree 2, or less,

$$A1(X) \equiv 1, \; B1(X) = X - X(1), \; C1(X) = (X - X(1)) ** 2/2.$$

Thus (7.3.28) characterized by (7.3.29) is the *Taylor Polynomial* $P\,(2; X, X(1))$. Similarly, $P\,(N; X, X(1))$ could be derived by this method.

### EXERCISES

1.  (a) Write explicitly the linear system defined by (7.3.2) and (7.3.1) for N = 3.
    (b) Solve the system in (a) to obtain (7.3.3) for N = 3.

2.  (a) Write explicitly the linear system defined by (7.3.5) and (7.3.1) for N = 3.
    (b) Solve the system in (a) to obtain (7.3.6) for N = 3.

The following exercises are included to inform the student of the *existence* of these formulas of Gauss, Stirling, Bessel, and Everett. Since the formulas are rather complicated, and most of the difference operators we have considered are involved, we present these exercises in the usual mathematical subscript notation and suggest, as added exercises, that the student *rewrite them in the one-line notation* of this text.

3.  Given: $x_k = x_0 + kh$; if $n = 2m$, then

$$P_n(x) = P_{2m}(x) = a_0 + a_1(x - x_0) + a_2(x - x_0)(x - x_1)$$
$$+ a_3(x - x_0)(x - x_1)(x - x_{-1}) + a_4(x - x_0)(x - x_1)(x - x_{-1})$$
$$(x - x_2) + \cdots + a_{2m}(x - x_0)(x - x_1)(x - x_{-1}) \cdots (x - x_{m-1})$$
$$(x - x_{-m+1})(x - x_m);$$

and if $n = 2m + 1$, then

$$P_n(x) = P_{2m+1}(x) = P_{2m}(x) + a_{2m+1}(x - x_0)(x - x_1)(x - x_{-1}) \cdots$$
$$(x - x_m)(x - x_{-m}).$$

(a) Find $P_3(x)$ characterized by $P_3(x_k) = f(x_k), k = -1(1)2$. [$k = -1(1)2$ is read: $k$ equals $-1$ in steps of 1 up to 2.] We write $f_k$ for $f(x_k)$. Observe that $P_3(x)$ is the first four terms of *Gauss' Forward Formula* at $x_0$:

$$(7.3.30a) \qquad P_n(x) = f_0 + \frac{\delta f_{(1/2)}}{h}(x - x_0) + \frac{\delta^2 f_0}{2!\,h^2}(x - x_0)(x - x_1)$$

$$+ \frac{\delta^3 f_{(1/2)}}{3!\,h^3}(x - x_0)(x - x_1)(x - x_{-1})$$

$$+ \frac{\delta^4 f_0}{4!\,h^4}(x - x_0)(x - x_1)(x - x_{-1})(x - x_2) + \cdots$$

$$+ \frac{\delta^{2m} f_0}{(2m)!\,h^{2m}}(x - x_0)(x - x_1)(x - x_{-1})(x - x_2)$$

$$\underbrace{\cdots (x - x_{-m+1})(x - x_m)}_{\text{last term if } n = 2m}$$

$$+ \frac{\delta^{2m+1} f_{(1/2)}}{(2m + 1)!\,h^{2m+1}}(x - x_0)(x - x_1)(x - x_{-1})$$

$$\underbrace{\cdots (x - x_m)(x - x_{-m}),}_{\text{last term if } n = 2m + 1}$$

the Lagrange Interpolation Polynomial characterized by

$$P_n(x_k) = f(x_k), k = -m(1)m, \text{ for } n = 2m,$$

$$\text{and} \quad P_n(x_k) = f(x_k), k = -m(1)\overline{m + 1}, \text{ for } n = 2m + 1.$$

(b) Show with $x = x_0 + hs$, i.e., $s$ is positive in the direction of $x_1$, that (7.3.30a) can be written:

$$(7.3.30b) \qquad P_n(x) = f_0 + s \cdot \delta f_{(1/2)} + \frac{s(s - 1)}{2!}\delta^2 f_0 + \frac{s(s^2 - 1^2)}{3!}\delta^3 f_{(1/2)}$$

$$+ \frac{s(s^2 - 1^2)(s - 2)}{4!}\delta^4 f_0 + \cdots$$

$$+ \frac{s(s^2 - 1^2)\cdots(s^2 - (m - 1)^2)(s - m)}{(2m)!}\delta^{2m} f_0$$

$$\text{(and if } n = 2m + 1)$$

$$+ \frac{s(s^2 - 1^2)\cdots(s^2 - m^2)}{(2m + 1)!}\delta^{2m+1} f_{(1/2)},$$

$$= f_0 + \sum_{k=0}^{m-1}\left[\binom{s + k}{2k + 1}\delta^{2k+1} f_{(1/2)} + \binom{s + k}{2k + 2}\delta^{2k+2} f_0\right]$$

$$\text{(if } n = 2m + 1) + \binom{s + m}{2m + 1}\delta^{2m+1} f_{(1/2)}.$$

**4.** Given: $x_k = x_0 + kh$; if $n = 2m$, then

$$P_n(x) = P_{2m}(x)$$
$$= a_0 + a_1(x - x_0) + a_2(x - x_0)(x - x_{-1})$$
$$+ a_3(x - x_0)(x - x_{-1})(x - x_1)$$
$$+ a_4(x - x_0)(x - x_{-1})(x - x_1)(x - x_{-2}) + \cdots$$
$$+ a_{2m}(x - x_0)(x - x_{-1})(x - x_1) \cdots$$
$$(x - x_{-m+1})(x - x_{m-1})(x - x_{-m});$$

and if $n = 2m + 1$, then

$$P_n(x) = P_{2m}(x) + a_{2m+1}(x - x_0)(x - x_{-1})(x - x_1) \cdots (x - x_{-m})(x - x_m).$$

(a) Find $P_3(x)$ characterized by $P_3(x_k) = f(x_k), k = -2(1)1$. Observe that $P_3(x)$ is the first four terms of *Gauss' Backward Formula at* $x_0$:

$$(7.3.31a) \quad P_n(x) = f_0 + \frac{\delta f_{(-1/2)}}{h}(x - x_0) + \frac{\delta^2 f_0}{2!\, h^2}(x - x_0)(x - x_{-1})$$

$$+ \frac{\delta^3 f_{(-1/2)}}{3!\, h^3}(x - x_0)(x - x_{-1})(x - x_1)$$

$$+ \frac{\delta^4 f_0}{4!\, h^4}(x - x_0)(x - x_{-1})(x - x_1)(x - x_{-2}) + \cdots$$

$$+ \frac{\delta^{2m} f_0}{(2m)!\, h^{2m}}(x - x_0)(x - x_{-1})(x - x_1) \cdots$$

$$(x - x_{m-1})(x - x_{-m})$$

$$(\text{and if } n = 2m + 1) + \frac{\delta^{2m+1} f_{(-1/2)}}{(2m + 1)!\, h^{2m+1}}$$

$$(x - x_0)(x - x_{-1})(x - x_1) \cdots (x - x_{-m})(x - x_m),$$

the Lagrange Interpolation Polynomial characterized by

$$P_n(x_k) = f(x_k), k = -m(1)m, \text{ for } n = 2m$$
$$\text{and} \quad P_n(x_k) = f(x_k), k = \overline{-m-1}(1)m, \text{ for } n = 2m + 1.$$

(b) Show with $x = x_0 + hs$, i.e., $s$ is positive in the direction of $x_1$, that (7.3.31a) can be written:

$$(7.3.31b) \quad P_n(x) = f_0 + s \cdot \delta f_{(-1/2)} + \frac{s(s+1)}{2!} \delta^2 f_0$$

$$+ \frac{s(s^2 - 1^2)}{3!} \delta^3 f_{(-1/2)}$$

$$+ \frac{s(s^2 - 1^2)(s+2)}{4!} \delta^4 f_0 + \cdots$$

$$+ \frac{s(s^2 - 1^2) \cdots (s^2 - (m-1)^2)(s+m)}{(2m)!} \delta^{2m} f_0$$

(and if $n = 2m + 1$)

$$+ \frac{s(s^2 - 1^2) \cdots (s^2 - m^2)}{(2m+1)!} \delta^{2m+1} f_{(-1/2)}$$

$$= f_0 + \sum_{k=0}^{m-1} \left[ \binom{s+k}{2k+1} \delta^{2k+1} f_{(-1/2)} + \binom{s+k+1}{2k+2} \delta^{2k+2} f_0 \right]$$

(and if $n = 2m + 1$) $+ \binom{s+m}{2m+1} \delta^{2m+1} f_{(-1/2)}.$

**5.** Compute the arithmetic mean of (7.3.30b) and (7.3.31b) to obtain *Stirling's Formula at $x_0$* ($s$ is positive in the direction of $x_1$):

$$(7.3.32a) \quad P_n(x_0 + hs) = f_0 + \frac{s}{2}(\delta f_{(1/2)} + \delta f_{(-1/2)}) + \frac{s^2}{2!} \delta^2 f_0$$

$$+ \frac{s(s^2 - 1^2)}{2 \cdot 3!} (\delta^3 f_{(1/2)} + \delta^3 f_{(-1/2)})$$

$$+ \frac{s^2(s^2 - 1^2)}{4!} \delta^4 f_0 + \cdots$$

$$+ \frac{s^2(s^2 - 1^2) \cdots (s^2 - (m-1)^2)}{(2m)!} \delta^{2m} f_0$$

(and if $n = 2m + 1$)

$$+ \frac{s(s^2 - 1^2) \cdots (s^2 - m^2)}{2 \cdot (2m+1)!} (\delta^{2m+1} f_{(1/2)}$$

$$+ \delta^{2m+1} f_{(-1/2)}),$$

which for $n = 2m$ is the Lagrange Interpolation Polynomial characterized by $P_n(x_k) = f(x_k)$, $k = -m(1)m$, i.e., the same as the polynomials (7.3.30 b) and (7.3.31b). But, for $n = 2m + 1$, Stirling's Formula is a polynomial of degree $2m + 1$ with coefficients involving the $2m + 3$ values $f(x_k)$, $k = \overline{-m-1(1)m+1}$, so that it is in general *not* the Lagrange Interpolation Polynomial for any $2m + 2$ of the points $(x_k, f(x_k))$, $k = \overline{-m-1(1)m+1}$, even though it does satisfy $P_n(x_k) = f(x_k)$, $k = -m(1)m$.

*Note.* If we use $\mu\delta^k f_0 = \frac{1}{2} (\delta^k f_{(1/2)} + \delta^k f_{(-1/2)})$, then Stirling's Formula can be written: if $n = 2m$,

(7.3.32b) $\quad P_n(x_0 + hs)$

$$= f_0 + \sum_{k=0}^{m-1} \left[ \binom{s+k}{2k+1} \mu\delta^{2k+1} f_0 + \frac{s}{2k+2} \binom{s+k}{2k+1} \delta^{2k+2} f_0 \right]$$

$$(\text{and if } n = 2m+1) + \binom{s+m}{2m+1} \mu\delta^{2m+1} f_0.$$

Stirling's Formula is *frequently used* for interpolation in the interval $x_0 - \frac{1}{2}h < x < x_0 + \frac{1}{2}h$. The *Symmetry* (see the corresponding Lozenge Diagram in §7.6) that results when we average (7.3.30b) and (7.3.31b) is the factor that renders Stirling's Formula *preferred* to either of Gauss' Formulas.

6. For the same reasons that Stirling's Formula is desirable for interpolation near the grid point $x_0$, we desire a similar formula *symmetric relative to the midpoint of a sub interval*, say $(x_0 + x_1)/2 = x_{(1/2)}$. Here we compute the arithmetic mean of Gauss' Forward Formula at $x_0$ (7.3.30b) and Gauss' Backward Formula[1] at $x_1$ with $s$ measured from[2] $x_0$. The latter formula is

$$P_n(x_0 + hs) = f_1 + (s-1)\delta f_{(1/2)} + \frac{(s-1)s}{2!} \delta^2 f_1$$

$$+ \frac{(s-1)s(s-2)}{3!} \delta^3 f_{(1/2)}$$

$$+ \frac{(s-1)s(s-2)(s+1)}{4!} \delta^4 f_1$$

$$+ \frac{(s-1)s(s-2)(s+1)(s-3)}{5!} \delta^5 f_{(1/2)} + \cdots$$

$$+ \frac{s(s^2-1^2)\cdots(s^2-(m-1)^2)(s-m)}{(2m)!} \delta^{2m} f_1$$

$$(\text{and if } n = 2m+1)$$

$$+ \frac{s(s^2-1^2)\cdots(s^2-(m-1)^2)(s-m)(s-m-1)}{(2m+1)!} \delta^{2m+1} f_{(1/2)}$$

characterized by $P_n(x_k) = f(x_k)$, $x_k = x_0 + kh$, $k = -m(1)m$ for $n = 2m$, and $k = \overline{-m-1}(1)m$ for $n = 2m+1$. Compute the average of this polynomial and (7.3.30b) to obtain *Bessel's Formula at* $x_{(1/2)}$:

[1]In (7.3.31b) $\delta^{2k} f_0$ is replaced by $\delta^{2k} f_1$ and $\delta^{2k+1} f_{(-1/2)}$ is replaced by $\delta^{2k+1} f_{(1/2)}$ for each $k = 0(1)m$.
[2]In Gauss' Backward Formula at $x_1$ we replace $s$ by $s-1$.

(7.3.33a)    $P_n(x_0 + hs) = \mu f_{(1/2)} + (s - \frac{1}{2})\delta f_{(1/2)} + \dfrac{s(s-1)}{2!}\mu\delta^2 f_{(1/2)}$

$+ \dfrac{s(s-1)(s-\frac{1}{2})}{3!}\delta^3 f_{(1/2)} + \cdots$

$+ \dfrac{s(s^2-1^2)\cdots(s^2-(m-1)^2)(s-m)}{(2m)!}\mu\delta^{2m} f_{(1/2)}$

(and if $n = 2m + 1$)

$+ \dfrac{s(s^2-1^2)\cdots(s^2-(m-1)^2)(s-m)(s-\frac{1}{2})}{(2m+1)!}\delta^{2m+1} f_{(1/2)}$

which for $n = 2m + 1$ is the Lagrange Interpolation Polynomial characterized by $P_n(x_k) = f(x_k)$, $x_k = x_0 + kh$, $k = -m(1)\overline{m+1}$. If $n = 2m$, then $P_n(x_k) = f(x_k)$, $x_k = x_0 + kh$, $k = \overline{-m+1}(1)m$, but the $(2m+1)th$ condition needed to characterize $P_n(x)$ is in general *neither* $P_n(x_{-m}) = f(x_{-m})$ *nor* $P_n(x_{m+1}) = f(x_{m+1})$, even though Bessel's Formula at $x_{(1/2)}$ involves both $f(x_{-m})$ and $f(x_{m+1})$ explicitly. Thus Bessel's Formula for $n = 2m$ is *not* the Lagrange Interpolation Polynomial for any $2m + 1$ of the $2m + 2$ points used in its definition.

*Note.* Bessel's Formula at $x_{(1/2)}$ is particularly useful when *subtabulation* in a table is required (set $s = \frac{1}{2}$). Bessel's Formula at $x_{(1/2)}$ has a form similar to (7.3.32b), namely:

(7.3.33b)    $P_n(x_0 + hs) = \mu f_{(1/2)} + (s - \frac{1}{2})\delta f_{(1/2)}$

$+ \sum_{k=1}^{m-1}\left\{\binom{s+k-1}{2k}\left[\mu\delta^{2k} f_{(1/2)} + \dfrac{s-\frac{1}{2}}{2k+1}\delta^{2k+1} f_{(1/2)}\right]\right\}$

$+ \binom{s+m-1}{2m}\mu\delta^{2m} f_{(1/2)}$

(and if $n = 2m + 1$)

$+ \dfrac{s-\frac{1}{2}}{2m+1}\binom{s+m-1}{2m}\delta^{2m+1} f_{(1/2)}.$

**7.** (a) In Gauss' Forward Formula at $x_0$ terminated with an odd difference ($n = 2m + 1$), replace the odd differences with

$$\delta^{2k+1} f_{(1/2)} = \delta^{2k} f_1 - \delta^{2k} f_0$$

to obtain *Everett's first formula at* $x_0$:

$$(7.3.34) \qquad P_n(x_0 + hs) = (1 - s)f_0 + \sum_{k=1}^{m} \binom{(1-s)+k}{2k+1} \delta^{2k} f_0$$

$$+ sf_1 + \sum_{k=1}^{m} \binom{s+k}{2k+1} \delta^{2k} f_1,$$

which is another representation (using *only even* differences), of the Lagrange Interpolation Polynomial characterized by $P_n(x_k) = f(x_k)$, $k = -m$ $(1)\overline{m+1}$.

(b) In Gauss' Forward Formula at $x_0$ terminated with an even difference $(n = 2m)$, replace the even differences with

$$\delta^{2k} f_0 = \delta^{2k-1} f_{(1/2)} - \delta^{2k-1} f_{(-1/2)}$$

to obtain *Everett's second Formula* at $x_0$:

$$(7.3.35) \qquad P_n(x_0 + hs) = f_0 + \sum_{k=1}^{m} \binom{s+k}{2k} \delta^{2k-1} f_{(1/2)}$$

$$- \sum_{k=1}^{m} \binom{-s+k}{2k} \delta^{2k-1} f_{(-1/2)},$$

which is another representation (using *only odd* differences) of the Lagrange Interpolation Polynomial characterized by $P_n(x_k) = f(x_k)$, $k = -m(1)m$. Since odd differences are seldom furnished with tables of functions, Everett's Second Formula is the least popular of the two formulas.

## 7.4. TRUNCATION ERROR IN POLYNOMIAL INTERPOLATION

In this section we will derive and discuss two representations, (7.4.4) and (7.4.12), of the truncation error for the estimation of F(X) on [A, B] by (any representation of) the Lagrange Interpolation Polynomial for any $N + 1$ distinct points in [A, B]. A few remarks are offered concerning the effect *choice of grid*, $X(J)$, $J \in //0, N//$, has on truncation error. Then, for equally spaced grid points, we list a representation of truncation error with a formula for *estimating* it for certain polynomials considered in §7.3. The method used to get (7.4.12) leads to a representation of truncation error for the Hermite Polynomial.

*Note.* This method is analogous to the usual method used to derive the Lagrange form of R(N; X, C) for Taylor Polynomial estimates to F(X) near X=C.

Let F(X) be a real function, defined and with a continuous (N + 1)*th* derivative on [A, B]. Let X(J), J ∈ //0, N//, be N + 1 *distinct* points in [A, B], and let P(N; X) be the Lagrange Interpolation Polynomial estimate to F(X) characterized by

(7.4.1)        $P(N; X(K)) = F(X(K)) \equiv F(K), K \in //0, N//.$

The truncation error of this estimate is

(7.4.2)                    $E(N; X) = F(X) - P(N; X)$

which satisfies the conditions [E(N; X) is zero at the grid points.]

(7.4.3)                    $E(N; X(K)) = 0, K \in //0, N//,$

and has the continuity properties of F(X) on [A, B].

One important representation of E(N; X) in (7.4.2) involves the (N + 1)*th* divided difference of F(X) at the N + 2 distinct points X(J), J ∈ //0, N//, and X, all in [A, B]. Specifically,

(7.4.4)      $E(N; X) = PROD(X - X(J)), J \in //0, N//,$
             $* [X(0), X(1), \cdots, X(N), X]F,$
             $\text{for } X \neq X(K), K \in //0, N//,$
             $= 0, \text{ for } X = X(K), K \in //0, N//, \text{ by (7.4.3).}$

This is clear. For, if X(J), J ∈ //0, N//, and X are distinct points in [A, B], then the definition of divided difference gives

(7.4.5)                    $F(X) = F(X(0)) + (X - X(0)) * [X(0), X]F$
                           $[X(0), X]F = [X(0), X(1)]F$
                           $+ (X - X(1)) * [X(0), X(1), X]F$
                $[X(0), X(1), X]F = [X(0), X(1), X(2)]F$
                           $+ (X - X(2)) * [X(0), X(1), X(2), X]F$

(7.4.5)                                    $\vdots$

$$[X(0), \cdots, X(N-2), X]F = [X(0), \cdots, X(N-1)]F$$
$$+ (X - X(N-1))$$
$$* [X(0), \cdots, X(N-1), X]F$$
$$[X(0), \cdots, X(N-1), X]F = [X(0), \cdots, X(N)]F$$
$$+ (X - X(N)) * [X(0), \cdots, X(N), X]F.$$

And, when $[X(0), \cdots, X(N-1), X]F$ is eliminated from the N*th* equation of (7.4.5) by substituting its value given in the $(N+1)th$ (last)equation of (7.4.5) and $[X(0), \cdots, X(N-2), X]F$ is eliminated from the $(N-1)th$ equation by substituting its value given by the new N*th* equation, etc, until $[X(0), X]F$ is eliminated from the first equation using the new second equation, we get [using (7.3.8)]

$$(7.4.6) \quad F(X) = F(X(0)) + (X - X(0)) * [X(0), X(1)]F$$
$$+ (X - X(0)) * (X - X(1)) * [X(0), X(1), X(2)]F + \cdots$$
$$+ (X - X(0)) * \cdots * (X - X(N-1))$$
$$* [X(0), X(1), \cdots, X(N)]F$$
$$+ (X - X(0)) * \cdots * (X - X(N))$$
$$* [X(0), \cdots, X(N), X]F$$
$$= P(N; X) + (PROD(X - X(J)), J \in //0, N//,)$$
$$* [X(0), \cdots, X(N), X]F$$
$$= P(N; X) + E(N; X).$$

The induction on N is clear.

Now we discuss in some detail this representation of truncation error for linear interpolation $(N = 1)$.[1]

$$F(X) = F(X(0)) + (X - X(0)) * [X(0), X(1)]F + E(1; X),$$

where

$$E(1; X) = (X - X(0)) * (X - X(1)) * [X(0), X(1), X]F.$$

---

[1]The student should consider the applicability of similar remarks for cases with N $>1$. An enlightening discussion of *absolute error* for linear interpolation is given in [2a].

First, observe for XX in [A, B] and XX $\neq$ X(0) and XX $\neq$ X(1), then

(7.4.7)     $[X(0), X(1), XX]F = \big((F(XX) - F(X(0)))/(XX - X(0))$
$- (F(X(1)) - F(X(0)))/(X(1) - X(0))\big)/$
$(XX - X(1)).$

Thus we cannot compute $[X(0), X(1), XX]F$ unless we know the value of $F(X)$ at XX, the point at which we are using $P(1; X)$ to estimate $F(X)$. However, if $[X(0), X(1), X]F$ does not change much as X varies over [A, B], and if we know $F(T)$ for some T in [A, B] with $T \neq X(0)$ and $T \neq X(1)$, then *one* estimate of $E(1; X)$ is

$$E(1; X) \doteq (X - X(0)) * (X - X(1)) * [X(0), X(1), T]F.$$

In the spirit of (2.2.3), we could *seek* bounds on $[X(0), X(1), X]F$, such as

(7.4.8a)          $M1 = MAX|[X(0), X(1), X]F|$, over $X \in [A, B]$,
$= $ constant,

or

(7.4.8b)     $M2 = G(X) \geq |[X(0, X(1), X]F|$, but $G(X) \leq M1$ on [A, B],

so that we may write

(7.4.9)     $|E(1; X)| \leq |(X - X(0)) * (X - X(1)) * M2|$
$\leq |(X - X(0)) * (X - X(1)) * M1|$, for X in [A, B].

*Note.* One should *not* jump to the conclusion that if $P(X) \geq F(X)$, then

(7.4.8c)     $GG(X) = ABS\big(((P(X) - F(X(0)))/(X - X(0))$
$- (F(X(1)) - F(X(0)))/(X(1) - X(0))\big)$
$/(X - X(1))\big)$
$\geq [X(0), X(1), X]F.$

The following example demonstrates that (7.4.8c) may *not* hold.

**Example 1.** Let $F(X) = COS(X)$, $[A, B] = [0, \pi/2]$, $X(0) = \pi/4, X(1) = \pi/3, T = \pi/6$, and let $P(X)$ be any convenient upper bound for $F(X)$ with $P(T) = SQRT(3)/2$

$+$ E for small E $>$ 0, say E $=$ 10 $**$ ($-5$). Then

$$[X(0), X(1), T]F = (2 * F(T) - 2 * SQRT(2) + 1) * (6/\pi) ** 2$$
$$= (SQRT(3) - 2 * SQRT(2) + 1) * (6/\pi) ** 2 < 0.$$

But

$$GG(T) = |(SQRT(3) + 2 * E - 2 * SQRT(2) + 1) * (6/\pi) ** 2|$$
$$< |[X(0), X(1), T]F|.$$

Yet, if F(X) $=$ SIN(X), [A, B] $=$ [0, $\pi/2$], X(0) $=$ $\pi/4$, X(1) $=$ $\pi/3$, and P(X) $\geq$ F(X) on [A, B], then GG(X) $\geq$ |[X(0), X(1), X]F| for X(0) $<$ X $<$ X(1). It is significant that SIN(X) is positive, increasing, and concave-down throughout the interval $(X(0), X(1))$. *In general*, if F(X) is positive, increasing, and concave-down on X(0) $<$ X $<$ X(1), then the slope of the secant through $(X(0), F(X(0)))$ and $(X, F(X))$ is greater than the slope of the secant through $(X(0), F(X(0)))$ and $(X(1), F(X(1)))$. Thus the numerator of [X(0), X(1), X]F, (7.4.7), is increased when we replace F(X) by P(X) [$\geq$ F(X)], and then

$$GG(X) \geq |[X(0), X(1), X]F|, \text{ for } X(0) < X < X(1).$$

Similar remarks apply when F(X) is negative, decreasing, and concave-up on X(0) $<$ X $<$ X(1), and in GG(X) we have P(X) $\leq$ F(X). The student should attempt to find other situations where (7.4.8c) holds.

Another important representation of E(N; X), (7.4.2), involves the (N $+$ 1)*th* derivative of F(X) at a mysterious point Z—compare (2.2.2b). Let I(N) be the smallest (closed) interval that contains the N $+$ 2 distinct points X(J), J $\in$ //0, N//, and X, all in [A, B]. Then

(7.4.10)     E(N; X) $=$ PROD (X $-$ X(J)), J $\in$ //0, N//,

            $*$ DER $**$ (N $+$ 1)F(Z)/(N $+$ 1) !,

            for some Z $=$ Z(X) in I(N),

            $=$ 0, for X $=$ X(J), J $\in$ //0, N//, by (7.4.3).

The proof of (7.4.10) goes much like the usual proof of Taylor's Formula with the Lagrange Form of the remainder: (i) invent a function, (ii) show that this function has properties that are the hypotheses of a well-known theorem, and (iii) apply the theorem to the function to obtain the desired result. Specifically, define

$$FF(X) = F(X) - P(N; X) - PROD (X - X(J)), J \in //0, N//, * K1,$$

where K1 is to be determined. Choose T any point in [A, B] where T is *not* one of the points X(J), J $\in$ //0, N//, and let I(N) be the smallest interval containing these N + 2 distinct points. For each choice of T, define a corresponding constant K1 = K1(T) in FF(X) by

(7.4.11)

$$FF(T) = F(T) - P(N; T) - PROD(T - X(J)), \; J \in //0, N//, * K1 = 0.$$

We obtain the desired form for K1(T) by applying Rolle's Theorem to FF(X), FF'(X), FF''(X), $\cdots$, DER $**$ (N + 1)FF(X). Since FF(X) vanishes at least N + 2 times in I(N), then FF'(X) vanishes at least N + 1 times[2] in I(N), so FF''(X) vanishes at least N times in I(N), etc., so

$$DER ** (N + 1)FF(X) = DER ** (N + 1)F(X) - (N + 1) ! * K1$$

vanishes at least once in I(N). Call one of these points Z = Z(T). Then

$$K1 = K1(T) = DER ** (N + 1)F(Z(T))/(N + 1)!.$$

We replace T by X, remembering that X is not one of the grid points and that Z depends on the choice of X; then (7.4.11) can be written

$$F(X) - P(N; X) = PROD(X - X(J)), J \in //0, N//,$$
$$* DER ** (N + 1)F(Z)/(N + 1)!$$

and the representation (7.4.10) is established for X not a grid point. The choice Z(X(K)) = X(K) in the *form* (7.4.10) gives E(N; X(K)) = 0 for K $\in$ //0, N//.

Thus, for each X in [A, B], we have

(7.4.12)     $E(N; X) = (X - X(0)) * (X - X(1)) * \cdots * (X - X(N))$
$$* DER ** (N + 1)F(Z)/(N + 1)!$$
$$= POLP(X) * DER ** (N + 1)F(Z)/(N + 1)!$$
for some Z in I(N),

where I(N) is the smallest closed interval containing the distinct points X and X(J), J $\in$ //0, N//, all in [A, B]. The *polynomial part* of E(N; X) is *named* POLP(X).

[2]At points *intermediate* to adjacent elements of X(0), X(1), ..., X(N), T.

*Note.* We use the notation $Z = Z(X)$, but this "mysterious" $Z$ also depends on the choice of F and the grid $X(J)$, $J \in //0, N//$. Generally, discussions of "choice of grid" versus "quality of the estimate" $F(X) \doteq P(N; X)$ are limited to a study of local maxima of $|POLP(X)|$ for various grids.

Sometimes we know enough about DER $** (N + 1)F(X)/(N + 1)$ ! to replace it with a bound $G(X)$, or a constant M1, so that we may write

(7.4.13)        $|E(N; X)| \leq |POLP(X) * G(X)|$

              or $\leq |POLP(X) * M1|$, for each X in [A, B].

Clearly, if $F(X)$ is any polynomial of degree $M \leq N$, then $M1 = 0$.

**Example 2.** For $F(X) = EXP(X), [A, B] = [-1, 1]$, and $X(J) = -1 + J * 2/9$, $J \in //0, 9//$, we have

        $MAX|EXP(Z)/10!|$, over $Z \in [-1, 1]$, $=EXP(1)/10!$, and

        $MIN|EXP(Z)/10!|$, over $Z \in [-1, 1]$, $=EXP(-1)/10!$,

so that[3] [using (7.4.12)], for each X in $[-1, 1]$,

        $|POLP(X)| * EXP(-1)/10! \leq |E(9: X)| \leq |POLP(X)| * EXP(1)/10!$,

where the polynomial part of $E(9; X)$ is

$POLP(X) = \big(X - (-1)\big) * \big(X - (-7/9)\big) * \big(X-(-5/9)\big) * \cdots$
$\qquad * \big(X - (7/9)\big) * \big(X - (1)\big)$
$\qquad = (X ** 2 - 1/81) * (X ** 2 - 9/81) * (X ** 2 - 25/81)$
$\qquad * (X ** 2 - 49/81) * (X ** 2 - 1).$

A sketch of POLP (X) is given in Figure 7.4.1. Here,

    $MAX|POLP(X)|$, over $X \in [-1, 1]$, $= MAX|POLP(X)|$, over $X \in [7/9, 1]$,
                    $\doteq |POLP(.935)| \doteq .0126$,

while the *smallest local* maximum of $|POLP(X)|$ is

    $MAX|POLP(X)|$, over $X \in [-1/9, 1/9]$, $=|POLP(0)| \doteq .000256$.

---

[3]In this case we are able to find a *lower bound* on the truncation error. Of course if DER $** (N + 1)$ $F(X)$ is zero *anywhere* in (A, B), then the lower bound obtained in this way is zero.

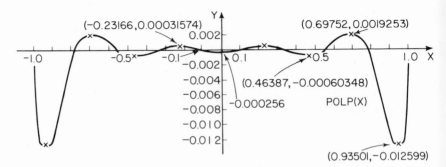

**Figure 7.4.1**

Remarks. (i) Whenever X is *very near* a grid point, then E(9: X) is small. (ii) If X *must* be chosen near the midpoint of some subinterval and if we *may choose* the subinterval that is to contain X, then the *best* choice is a subinterval nearest the midpoint of $[-1, 1]$[4].

It is clear that the choice of grid X(J), J $\in$ //0, N//, determines the location and magnitude of local maxima and minima of POLP(X).

**Example 3.** Suppose X(0), X(1), X(2), and X(3) are bunched together and X(4) is widely separated from the other four grid points. Figure 7.4.2. contains part of POLP (X) for such grid points. Notice that the local minimum between X(3) and X(4) does not occur at the midpoint of the interval. Why?

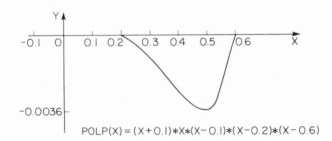

POLP(X) = (X + 0.1)*X*(X − 0.1)*(X − 0.2)*(X − 0.6)

**Figure 7.4.2**

The question naturally arises: Is there a choice for the grid X(J), J $\in$ //0, N//, that is *best* in the sense that the maximum of POLP(X) is as small as possible on a specified interval containing the grid? Also, what is the best choice?

If the interval [A, B] on which the interpolation polynomial is to be evaluated is $[-1, 1]$,[5] then the answer to the first question is YES, and the second question is answered by choosing (the *Chebyshev Abscissas*)

---

[4]This choice minimizes the largest of the factors X − X(K) in (7.4.12).
[5]If [A, B] is not $[-1, 1]$, then with the change of variable X = T * (B − A)/2 + (B + A)/2, F(X) on [A, B] becomes F$\big($X(T)$\big)$ on $[-1, 1]$.

(7.4.14)     $X(K) = COS((2 * K + 1) * \pi/(2 * N + 2)), K \in //0, N//.$

These are the zeros of $T(N + 1; X)$, the Chebyshev Polynomial of degree $N + 1$, where (see §8.4, Example 4)

$$T(0; X) \equiv 1$$
$$T(1; X) = X$$
$$T(2; X) = 2 * X ** 2 - 1$$
$$T(3; X) = 4 * X ** 3 - 3 * X$$
$$\vdots$$
$$T(N; X) = 2 * X * T(N - 1; X) - T(N - 2; X).$$

With $X(J), J \in //0, N//$, defined by (7.4.14), then

(7.4.15)     $T(N + 1; X) = PROD(X - X(J)), J \in //0, N//, * 2 ** N$
$$= POLP(X) * 2 ** N$$

is such that $|T(N + 1; X)| \leq 1$ on $[-1, 1]$ and $|T(N + 1; X)|$ takes the value *unity* at

$$X = COS(M * \pi/(N + 1)), M \in //0, N + 1//.$$

In view of (7.4.15), we may write (7.4.12) *with the Chebyshev Abscissas* in the form

(7.4.16)     $E(N; X) = T(N + 1; X) * 2 ** (-N)$
$$* DER ** (N + 1)F(Z)/(N + 1)!.$$

**Example 4.** For

$$F(X) = EXP(X), \quad [A, B] = [-1, 1],$$
$$X(K) = COS((2 * K + 1) * \pi/(2 * 10)), K \in //, 0, 9//,$$

the Chebyshev Abscissas, and

$$M1 = MAX(EXP(X)/10!), \text{ over } X \in [-1, 1], = EXP(1)/10!$$

we have [using (7.4.16)]

$$|E(9; X)| \leq |T(10; X) * 2 ** (-9) * EXP(1)/10!|, \text{ for each } X \text{ in } [-1, 1].$$

A sketch of

$$T(10;X) * 2 ** (-9) = (512 * X ** 10 - 128 * X ** 8 + 1120 * X ** 6$$
$$- 400 * X ** 4 + 50 * X ** 2 - 1)/512$$

is given in Figure 7.4.3.

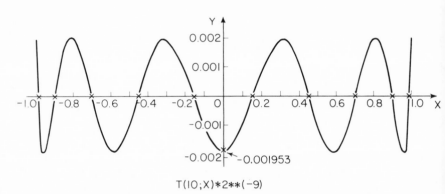

$$T(10;X)*2**(-9)$$

**Figure 7.4.3**

The local maxima of $|T(10;X) * 2 ** (-9)|$ on $[-1, 1]$ are *all* equal to $2 ** (-9) \doteq$ .00195. In Example 2, the maximum of $|POLP(X)|$ on $[-1/9, 1/9]$ is .000256 $< 2$ $** (-9)$, but the maximum of $|POLP(X)|$ on $[7/9, 1]$ is .0126 $> 2 ** (-9)$.

SUMMARY

1. If one is *free* to choose the grid points X(J), J $\in$ //0, N//, anywhere in $[-1, 1]$, and if it is decided to use P(N; X) as an estimate to F(X) at points in $[-1, 1]$, to be determined *after* specifying the grid, then generally the *best* choice for grid points are the *Chebyshev Abscissas*: zeros of T(N + 1; X). This choice does *not necessarily* imply that the largest local maximum of $|E(N; X)|$ is minimized, since $|DER ** (N + 1)F(Z(X))|$ *may not* assume its local maxima where POLP(X) does. A similar reservation is implicit in any recommendation pertaining to a choice of grid and/or estimating function given below.

2. If one is free to choose only equally spaced grid points, and it is decided to use P(N; X) as an estimate to F(X) *near one grid point* [call it X(0)]. then grid points should be chosen on both sides of X(0), and something like Stirling's Formula, (7.3.32), is recommended.

3. If one is free to choose only equally spaced grid points, and it is decided to use $P(N; X)$ as an estimate to $F(X)$ *between two consecutive grid points* [call them $X(0)$ and $X(1)$, where $X(0) < X(1)$], then grid points should be chosen to the left of $X(0)$ and to the right of $X(1)$, and something like Bessel's Formula, (7.3.33), is recommended.

From (7.4.4) and (7.4.12) we have, for $X \neq X(J)$, $J \in //0, N//$,

$$(7.4.17) \quad [X(0), \ldots, X(N), X]F = DER ** (N + 1)F(Z)/(N + 1)!$$

for some $Z$ in $I(N)$.

Suppose that interpolation in a table of $F(X)$ is required, and we have decided to use the Lagrange Interpolation Polynomial $P(N; X)$ characterized by (7.3.1). If we do not know $F(X)$ or $DER ** (N + 1)F(X)$ well enough to obtain bounds on $E(N; X)$ like (7.4.9) or (7.4.13), we sometimes use the *estimate*

$$(7.4.18) \qquad E(N; X) \doteq POLP(X) * [X(0), \ldots, X(N), T]F,$$

where $F(T)$ is in the table, say $T = X(N + 1)$, or $T = X(-1)$.

In general, if $P(N; X)$ is any representation of the Lagrange Interpolation Polynomial characterized by ($H > 0$, and $Q$, $I1$, and $I2$ are integers, with $N = I2 - I1 \geq 0$)

$$(7.4.19) \quad \begin{aligned} P(N; X(Q + K)) &= F(X(Q + K)), \\ X(Q + K) &= X(Q) + H * K, K \in //I1, I2//, \end{aligned}$$

then[6]

$$(7.4.20a) \qquad \begin{aligned} E(N; X) &= PROD(X - X(Q + K)), K \in //I1, I2//, \\ &* DER ** (N + 1)F(Z)/(N + 1)!. \end{aligned}$$

With $X(S) = X(Q) + H * S$ we may write

$$(7.4.20b) \qquad \begin{aligned} E(N; X(S)) &= H ** (N + 1) * PROD(S - K), K \in //I1, I2//, \\ &* DER ** (N + 1)F(Z)/(N + 1)!, \end{aligned}$$

and estimates corresponding to (7.4.18) are

---

[6](7.4.20a) holds even if the $X(Q + K)$, $K \in //I1, I2//$, are not equally spaced.

(7.4.20c)     $E(N; X(S)) \doteq H ** (N + 1) * PROD(S - K), K \in //I1, I2//,$

$* [X(I1), \ldots, X(I2), X(I2 + 1)]F$

(7.4.20d)              $or \doteq H ** (N + 1) * PROD(S - K), K \in //I1, I2//,$

$* [X(I1 - 1), X(I1), \ldots, X(I2)]F.$

The following relations allow us to write the estimates (7.4.20c, d) in other forms—a choice is usually made dependent on the availability of tables of differences of the function F(X).

(7.4.21a)     $[X(0), X(1), \ldots, X(N + 1)]F$

$= \Delta ** (N + 1)F(0)/(H ** (N + 1) * (N + 1)!)$

(7.4.21b)     $[X(-1), X(0), \ldots, X(N)]F$

$= \nabla ** (N + 1)F(N)/(H ** (N + 1) * (N + 1)!)$

(7.4.21c)     $[X(Q - M), \ldots, X(Q), \ldots, X(Q + M + 1)]F$

$= \delta ** (2 * M + 1)F(Q + .5)/(H ** (2 * M + 1)$

$* (2 * M + 1)!)$

(7.4.21d)     $[X(Q - M - 1), \ldots, X(Q), \ldots, X(Q + M + 1)]F$

$= \delta ** (2 * M + 2)F(Q)/(H ** (2 * M + 2) * (2 * M + 2)!)$

(7.4.21e)     $[X(Q - M - 1), \ldots, X(Q), \ldots, X(Q + M)]F$

$= \delta ** (2 * M + 1)F(Q - .5)/(H ** (2 * M + 1)$

$* (2 * M + 1)!).$

For example, for *Newton's Forward Difference Formula* (7.3.4), we set Q = 0, I1 = 0, and I2 = N in equations (7.4.19) and (7.4.20a, b, c) and get [using (7.4.21a)] for some Z in I(N),

(7.4.22)     $E(N; X(S)) = H ** (N + 1) * PROD(S - K), K \in //0, N//,$

$* DER ** (N + 1)F(Z)/(N + 1)!$

$\doteq PROD(S - K), K \in //0, N//,$

$* \Delta ** (N + 1)F(0)/(N + 1)!.$

**Exercise 1**. Define estimates for *Newton's Backward Difference Formula* (7.3.7). *Hint*. Use (7.4.21b).

**Exercise 2**. Define estimates for the formulas considered in the Exercises 3 through 7 of §7.3.

Finally, for the estimation of F(X) on [A, B] by the *Hermite Polynomial* $P(2 * N + 1; X)$, (7.3.22a), characterized by (7.3.22b), the truncation error may be written [I(N) is the smallest interval containing the distinct points X(J), $J \in //0, N//$, and X] for some $Z = Z(X)$ in I(N),

$$(7.4.23) \quad E(2 * N + 1; X) = (POLP(X)) ** 2$$
$$* DER ** (2 * N + 2) F(Z)/(2 * N + 2)!.$$

Notice that the $(2 * N + 2)th$ derivative factor insures that $E(2 * N + 1; X) \equiv 0$ if F(X) is *any* polynomial of degree $M \leq 2 * N + 1$. The proof of (7.4.23) is entirely analogous to that for (7.4.12). In particular, define

$$FF(X) = F(X) - P(2 * N + 1; X) - ((X - X(0)) * \cdots$$
$$* (X - X(N))) ** 2 * K1,$$

where constant $K1 = K1(T)$ is such that $FF(T) = 0$. Rolle's Theorem applied to FF(X) implies that $FF'(X) = 0$ at $N + 1$ points *intermediate* to the points $X(J), J \in //0, N//$, and T. But FF'(X) also vanishes at $X(J), J \in //0, N//$. Thus FF'(X) vanishes at $2 * N + 2$ distinct points in I(N), and FF''(X) vanishes at $2 * N + 1$ distinct points, etc., so

$$DER ** (2 * N + 2)FF(X) = DER ** (2 * N + 2)F(X) - (2 * N + 2)! * K1$$

vanishes at at least one point in I(N), call it $Z = Z(T)$. Thus

$$K1 = K1(T) = DER ** (2 * N + 2)F(Z(T))/(2 * N + 2)!,$$

and (7.4.23) is established.

**Exercise 3.** Use this method of proof to establish the representation, (7.4.24c). The truncation error for the estimation of F(X) on [A, B] by the polynomial $[M \leq N + 1$, and the A(K, X) and B(K, X) are polynomials of degree K or less—not required for this problem. Compare (7.3.22) and (7.3.27).]

$$(7.4.24a) \quad P(N + M; X) = \sum F(X(K)) * A(K, X), K \in //0, N//,$$
$$+ \sum F'(X(K)) * B(K, X), K \in //0, M - 1//,$$

of degree $N + M$ or less, characterized by[7]

---

[7]We could have chosen any M of the X(K) and obtained a representation like (7.4.24c) with the appropriate $(X - X(K)) ** 2$.

$X(J), J \in //0, N//$, are distinct points in $[A, B]$

(7.4.24b) $\quad P(N + M; X(K)) = F(X(K)), K \in //0, N//,$

$\quad P'(N + M; X(K)) = F'(X(K)), K \in //0, M - 1//,$

is, for some Z in I(N)

(7.4.24c) $\quad E(N + M; X) = ((X - X(0)) * \cdots * (X - X(M - 1))) ** 2$

$\quad * (X - X(M)) * \cdots * (X - X(N))$

$\quad * DER ** (N + M + 1)F(Z)/(N + M + 1)!.$

A discussion of bounds for (7.4.23) or (7.4.24c) would parallel the above discussion of bounds for (7.4.12): see (7.4.13), (7.4.18), and (7.4.8).

If one used the data of Example 2 [below (7.4.13)] and the corresponding Hermite Polynomial, P(19; X), to estimate EXP(X) on $[-1, 1]$, then E(19; X), (7.4.23) with N = 9, would have the factor $(POLP(X)) ** 2$ where POLP(X) is sketched in Figure 7.4.1. We are not surprised if P(19; X) gives a better estimate to EXP(X) on $[-1, 1]$ than does the Lagrange Interpolation Polynomial P(9; X). For both polynomials represent *educated* guesses at EXP(X), but P(19; X) is a polynomial of degree 19 while P(9; X) is of degree 9. A more realistic comparison of Hermite and Lagrange Interpolation Polynomial is obtained by comparing Example 2 and the following Example 5.

**Example 5.** For $F(X) = EXP(X), [A, B] = [-1, 1], X(J) = -1 + .5 * J, J \in //0, 4//$, we have

$MAX|EXP(Z)/10!|$, over $Z \in [-1, 1], = EXP(1)/10!$

so that [using (7.4.23)]

$E(9; X) \leq POLP(X) ** 2 * EXP(1)/10!$, for each X in $[-1, 1]$,

where

$POLP(X) = (X - (-1)) * (X - (-.5)) * (X - 0) * (X - .5) * (X - 1)$

$= X * (X ** 2 - .25) * (X ** 2 - 1).$

A sketch of $POLP(X) ** 2$ is given in Figure 7.4.4. Here, $POLP(X) ** 2$ takes its local maxima in $[-1, 1]$ at

$X \doteq \pm .8222$, and $X \doteq \pm .2720,$

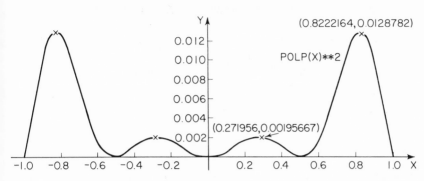

**Figure 7.4.4**

and

$$POLP(\pm .8222) ** 2 \doteq .0129, \text{ while } POLP(\pm .2720) ** 2 \doteq .0020.$$

Compare Example 2. In this example, *if we had chosen* the grid to be the *Chebyshev Abscissas*, (7.4.14),

$$X(K) = COS\big((2 * K + 1) * \pi/10\big), K \in //0, 4//,$$

then the Chebyshev Polynomial, (7.4.15),

$$T(5; X) = 2 ** 4 * POLP(X)$$

and its square

$$T(5; X) ** 2 = 2 ** 8 * POLP(X) ** 2$$

take their maximum value $(+1)$ at

$$X = COS(M * \pi/5), M \in //0, 5//.$$

With this choice of grid all local maxima of $POLP(X) ** 2$ are equal, and equal to $2 ** (-8) = .00390625$. Recall, in Example 4 [below (7.4.16)] the local maxima of $|POLP(X)| = 2 ** (-9) * |T(10; X)|$ were all equal to $2 ** (-9)$.

CONCLUSION: We cannot say which type polynomial is *best*. We look until we find one that gives satisfactory results—often it is neither the Lagrange nor the Hermite Polynomial. Recall Remark 9 at the end of §1.5.

## 7.5 EVALUATING LAGRANGE POLYNOMIALS. AITKEN'S PROCESS

If the Lagrange Interpolation Polynomial $P(N; X)$ characterized by

$$(7.5.1) \qquad P(N; X(J)) = F(X(J)), J \in //0, N//,$$

is represented in the form

$$(7.5.2) \qquad P(N; X) = \sum A(K) * X ** K, K \in //0, N//,$$

and if only rational operations $(+, -, *, /)$ may be used, then an economical method for evaluating $P(N; X)$ at $X = XX \neq X(J), J \in //0, N//,$ is

$$(7.5.3) \qquad P(N; XX) = ( \cdots ((A(N) * XX + A(N - 1)) * XX$$
$$+ A(N - 2)) * XX + \cdots ) * XX + A(0),$$

which requires N additions and N multiplications. This method, (7.5.3), is generally preferred for use on electronic digital computers when a polynomial is *given* in the form (7.5.2).

Suppose $P(N; X)$ is represented in the form (7.2.5)

$$(7.5.4) \qquad P(N; X) = \sum F(X(K)) * LC(N, K; X), K \in //0, N//,$$

where the Lagrange Coefficients are given *explicitly* as polynomials in X, (7.3. 12),

$$(7.5.5) \qquad LC(N, K; X) = (PROD(X - X(J)), J \in //0, N//, \text{ and } J \neq K,)/$$
$$(PROD(X(K) - X(J)), J \in //0, N//, \text{ and } J \neq K,),$$

or as polynomials in S, (7.3.13). Then, to compute $P(N; X)$ at $X = XX \neq X(J), J \in //0, N//,$ we *could evaluate* the appropriate polynomials (Lagrange Coefficients) at $X = XX$ and sum the products in (7.5.4). Unless these Lagrange Coefficients are to be used with several functions $F(X)$ or unless they have already been tabulated, this method is generally *not recommended* when only *evaluation* of $P(N; X)$ at specific points is required. It is usually better to read-off from the form (7.5.4) the interpolation points $(X(J), F(X)), J \in //0, N//,$ and use one of the following methods to compute $P(N; XX)$.

We list below, as a summary, several important cases. The grid points involved in the recommended representation of the Lagrange Polynomial $P(N; X)$ are assumed renumbered in each case as indicated in the associated figure.

The recommended representation of P(N; X) in each case is presented with a list of useful computing aids. Except in Case V, we assume a uniform grid. In Case V, Aitken's process is discussed as one of several similar processes which require N * (N + 1)/2 *linear interpolations* for the evaluation of Lagrange Polynomials where the grid is not necessarily uniform. Aitken's Process is particularly useful for a study of the "smallest N" problem when we do not have available a *usable* representation of the truncation error for the estimation of F(X) by P(N; X).

**Case Ia.** [N = 2 * M; X(J) = X(0) + H * J, for each J ∈ // − M, M//; and 0 ≤ S ≤ .5.]

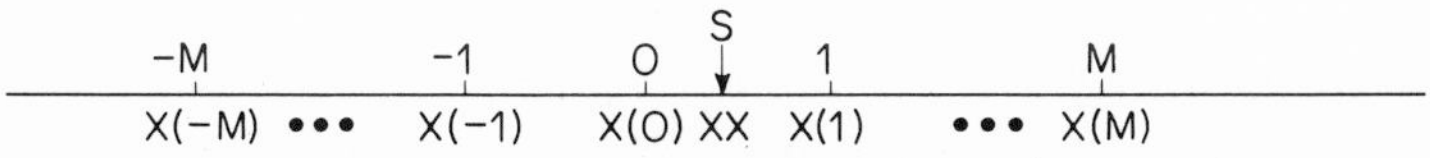

$$\begin{array}{ccccccc} & & & & \overset{S}{\downarrow} & & \\ \underline{-M} & & -1 & 0 & & 1 & M \\ X(-M) & \bullet\bullet\bullet & X(-1) & X(0) \; XX & X(1) & \bullet\bullet\bullet & X(M) \end{array}$$

**Figure 7.5.1**

RECOMMENDED FORM A. If the Lagrange Coefficients LC(N, K; XX) = LC (N, K; X(0) + H * S) in the form (7.3.13) have been tabulated (e.g., see [7]) and if

$$S = \big(XX - X(0)\big)/H$$

is an argument in the table, then *read* the Lagrange Coefficients LC(N, K: X(0) + H * S) = A(K, S) from the table and compute the sum (7.5.4)

(7.5.6)    P(N; XX) = P(N; X(0) + H * S)

$$= \sum F\big(X(K)\big) * A(K, S), \; K \in // -M, M//.$$

*Computing Aids.* A table of Lagrange Coefficients for 2 * M + 1 points with S [= (XX − X(0))/H] an argument in the table.

*Note.* Most tables of Lagrange Coefficients are published for S ∈ //0, T, .5//, for T = 10 ** (−2) or T = 10 ** (−3).

RECOMMENDED FORM B. Stirling's Formula at X(0), (7.3.32b).

(7.5.7)    P(N; XX) = P(N; X(0) + H * S)

$$= F(0) + \sum \big(BINCO(S + K, 2 * K + 1)$$

$$* \mu\delta ** (2 * K + 1) \, F(0)$$

$$+ S/(2 * K + 2) * BINCO(S + K, 2 * K + 1)$$

$$* \delta ** (2 * K + 2)F(0)\big), \; K \in //0, M - 1//.$$

*Computing Aids.* A table of the binomial coefficient function, and a table of central differences of F(X) containing even central differences at X(0), and [since $\mu\delta ** (K)F(0) = .5 * (\delta ** (K)F(.5) + \delta ** (K)F(-.5))$] *odd* central differences at $X(.5) = X(0) + H * (.5)$ and $X(-.5) = X(0) - H * (.5)$.

**Case Ib.** [$N = 2 * M$; $X(J) = X(0) + H * J$, for each $J \in // - M, M//$; and $-.5 \leq S \leq 0$.]

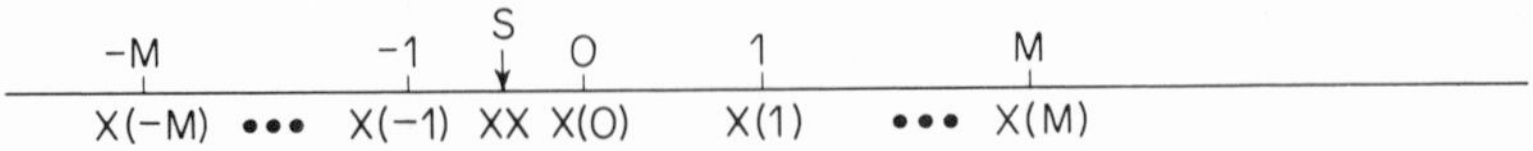

**Figure 7.5.2**

RECOMMENDED FORM A. Lagrange Coefficients are usually tabulated only for the choice of grid, XX, and $0 \leq S \leq .5$, in Case Ia. The symmetries of the grid about X(0) and of the form (7.5.5) for LC(N, K; X) permit the use in Case Ib of a table of Lagrange Coefficients which was designed for use in Case Ia. The *rule*: if

$$S = (XX - X(0))/H \text{ and } -.5 \leq S \leq 0,$$

then the Lagrange Coefficients LC(N, K; XX) = A(K, S), S < 0, may be obtained from a table of Lagrange Coefficients designed for use with Case Ia by reading the entries in row $-S$ (>0) *from right to left*. That is, A(K, S), S < 0, for Case Ib is equal to A(-K, -S), (-S) > 0, for case Ia, Thus

(7.5.8)     $P(N; XX) = P(N: X(0) + H * S)$

$$= \sum F(X(K)) * A(-K, -S), K \in // - M, M//.$$

*Computing Aids.* Same as that needed for Recommended Form A of Case Ia.

RECOMMENDED FORM B. Stirling's Formula at X(0), (7.3.32b).

*Computing Aids.* Same as those needed for Recommended Form B of Case Ia.

**Case II.** [$N = 2 * M + 1$; $X(J) = X(0) + H * J$, $J \in // - M, M + 1//$; and $0 \leq S \leq 1$.]

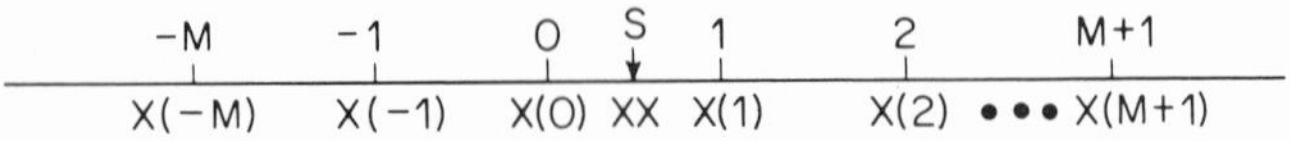

**Figure 7.5.3**

RECOMMENDED FORM. Bessel's Formula at X(.5), (7.3.33b), with $S = (XX - X(0))/H$ and $0 \leq S \leq 1$. With $N = 2 * M$,

(7.5.9)    $P(N; XX) = P\big(N; X(0) + H * S\big)$

$= \mu F(.5) + (S - .5) * \delta F(.5)$

$+ \text{BINCO}(S + M - 1, 2 * M) * \mu\delta ** (2 * M)F(.5)$

$+ \sum \text{BINCO}(S + K - 1, 2 * K) * \big(\mu\delta ** (2 * K)F(.5)$

$+ (S - .5) * \delta ** (2 * K + 1)F(.5)/(2 * K + 1)\big),$

$K \in //1, M - 1//.$

*Note.* This formula with $S = .5$ is highly recommended for subtabulation in a table of $F(X)$.

*Computing Aids.* A table of the binomial coefficient function, and a table of the appropriate central differences.

**Case III.** [Any N;   $X(J) = X(0) + H * J, J \in //0, N//$; and $-1 \leq S \leq 1$.]

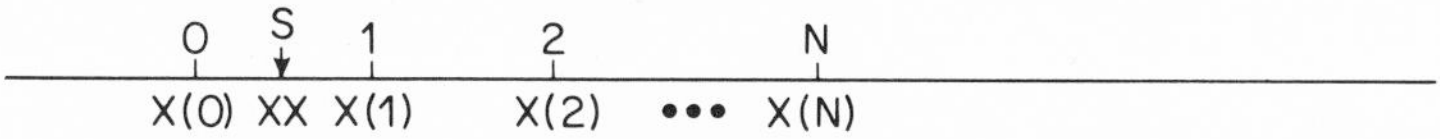

**Figure 7.5.4**

RECOMMENDED FORM. Newton's Forward Difference Formula at $X(0)$, (7.3.4), with $S = \big(XX - X(0)\big)/H$ and $-1 \leq S \leq 1$.

(7.5.10)    $P(N; XX) = P\big(N; X(0) + H * S\big)$

$= \sum \text{BINCO}(S, K) * \Delta ** (K)F(0), K \in //0, N//.$

*Note.* This formula with $S = -1$, is often used to *extend a table* of $F(X)$ to include the grid point $X(-1)$, then $X(-2)$, etc.—especially when the appropriate N is known.

*Computing Aids.* A table of the binomial coefficient function, and the appropriate table of forward differences of $F(X)$ at $X(0)$.

*Note.* When this method is being used to extend a table of $F(X)$ and when the $\big(X(-1), F(-1)\big)$ has been computed, then only one (upper) diagonal need be added to Table 6.2.3 to produce the table of forward differences at $X(-1)$ required to extend the table of $F(X)$ to include $\big(X(-2), F(-2)\big)$.

**Case IV.** [Any N;   $X(J) = X(0) + H * J, J \in //0, N//$; and $-1 \leq S \leq 1$.]

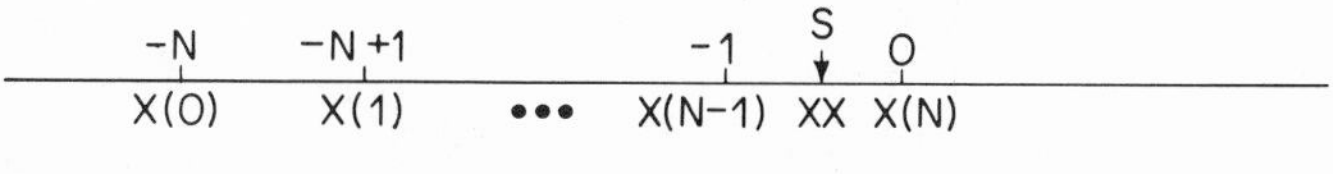

**Figure 7.5.5**

RECOMMENDED FORM. Newton's Backward Difference Formula at X(N), (7.3.7) with $S = (XX - X(N))/H$ and $-1 \le S \le 1$.

(7.5.11)  $P(N; XX) = P(N; X(N) + H * S)$
$$= \sum (-1) ** K * BINCO(-S, K)$$
$$* \nabla ** (K)F(N), K \in //0, N//.$$

*Note.* This formula with $S = 1$ is often used to *extend a table* of F(X) to include the grid point X(N + 1), then X(N + 2), etc.—especially when the appropriate N is known.

*Computing Aids.* A table of the binomial coefficient function, and the appropriate table of backward differences of F(X) at X(N).

*Note.* When this method is being used to extend a table of F(X) and when the $(X(N + 1), F(N + 1))$ has been computed, then only one (lower) diagonal need be added to Table 6.2.4 (set $K = N$) to produce the table of backward differences at X(N+1) required to extend the table of F(X) to include $(X(N+2), F(N+2))$.

**Case V.** [Any N; $X(J), J \in //0, N//$, any not necessarily uniform grid; and any $X = XX$ *not* a grid point.]

**Figure 7.5.6**

RECOMMENDED FORM. Aitken's Process. An enlightening geometric interpretation of Aitken's Process is given in [2b]. See also [3]. We denote the Lagrange Polynomial which agrees with F(X) at X(P) and X(Q) by I(P, Q; X). And, in general, the indices of the points that are used to characterize a Lagrange Polynomial appear as subscripts (before the semicolon) in the symbol $I(\cdots; X)$. We write (all determinants are second order)

$$I(P, Q; X) = \begin{vmatrix} F(P) & X(P) - X \\ F(Q) & X(Q) - X \end{vmatrix} / (X(Q) - X(P))$$

$$I(P, R; X) = \begin{vmatrix} F(P) & X(P) - X \\ F(R) & X(R) - X \end{vmatrix} / (X(R) - X(P)).$$

A simple calculation shows that

$$I(P, Q, R; X) = \begin{vmatrix} I(P, Q; X) & X(Q) - X \\ I(P, R; X) & X(R) - X \end{vmatrix} / (X(R) - X(Q)),$$

so that the Lagrange Polynomial $P(2; X)$ characterized by $P\big(2; X(K)\big) = F(K)$, $K = P, Q, R$ is given by three linear interpolations. *In general,* the Lagrange Interpolation Polynomial

$$P(N; X) \equiv I(0, 1, 2, \ldots, N; X)$$

characterized by

$$P\big(N; X(K)\big) = F\big(X(K)\big) \equiv F(K), K \in //0, N//,$$

may be obtained by the $N * (N + 1)/2$ linear interpolations indicated below. Of course, execution of the indicated operations is practical only when *evaluation*[1] of $P$ $(N; X)$ is desired for a particular value of X, say XX, so that the elements in the determinants are *numbers*. There is very little advantage here to having a uniform grid. Compute in the order indicated

$$I(0, K; XX) = \begin{vmatrix} F(0) & X(0) - XX \\ F(K) & X(K) - XX \end{vmatrix} / \big(X(K) - X(0)\big), K \in //1, N//,$$

then

$$I(0, 1, K; XX) = \begin{vmatrix} I(0, 1; XX) & X(1) - XX \\ I(0, K; XX) & X(K) - XX \end{vmatrix} / \big(X(K) - X(1)\big), K \in //2, N//,$$

then

$$I(0, 1, 2, K; XX) = \begin{vmatrix} I(0, 1, 2; XX) & X(2) - XX \\ I(0, 1, K; XX) & X(K) - XX \end{vmatrix} / \big(X(K) - X(2)\big), K \in //3, N//,$$

etc. until we have

$$I(0, 1, 2, \ldots, N; XX) = \begin{vmatrix} I(0, 1, 2, \cdots, N-2, N-1; XX) & X(N-1) - XX \\ I(0, 1, 2, \cdots, N-2, N; XX) & X(N) - XX \end{vmatrix}$$
$$/ \big(X(N) - X(N-1)\big).$$

The schematic diagram in Table 7.5.1 is useful as a summary, and for discussions of Aitken's Process. Notice that elements of the determinants needed above occur in Table 7.5.1 at appropriate corners of rectangles.

[1]Recall, if the coefficients of $P(N; X)$ in (7.5.2) are available, then we would use (7.5.3) to compute $P(N; XX)$.

**Table 7.5.1** AITKEN'S PROCESS

| X(J) | F(J) | Degree 1 | Degree 2 | Degree 3 | X(J) − XX |
|------|------|----------|----------|----------|-----------|
| X(0) | F(0) |          |          |          | X(0) − XX |
| X(1) | F(1) | I(0, 1; XX) |       |          | X(1) − XX |
| X(2) | F(2) | I(0, 2; XX) | I(0, 1, 2; XX) |   | X(2) − XX |
| X(3) | F(3) | I(0, 3; XX) | I(0, 1, 3; XX) | I(0, 1, 2, 3; XX) | X(3) − XX |

Besides its obvious usefulness to *evaluate* a Lagrange Polynomial P(N; X) characterized by (7.5.1) where the grid need not be uniform, *Aitken's Process has another important application.* Suppose that a table of F(X) is given $\{(X(J), F(J)) \,|\, J \in //0, T//\}$ where the grid is not necessarily uniform, also suppose that no usable representation of the truncation error, (7.4.12), E(N; X) = F(X) − P(N; X), is available to determine a *required* suitable N in (7.5.1) to insure that |E(N; X)| will be sufficiently small for a specified value X = XX. An *estimate* to the required N may be obtained from Table 7.5.1 where Aitken's Process has been applied to the given table of F(X): Read the *numbers* on the upper diagonal of Table 7.5.1,

(7.5.12)     F(0), I(0, 1; XX), I(0, 1, 2; XX), I(0, 1, 2, 3; XX), etc.

and as soon as two consecutive elements, I(0, 1, 2, ..., M; XX) and I(0, 1, 2, ..., M, M + 1; XX), in the sequence (7.5.12) are nearly equal [and the computed elements that follow these in (7.5.12) differ little from I(0, 1, 2, ..., M; XX)], then M is taken as an estimate to the "smallest N" such that P(N; X) characterized by (7.5.1) estimates F(X) at X = XX with the "least practical" truncation error.

*Motivation* (certainly not a proof that an N chosen in this way is best in the sense suggested) for this method of choosing this "smallest N" is: If the value of the M*th* degree Lagrange Polynomial at XX differs little from the value of higher-degree Lagrange Polynomials at XX where characterizations of these higher-degree polynomials involve only additional given tabulated points, *then perhaps*, at least near XX, I(0, 1,2, ..., M; X) is close to the polynomial guaranteed by Weierstrass' Theorem. Of course there is *no reason to believe* that I(0, 1, 2, ..., M; XX) = F(XX), even if the next 100 numbers in the sequence (7.5.12) are equal to I(0, 1, 2, ..., M; XX). However, *usable* estimates to such a "smallest N" are often found in this way.

The character of POLP(X) in (7.4.12), see Figure 7.4.1, suggests that the elements $\{(X(J), F(J)) \,|\, J = 0, 1, 2, ...\}$ to be used in Aitken's Process should be chosen so that not all of the points X(J), J ∈ //0, M//, appear on one side of XX.

**Example.** Given F(X) = EXP(X) and the table $\{(X(J), F(J)) \,|\, X(J) = .1 * J, J \in //0, 4//\}$. Apply Aitken's Process to evaluate the Lagrange Polynomial P(4; X), characterized by P(4; X(K)) = F(K), K ∈ //0, 4//, at X = XX = .25.

*Solution.* In this case, Table 7.5.1 becomes Table 7.5.2,

**Table 7.5.2** Aitken's Process: $F(X) = EXP(X)$, $XX = .25$

| J | X(J) | F(J) | Degree 1 | Degree 2 | Degree 3 | Degree 4 | X(J) − XX |
|---|------|------|----------|----------|----------|----------|-----------|
| 0 | 0 | 1.0000 | | | | | −.25 |
| 1 | .1 | 1.1052 | 1.26300 | | | | −.15 |
| 2 | .2 | 1.2214 | 1.27675 | 1.28362 | | | −.05 |
| 3 | .3 | 1.3499 | 1.29158 | 1.28444 | 1.28403 | | .05 |
| 4 | .4 | 1.4918 | 1.30738 | 1.28519 | 1.28402 | 1.28404 | .15 |

where $XX = .25$, and in the calculation the given data is assumed exact as listed.

Thus $P(4; .25) = I(0, 1, 2, 3, 4; .25) = 1.28404 \doteq EXP(.25)[= 1.284025]$ where the last digit listed is in doubt, and $P(4; .25) \doteq EXP(.25)$ correct to four decimal places. It appears that the third degree Lagrange Polynomial $I(0, 1, 2, 3; X)$ is adequate to estimate $EXP(X)$ near $X = .25$ to the accuracy of the given data. Indeed, the second bound in (7.4.13) may be used with $N = 3$, and $XX = .25$ to show that $I(0, 1, 2, 3; XX)$ differs from $EXP(XX)$ by less than .00001 if the given data is exact and round-off error is not significant.

## 7.6  THE LOZENGE DIAGRAM

The *Lozenge Diagram* is a schematic device useful in defining various representations of the Lagrange Polynomial $P(N; X)$ for a uniform grid with mesh H. *In this section* we assume that the argument of $P(N: X)$ has the form

$$X = X(0) + H * S.$$

The reader is referred to Table 6.2.5 and (6.2.8) for relations between *forward differences* (used exclusively in this section) and the other differences involved in familiar representations of $P(N; X)$.

For the purpose of simplifying the appearance of the Lozenge Diagram in Table 7.6.1 we write the binomial coefficient function, (6.5.4), in the form

(7.6.1)    $C(S, K) = BINCO(S, K)$

$$= (1/K!) * PROD(S - J), J \in //0, K - 1//,$$

where S is measured from $X(0)$

(7.6.2)                    $S = (X - X(0))/H.$

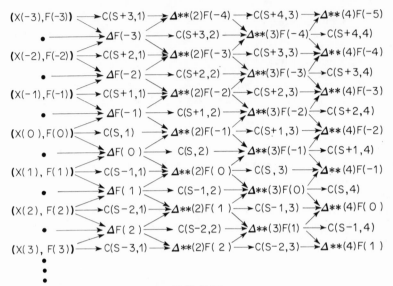

**Table 7.6.1**

A *polygon on the Lozenge Diagram* is characterized by the following conditions.

1. Each column of the Lozenge Diagram through which the polygon passes (including the first column where it starts and the column where it terminates) contains exactly one *corner* of the polygon.

2. A *starting* corner may be *at* a tabulated point or *at* a point midway between two consecutive tabulated points in the first column. An *interior* corner may be *at* a difference or *at* a binomial coefficient between two differences.

3. The polygon is defined by listing a sequence of *directed steps*: directions for passing from one corner to the next along the polygon.

4. As indicated by the arrows in Table 7.6.1, three directed steps are possible *from* a starting corner which is at a grid point, or *from* an interior corner at a difference. The *names* of directed steps are: UR (upper right); HR (horizontal to the right); LR (lower right).

   *Note.* The directed steps are always to the right.

5. Only the directed step HR (horizontal to the right) is permitted *from* a starting corner midway between two tabulated points, or *from* an interior corner at a binomial coefficient.

6. The polygon *terminates at a difference*. In particular, if N directed

steps are used to define the polygon, then the terminal corner is $\Delta **$ (N)F(Q), where (X(Q), F(Q)) is a tabulated point.

We can *define a representation* of the Lagrange Polynomial P(N; X) characterized by

(7.6.3)      P(N; X(K)) = F(X(K)) $\equiv$ F(K), K $\in$ //Q, Q + N//,

where F(K), K $\in$ //Q, Q + N//, are those values of F(X) involved in the difference $\Delta **$ (N)F(Q) at the terminal corner of a given *polygon on the Lozenge Diagram*, by applying the following rules.

1. Let (X(P), F(P)) denote the starting corner of the given polygon on the Lozenge Diagram, and let this polygon be defined by the ordered set of directed steps

(7.6.4)      D(1), D(2), . . . , D(N), [each D(K) = UR, or HR, or LR]

where D(1) is the directed step *from* the first corner (X(P), F(P)) to the second corner (counting from left to right) along the polygon, and D(2) is the directed step from the second corner to the third corner along the polygon, etc. That is, D(K), with the K*th* corner, defines the (K + 1)*th* corner.
2. Corresponding to each D(K), let B(K) denote the *function* of differences and binomial coefficients that results from applying the following rules.

(a) If D(K) = UR, then the (K + 1)*th* corner will be at a difference, so *define* B(K) to be the difference at the corner reached times the coefficient immediately below the corner reached. With the obvious abbreviations we write

(7.6.5a)      B(K) = (diff. at c. r.) $*$ (coeff. below c. r.).

(b) If D(K) = LR, then the (K + 1)*th* corner is at a difference, so define

(7.6.5b)      B(K) = (diff. at c. r.) $*$ (coeff. above c. r.).

(c) If D(K) = HR, *and* the (K + 1)*th* corner is at a difference, then define

(7.6.5c)      B(K) = (diff. at c. r.)
                       $*$ .5 $*$ ((coeff. above c. r.) + (coeff. below c. r.)).

(d) If $D(K) = HR$, *and* the $(K + 1)th$ corner is at a binomial coefficient, then define

(7.6.5d)     $B(K) = $ (coeff. at c. r.)
$$* .5 * ((\text{diff. above c. r.}) + (\text{diff. below c. r.})).$$

3. Write the Lagrange Polynomial $P(N; X)$ characterized by (7.6.3) as the sum

(7.6.6)     $P(N; X) = P(N; X(0) + H * S)$
$$= F(P) + \sum B(K), K \in //1, N//.$$

*Note.* The conditions (7.6.3) may also be written

(7.6.3b)   $P(N; X(S)) = P(N; X(0) + H * S) \equiv F(S), S \in //Q, Q + N//.$

**Example 1.** Newton's Forward Difference Formula at $X(0)$, (7.5.10), is obtained by this method when we define the polygon on the Lozenge Diagram by specifying the starting corner to be at $(X(P), F(P)) = (X(0), F(0))$ and for (7.6.4) choose

$$D(K) = LR, K \in //1, N//,$$

so that the terminal corner is at $\Delta ** (N)F(0)$, and $Q = 0$ in (7.6.3). Then (7.6.5b) becomes

$$B(K) = \Delta ** (K)F(0) * C(S, K), K \in //1, N//,$$

so (7.6.6) becomes

(7.6.7)     $P(N; X) = P(N; X(0) + H * S) = F(0) + \sum B(K), K \in //1, N//,$
$$= F(0) + \sum \Delta ** (K)F(0) * C(S, K), K \in //1, N//,$$

the Lagrange Polynomial characterized by (7.6.3) or (7.6.3b) with $Q = 0$. Clearly, (7.6.7) is identical to (7.5.10).

**Example 2.** Newton's Backward Difference Formula at $X(N)$, (7.5.11), is obtained by this method when we define $(X(P)), F(P)) = (X(N), F(N))$ and for (7.6.4) choose

$$D(K) = UR, K \in //1, N//,$$

so that the terminal corner is at $\Delta ** (N) F(0)$, and $Q = 0$ in (7.6.3). Then (7.6.5a) becomes

$$B(K) = \Delta ** (K)F(N - K) * C(S - N + K - 1, K), K \in //1, N//,$$

and (7.6.6) becomes

(7.6.8)    $P(N; X(0) + H * S)$

$$= F(N) + \sum \Delta ** (K)F(N - K) * C(S - N + K - 1, K), K \in //1, N//,$$

the Lagrange Polynomial characterized by (7.6.3) with $Q = 0$. After noting (7.6.2), (6.5.8), and Table 6.2.5, we see that (7.6.8) is identical to (7.5.11).

**Example 3.** Stirling's Formula at $X(0)$, (7.5.7), where $N = 2 * M$, is obtained by this method when we define $(X(P), F(P)) = (X(0), F(0))$ and (7.6.4) to be

$$D(K) = HR, K \in //1, 2 * M//,$$

so that the terminal corner is at $\Delta ** (2 * M)F(-M)$, and $Q = -M$ in (7.6.3). Then, (7.6.5d) becomes

$$B(2 * K - 1) = C(S + K - 1, 2 * K - 1) * .5 * (\Delta ** (2 * K - 1)F(-K)$$
$$+ \Delta ** (2 * K - 1)F(-K + 1)), K \in //1, M//,$$

and (7.6.5c) becomes

$$B(2 * K) = \Delta ** (2 * K)F(-K)$$
$$* .5 * (C(S + K, 2 * K) + C(S + K - 1, 2 * K)), K \in //1, M//.$$

And (7.6.6) becomes

(7.6.9)        $P(N; X(0) + H * S)$

$$= F(0) + \sum (B(2 * K - 1) + B(2 * K)), K \in //1, M//.$$

This, using (7.6.1), Table 6.2.5, and (6.2.9), is seen to be Stirling's Formula at $X(0)$ characterized by $P(N; X(K)) = F(X(K)), K \in // -M, M//.$

**Example 4.** Bessel's Formula at $X(.5)$, (7.5.9) where $N = 2 * M + 1$, is obtained by this method when we define $(X(P), F(P)) = (X(.5), F(.5))$ and (7.6.4) to be

$$D(K) = HR, K \in //1, 2 * M + 1//,$$

so that the terminal corner is at $\Delta ** (2 * M + 1)F(-M)$, and $Q = -M$ in (7.6.3). Then (7.6.5c) becomes

$$B(2 * K - 1) = \Delta ** (2 * K - 1)F(-K + 1) * .5 * \big(C(S + K - 1, 2 * K - 1)$$
$$+ C(S + K - 2, 2 * K - 1)\big), K \in //1, M + 1//,$$

and (7.6.5d) becomes

$$B(2 * K) = C(S + K - 1, 2 * K) * .5 * \big(\Delta **(2 * K)F(-K)$$
$$+ \Delta ** (2 * K)F(-K + 1)\big), K \in //1, M//.$$

And (7.6.6) becomes

$$(7.6.10) \qquad P\big(N; X(0) + H * S\big) = F(.5) + B(2 * M + 1)$$
$$+ \sum \big(B(2 * K - 1) + B(2 * K)\big), K \in //1, M//.$$

This is Bessel's Formula at $X(.5)$ characterized by $P\big(N; X(K)\big) = F\big(X(K)\big), K \in // - M, M + 1//$.

**Example 5.** Another representation of the polynomial which is Newton's Forward Difference Formula at $X(0)$, or equivalently Newton's Backward Difference Formula at $X(N)$, is obtained when we define $\big(X(P), F(P)\big) = \big(X(1), F(1)\big)$, and (7.6.4) to be

$$D(K) = LR, K \in //1, N - 1//, \text{ and } D(N) = UR,$$

so that the terminal corner of this polygon on the Lozenge Diagram is at $\Delta ** (N)F(0)$, and $Q = 0$ in (7.6.3). Then, with (7.6.5b) and (7.6.5a),

$$B(K) = \Delta ** (K)F(1) * C(S - 1, K), K \in //1, N - 1//,$$

and

$$B(N) = \Delta ** (N)F(0) * C(S - 1 N).$$

Then (7.6.6) becomes

$$(7.6.11) \qquad P\big(N; X(0) + H * S\big) = F(1) + \sum B(K), K \in //1, N//.$$

This is the Lagrange Polynomial characterized by $P\big(N; X(K)\big) = F\big(X(K)\big), K \in //0, N//$. Then (7.6.11) is equivalent to (7.6.7) in Example 1, and (7.6.8) in Example 2.

SUMMARY

If a set of N directed steps (7.6.4) is used to define a polygon on the Lozenge Diagram which begins at $(X(P), F(P))$ and terminates at the difference $\Delta ** (N)F(Q)$, *then* (7.6.6) is *the* Lagrange Polynomial of degree N in S $= (X - X(0))/H$ characterized by the N + 1 conditions (7.6.3b). The characterizing properties of the Lagrange Polynomial obtained in this way depend only on the difference at the terminal corner, not on the particular polygon traversed to reach this difference.

A generalization of this method for defining various representations of Lagrange Polynomials is obtained when we allow (except *from* the first column) directed steps to the left. Define directed steps to the left and their contributions corresponding to (7.6.5a, b, c, d) as follows: (c. s. = corner at *start* of the directed step)

                 UL(upper left)

(7.6.12a)          $B(K) = -$ (diff. at c. s.) $*$ (coeff. above c. s.)

                 LL(lower left)

(7.6.12b)          $B(K) = -$ (diff. at c. s.) $*$ (coeff. below c. s.)

                 HL(horizontal to the left)

From a difference:

(7.6.12c)     $B(K) = -$ (diff. at c. s.)
              $* .5 *$ ((coeff. above c. s.) $+$ (coeff. below c. s.)).

From a coefficient:

(7.6.12d)     $B(K) = -$ (coeff. at c. s.)
              $* .5 *$ ((diff. above c. s.) $+$ (diff. below c. s.)).

If a set of M directed steps

(7.6.13)      $D(K), K \in //1, M//$, [each $D(K) = $ UR, HR, LR, UL, HL, or LL]

are used to define a polygon on the Lozenge Diagram which begins at $(X(P),$

F(P)) and terminates at the difference $\Delta ** (N)F(Q)$, $N \leq M$, *then*

(7.6.14)     $P(N; X(0) + H * S) = F(P) + \sum B(K)$, $K \in //1, M//$,

is *the* Lagrange Polynomial of degree N in $S = (X - X(0))/H$ characterized by (7.6.3b)

$$P(N; X(0) + H * S)) = F(S), S \in //Q, Q + N//.$$

*Note.* In this generalization a polygon on the Lozenge Diagram may contain closed loops (a segment of the polygon that is traversed in *both* directions is also considered a closed loop), and the sum of the contribution to (7.6.14) of the directed steps that define the loop is *zero*.

**Example 6.** Define $(X(P), F(P)) = (X(0), F(0))$, and $D(1) = HR$, $D(2) = HR$, $D(3) = LL$. The terminal corner is at $\Delta F(0)$, so $N = 1$ and $Q = 0$. Then, using (7.6.5d), (7.6.5c), and (7.6.12b), the form (7.6.14) becomes

$$P(1, X(0) + H * S) = F(0) + C(S, 1) * .5 * (\Delta F(-1) + \Delta F(0))$$
$$+ \Delta ** (2)F(-1) * .5 * (C(S + 1, 2) + C(S, 2))$$
$$- \Delta ** (2)F(-1) * C(S, 2)$$
$$= F(0) + S * (F(1) - F(0))$$
$$= F(0) + \Delta F(0) * C(S, 1),$$

which is the same polynomial that we would obtain if we chose $M = 1$, $(X(P), F(P)) = (X(0), F(0))$, and $D(1) = LR$.

## SUGGESTED READING

1. Birkhoff, G. and S. MacLane (1953): *A Survey of Modern Algebra.* The MacMillan Company. New York. (Page 303.)

2. Todd, J. (Ed.)(1962): *Survey of Numerical Analysis.* McGraw-Hill Book Company, New York.

2a. —————. (Page 54.)

2b. —————. (Page 39.)

3. Milne, W E. (1949): *Numerical Calculus.* Princeton University Press. Princeton, N. J. (Page 69.)

4. Hamming, R. W. (1962): *Numerical Methods for Scientists and Engineers.* McGraw-Hill Book Company, New York.

5. Kunz, K. S. (1957): *Numerical Analysis*. McGraw-Hill Book Company, New York.

6. Davis, P. J. (1963); *Interpolation and Approximation*. Blaisdell Publishing Company. New York.

7. *Handbook of Mathematical Functions with Formulas, Graphs, and Mathematical Tables* (1964): National Bureau of Standards Applied Mathematics Series 55. (Note particularly the tables of Lagrange coefficients. Page 900.)

# 8 LEAST SQUARE ESTIMATES

In Chapter 7 we considered Lagrange Interpolation Polynomials in the form (7.1.1)

$$(8.1.1) \qquad P(N; X) = \sum A(K) * U(K, X), K \in //0, N//,$$

where the $U(K, X)$ are various polynomials[1] of degree $K$ in $X$, and the coefficients $A(K), K \in //0, N//$, are characterized by the $N + 1$ conditions, for each $J \in //0, N//$,

$$(8.1.2) \qquad P(N; X(J)) = \sum A(K) * U(K, X(J)), K \in //0, N//,$$
$$= F(X(J)) \equiv F(J).$$

The function $P(N; X)$ *agrees* with $F(X)$ on a specified set of points $(X(J), F(J)), J \in //0, N//$, and *estimates* $F(X)$ at intermediate points with truncation error given by (7.4.12).

In practice, it frequently happens that a function $P(X)$ is required to estimate values intermediate to elements of a table of $FF(X)$ obtained by experiment, where the *form* of the function $F(X)$ defined by a similar experiment executed under ideal conditions *is known*. For example, consider the straight line $F(X) = .5 * X$, and the table $(X(J), FF(J)), J \in //0, 10//$, plotted in Figure

[1]See (7.2.1), (7.3.2), and (7.3.5).

258

8.1.1, where FF(J) is obtained from $F(X(J)) = F(J)$ by rounding (using the usual rule) to one decimal place. In this example the line might correspond (with the appropriate units) to the ideal relation between force and deflection for a particular coil spring, while the FF(J), $J \in //0, 10//$, correspond to *measured deflections* with the ideal spring and exact weights.

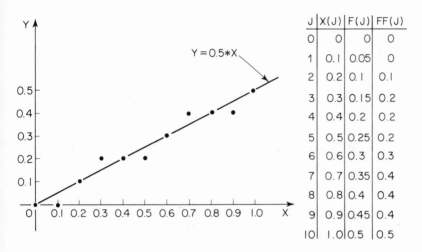

| J | X(J) | F(J) | FF(J) |
|---|---|---|---|
| 0 | 0 | 0 | 0 |
| 1 | 0.1 | 0.05 | 0 |
| 2 | 0.2 | 0.1 | 0.1 |
| 3 | 0.3 | 0.15 | 0.2 |
| 4 | 0.4 | 0.2 | 0.2 |
| 5 | 0.5 | 0.25 | 0.2 |
| 6 | 0.6 | 0.3 | 0.3 |
| 7 | 0.7 | 0.35 | 0.4 |
| 8 | 0.8 | 0.4 | 0.4 |
| 9 | 0.9 | 0.45 | 0.4 |
| 10 | 1.0 | 0.5 | 0.5 |

**Figure 8.1.1**

**Problem.** Using only the table $(X(J), FF(J))$, $J \in //0, 10//$, in Figure 8.1.1, and the knowledge that F(X) is a linear polynomial, *define* a function P(X) that can be used to estimate $F(X) = .5 * X$ on [0, 1].

SOLUTION 1. Define $P(X) = P(10; X)$, the Lagrange Polynomial using *all* eleven tabulated points. Not recommended, since $P(10; X)$ has at least five critical points which are either local maxima or minima.

SOLUTION 2. Choose *two* elements from the table and define $P(X) = P(1; X)$, the corresponding linear Lagrange Polynomial. Not recommended without a reliable method for choosing the two points.

SOLUTION 3. (Graphical). Place a straightedge, using engineering judgement, on a plot of the points and draw a line that "looks close" to most of the points, but possibly passes through none of them. Often used when an electronic computer is not available, or when a quick estimate of F(X) is desired. In this case, estimates to F(X) are *read* from the graph and are limited (at best) to plotting accuracy.

*Note.* In this particular case, that marvelous and mysterious quality, "engineering judgement," might involve criteria for "looks close" like:

1. Pick a line, P(X), so that the maximum absolute error at the tabulated points

is minimized[2]

(8.1.3)     $\text{MAX}|P(X(J)) - FF(J)|$, over $J \in //0, 10//, = \text{minimum}$;

or

2. Pick a line, $P(X)$, so that the sum of the absolute error at all tabulated points is a minimum

(8.1.4)     $\sum |P(X(J)) - FF(J)|, J \in //0, 10//, = \text{minimum}$;

or

3. Pick a line, $P(X)$, so that the sum of the squares of the error at all tabulated points is a minimum

(8.1.5)     $\sum (P(X(J)) - FF(J)) ** 2, J \in //0, 10//, = \text{minimum}$.

SOLUTION 4. (Least-Squares). Define the coefficients A and B in the polynomial form $P(X) = A * X + B$ so that (8.1.5) is satisfied. Highly recommended when *more points* than coefficients are involved, and when execution of the method is to be on an electronic computer.

In § 8.2 we develop an algorithm which may be applied to *compute* the coefficients $A(K), K \in //0, N//$, of the form

(8.1.6)          $P(X) = \sum A(K) * U(K, X), K \in //0, N//$,

where the functions $U(K, X), K \in //0, N//$, are assumed specified, and where a *least-squares* condition like (8.1.5) is satisfied. For example, if this method is applied to the table $(X(J), FF(J)), J \in //0, 10//$, in Figure 8.1.1 with $U(0, X) = X$ and $U(1, X) \equiv 1$, then the solution (8.2.7) of (8.2.5) determines $P(X) = .5 * X - .00454545$ satisfying (8.1.5). Note that $P(X)$ does *not* agree with $FF(J)$ at any of the points $X(J), J \in //0, 10//$, that $P(X)$ is parallel to $F(X) = .5 * X$, that

$.0125 = \sum (F(J) - FF(J)) ** 2, J \in //0, 10//,$
$> \sum (P(X(J)) - FF(J)) ** 2, J \in //0, 10//, \doteq .0122727,$

and that

---

[2]We use FF(J), since the exact value of F(J) is often not available. The appropriate minimum is seldom achieved by graphical methods.

$.05 = \text{MAX}|F(J) - FF(J)|$, over $J \in //0, 10//$,

$< \text{MAX}|P(X(J)) - FF(J)|$, over $J \in //0, 10//$, $\doteq .054545$.

In §8.3 a generalization of the method of §8.2 is considered where *certain elements* of the set $(X(J), F(J)), J \in //0, N1//$, involved in a condition like (8.1.5) are allowed to influence the choice of coefficients in P(X) *more* than other elements involved in the condition.

Finally, in §8.4, we offer some remarks concerning least-square estimates *over an interval* (A, B), where a condition corresponding to (8.1.5) involves a definite integral over (A, B).

When the coefficients $A(K), K \in //0, N//$, in (8.1.6) are determined so that the condition (8.1.3) is satisfied, then P(X) is called a *best approximation in the Chebyshev sense*. In this case the $A(K), K \in //0, N//$, are varied so that *each* $|P(X(J)) - F(J)| \leq M$ for the constant M as small as possible. The $A(K), K \in //0, N//$, are often determined as a solution of a linear programming problem where $|P(X(J)) - F(J)| \leq M$ is replaced by a pair of constraints

$$P(X(J)) - F(J) \leq M \ and - (P(X(J)) - F(J)) \leq M,$$

and the function to be minimized is $F = M = $ (constant to be determined). See Example 3 in §4.9.

In Chapter 4 we considered the problem of solving linear systems. We saw that underdetermined linear systems have many solutions, and that overdetermined linear systems have no solution. Least-square methods are useful when an "almost solution" to an overdetermined linear system is required.


## 8.2. LEAST SQUARE ESTIMATES OVER A FINITE GRID

In this section we describe an algorithm for computing the coefficients $A(K), K \in //0, N//$, of the form

(8.2.1)          $P(X) = \sum A(K) * U(K, X), K \in //0, N//$,

where the functions $U(K, X), K \in //0, N//$, are assumed specified, and where P(X) is to be used to estimate F(X) on an interval (A, B) containing the distinct grid points $X(J), J \in //0, N1//, N1 > N$. The *residuals at the grid points* are written, for each $J \in //0, N1//$,

(8.2.2)   $R(J) \equiv F(X(J)) - P(X(J))$

$= F(X(J)) - \sum A(K) * U(K, X(J)), K \in //0, N//,$

$\equiv F(J) - \sum A(K) * U(K, J), K \in //0, N//.$

The coefficients $A(K), K \in //0, N//$, will be chosen so that $P(X)$ is an estimate to $F(X)$ *best in the least-square sense at the grid points* $X(J), J \in //0, N1//$, characterized by [compare (8.1.5)]

(8.2.3)  $\sum R(J) ** 2, J \in //0, N1//,$

$= \sum (F(J) - \sum A(K) * U(K, J), K \in //0, N//, ) ** 2, J \in //0, N1//,$

$= $ minimum.

For this discussion the $F(X(J)) \equiv F(J)$ and the $U(K, X(J)) \equiv U(K, J)$ are assumed to be exact values of $F(X)$ and the $U(K, X)$ at the grid points. We do *not* require that *any* $R(J)$ be zero.

*Note.* Here we assume that $N1 > N$. When the linear system $R(J) = 0, J \in //1, N1//$, is written: $J \in //1, N1//$,

$\sum U(K, J) * A(K), K \in //0, N//, = F(J),$

with corresponding matrix equation $Q * S = F$, see (8.2.6), we assume that $RANK(Q) = N$, and $RANK((Q|F)) = N + 1$. That is, we are considering a linear system which is inconsistent because it is *overdetermined* (more equations than unknowns, and there is no set of coefficients which make all of the residuals zero). This method is applicable when this linear system is inconsistent with $RANK(Q) < N$, but then there are *many* least-square solutions. If this linear system is consistent, then its solutions are solutions of (8.2.5) but they may be obtained more economically by the methods of Chapter 4. Of course, if the linear system is consistent, then there is a set of coefficients $A(K), K \in //0, N//$, which make all the residuals (8.2.2) zero, and we have an interpolation function. As a *rule of thumb*, when the method of least-squares is applied, $N1$ should be chosen so that $N < N1 < 2 * N$. See the Exercise below.

The form in (8.2.3) to be minimized is a nonnegative quadratic polynomial in the *variables* $A(K), K \in //0, N//$. Thus the desired coefficients are components of a solution $S = (A(0), A(1), \ldots, A(N))$ of the (linear) *normal equations:* for each $M \in //0, N//$,

(8.2.4a)  PAR $** (1$ in $M$th position$) (\sum R(J) ** 2, J \in //0, N1//, )$

$= \sum - 2 * (F(J) - \sum A(K) * U(K, J), K \in //0, N//, )$

$* U(M, J), J \in //0, N1//,$

$= 0.$

The normal equations may be written, for each $M \in //0, N//$,

$$(8.2.4b) \quad \sum \left( \sum A(K) * U(K, J) \right) * U(M, J), K \in //0, N//, ), J \in //0, N1//,$$
$$= \sum A(K) * \left( \sum U(K, J) * U(M, J), J \in //0, N1//, \right), K \in //0, N//,$$
$$= A(0) * \sum U(0, J) * U(M, J), J \in //0, N1//,$$
$$+ A(1) * \sum U(1, J) * U(M, J), J \in //0, N1//,$$
$$+ \cdots + A(N) * \sum U(N, J) * U(M, J), J \in //0, N1//,$$
$$= \sum F(J) * U(M, J), J \in //0, N1//.$$

The matrix equation equivalent to the normal equations (8.2.4b) is

$$(8.2.5) \qquad TRAN(Q) * Q * S = TRAN(Q) * F,$$

where

$$(8.2.6) \quad Q = \begin{bmatrix} U(0,0) & U(1,0) & U(2,0) & \cdots & U(N,0) \\ U(0,1) & U(1,1) & U(2,1) & \cdots & U(N,1) \\ U(0,2) & U(1,2) & U(2,2) & \cdots & U(N,2) \\ \vdots & \vdots & \vdots & & \vdots \\ U(0,N1) & U(1,N1) & U(2,N1) & \cdots & U(N,N1) \end{bmatrix},$$

$$S = \begin{bmatrix} A(0) \\ A(1) \\ A(2) \\ \vdots \\ A(N) \end{bmatrix}, \quad \text{and} \quad F = \begin{bmatrix} F(0) \\ F(1) \\ F(2) \\ \vdots \\ F(N1) \end{bmatrix}.$$

It can be shown that (theoretically) if $RANK(Q) = N$, then

$$DET(TRAN(Q) * Q) \neq 0,$$

so that the coefficients in $P(X)$, (8.2.1), which estimates $F(X)$ "best" in the least-square sense at the grid points $X(J)$, $J \in //0, N1//$, (8.2.3), are given by

$$(8.2.7) \qquad S = INV(TRAN(Q) * Q) * TRAN(Q) * F.$$

In practice, $DET(TRAN(Q) * Q)$ is often so small that inherent error, see (4.6.3, 4, 7), is significant in the calculation of S when using (8.2.7) or Crout

Reduction on (8.2.5). But frequently, with either of these computed solutions taken as a first guess, Gauss-Seidel Iteration on (8.2.5) leads to a usable solution S.

If in (8.2.1) the functions U(K, X) are polynomials of degree exactly K, then P(X) satisfying (8.2.3) is called a *least-square polynomial.* If N = N1, then the least-square polynomial is the Lagrange Interpolation Polynomial passing through the grid points, and each R(J), (8.2.2), is zero.

A test on the quality of our computed solution S = (A(0), A(1), . . . , A(N)) usually involves calculation of the residuals (8.2.2), the sum of squares of them (8.2.3), and residuals at some *other* points in (A, B) where F(X) is known. Again, art may play a significant role when choosing N and N1, the points (X(J), F(J)), J ∈ //0, N1//, to be used in (8.2.3), and when making a decision to accept or reject a particular P(X).

1. Write the equations of three lines where each line contains one side of a triangle [say, with vertices (0, 0), (1, 0), and (. 5, . 5 ∗ SQRT (3))]. Write the corresponding matrix equation Q ∗ S = F, where the elements of S are X and Y. Find the least-square solution S = (XX, YY) of this linear system. Locate the point in your triangle which corresponds to the least-square solution. Compare Figure 4.2.1. See the Note, page 262.

## 8.3. WEIGHTED LEAST SQUARE ESTIMATES OVER A FINITE GRID

It may happen that one has reason to want *some* of his data, (X(J), F(J)), J ∈ //0, N1//, to influence the choice of coefficients in (8.2.1) more than the other points involved in (8.2.3).

If the *weights* W(J), J ∈ //0, N1//, are positive numbers, then

(8.3.1)     P(X) = ∑ A(K) ∗ U(K, X), K ∈ //0, N//,

"best" estimates F(X) *at the grid points* X(J), J ∈ //0, N1//, in the *weighted least-square sense* when the coefficients A(K), K ∈ //0, N//, are chosen so that [compare (8.2.3)]

(8.3.2)　　　$\sum W(J) * R(J) ** 2, J \in //0, N1//,$

$= \sum W(J) * (F(J) - \sum A(K) * U(K, J), K \in //0, N//,) ** 2, J \in //0, N1//,$

$= $ minimum.

In this case the *normal equations* may be written [compare (8.2.4b)], for each $M \in //0, N//,$

(8.3.3)　　　$\sum A(K) * (\sum W(J) * U(K, J) * U(M, J), J \in //0, N1//, ),$

　　　　　$K \in //0, N//,$

　　　　$= \sum W(J) * F(J) * U(M, J), J \in //0, N1//.$

The corresponding matrix equation is [compare (8.2.5)]

(8.3.4)　　　$TRAN(Q) * W * Q * S = TRAN(Q) * W * F,$

where the diagonal *weighting matrix* has the form

$$W = \begin{bmatrix} W(0) & 0 & 0 & \cdots & 0 \\ 0 & W(1) & 0 & \cdots & 0 \\ 0 & 0 & W(2) & \cdots & 0 \\ \vdots & \vdots & \vdots & & \vdots \\ 0 & 0 & 0 & \cdots & W(N1) \end{bmatrix}.$$

Remarks analogous to those of §8.2 concerning solvability of (8.2.5) apply here for (8.3.4).

## 8.4. LEAST SQUARE ESTIMATES OVER AN INTERVAL

This section is presented as a *list* of several important cases. We assume that the reader will investigate further some of these in more comprehensive texts listed in Suggested Reading, at the end of this chapter.

For various choices of interval $(A, B)$, weighting function $W(X)$ which is nonnegative and integrable on $(A, B)$, and functions $U(K, X), K \in //0, N//,$ also integrable on $(A, B)$, we seek a function

(8.4.1)　　　$P(X) = \sum A(K) * U(K, X), K \in //0, N//,$

which "best" estimates F(X) *on the interval* (A, B) in the *weighted least-square sense.* The coefficients A(K), K $\in$ //0, N//, are chosen so that

(8.4.2) $\int$ W(T) * (F(T) $-$ $\sum$ A(K) * U(K, T), K $\in$ //0, N//, ) ** 2,

over T $\in$ (A, B),

$=$ minimum.

The functions U(K, X), K $\in$ //0, N//, are usually chosen to be elements of a set of functions {U(J, X)|J $\in$ //0, $\infty$//} *orthogonal over* (A, B) *relative to the weighting function* W(X):

(8.4.3) $\int$ W(T) * U(P, T) * U(Q, T), over T $\in$ (A, B), $=$ 0, for P $\neq$ Q.

When each U(J, X) is a polynomial of degree J then {U(J, X)|J $\in$ //0, $\infty$ //} is a family of *orthogonal polynomials*—orthogonal over (A, B) relative to W(X).

The coefficients A(K), K $\in$ //0, N//, in the following five examples are usually computed using numerical integration methods like those considered in Chapter 10.

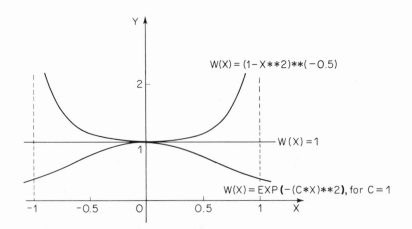

**Figure 8.4.1**

**Example 1.** [Fourier (Trigonometric) Polynomials]. If we choose (A, B) $=$ $(-\pi, \pi)$, W(X) $\equiv$ 1, N $=$ 2 * M, and the functions

(8.4.4a)

U(2 * K, X) $=$ COS (K * X), K $\in$ //0, M//,

U(2 * K $+$ 1, X) $=$ SIN ((K $+$ 1) * X), K $\in$ //0, M $-$ 1//, which are orthogonal over $(-\pi, \pi)$ relative to $W(X) \equiv 1$, then the coefficients $A(K), K \in //0, N//$, in (8.4.1) satisfying (8.4.2) are the Fourier Coefficients

(8.4.4b) $\qquad A(0) = \int F(T)$, over $T \in (-\pi, \pi)$, $/(2 * \pi)$

$$A(2*K+1) = \int F(T) * SIN((K+1) * T), \text{ over } T \in (-\pi, \pi), /\pi$$

$$\text{for } K \in //0, M-1//,$$

$$A(2*K) = \int F(T) * COS(K*T), \text{ over } T \in (-\pi, \pi), /\pi$$

$$\text{for } K \in //1, M//.$$

**Example 2.** (Estimates Using Orthogonal Polynomials). If the $U(K, X), K \in //0, N//$, are orthogonal polynomials, orthogonal over $(A, B)$ relative to $W(X)$, satisfying (8.4.3), then the coefficients $A(K), K \in //0, N//$, in (8.4.1) satisfying (8.4.2) are given by

(8.4.5) $\qquad A(K) = \int W(T) * F(T) * U(K, T), \text{ over } T \in (A, B), /$

$$\int W(T) * U(K, T) ** 2, \text{ over } T \in (A, B).$$

**Example 3.** (The Legendre Estimate: Constant Weight Function). This is Example 2 with $(A, B) = (-1, 1)$, and $W(X) \equiv 1$. The coefficients in (8.4.1) satisfying (8.4.2) are then, for each $K \in //0, N//$,

(8.4.6) $\qquad A(K) = (2*K + 1)/2 * \int F(T) * PL(K, T), \text{ over } T \in (-1, 1),$

where the $U(K, X) = PL(K, X)$ are the *Legendre Polynomials*

$$PL(0, X) \equiv 1, \quad PL(1, X) = X, \quad PL(2, X) = .5 * (3 * X ** 2 - 1),$$
$$PL(3, X) = .5 * (5 * X ** 3 - 3 * X),$$
$$PL(4, X) = (35 * X ** 4 - 30 * X ** 2 + 3)/8,$$

and in general we have the recurrence relation for Legendre Polynomials

(8.4.7) $\qquad PL(K + 1, X) = (2 * K + 1)/(K + 1) * X * PL(K, X)$
$$-K/(K + 1) * PL(K - 1, X).$$

**Example 4.** (Chebyshev Approximation). (Magnifies Error at Ends of the Interval). This is Example 2 with $(A, B) = (-1, 1)$, and $W(X) = 1/SQRT(1 - X ** 2)$. The coefficients in (8.4.1) satisfying (8.4.2) are then

(8.4.8a)     $A(0) = \int (1 - X ** 2) ** (-.5) * F(X)$, over $X \in (-1, 1), /\pi$

and for $K \in //1, N//$,

(8.4.8b)     $A(K) = \int (1 - X ** 2) ** (-.5) * F(X) * T(K; X)$,

over $X \in (-1, 1), * 2/\pi$,

where the $U(K, X) = T(K; X)$ are the *Chebyshev Polynomials*

$$T(0; X) \equiv 1, \quad T(1; X) = X, \quad T(2; X) = 2 * X ** 2 - 1,$$

and in general

(8.4.9)     $T(K + 1; X) = 2 * X * T(K; X) - T(K - 1; X)$.

Some properties of Chebyshev Polynomials were discussed in §7.4, see (7.4.14), et seq.

We have listed only three specific forms for $P(X)$ in (8.4.1). Other important examples are obtained when in Example 2 we choose $(A, B) = (-\infty, +\infty)$ and $W(X) = EXP(-(C * X) ** 2)$ for the Hermite Estimate, and choose $(A, B) = (0, + \infty)$ and $W(X) = EXP(-C * X)$ to obtain the Laguerre Estimate.

Even if we could execute the integration in (8.4.2) with the least-square $P(X)$ substituted, and if the value of this integral is K1, then we *cannot* (we could in the discrete case) say anything specific about the maximum of the error of the estimate, $E(X) = F(X) - P(X)$, at the grid points. For, at some $X(J)$ we could have $E(X(J)) ** 2 = (F(X(J)) - P(X(J))) ** 2$ large, but $E(X) ** 2$ could become small near $X(J)$ so fast that this contribution to K1 is very small. However, a sketch of $E(X)$ on $(A, B)$ is often used (with K1) to determine the acceptability of $P(X)$.

If a computed least-square function $P(X)$ in the form (8.4.1) is *not* acceptable as an estimate to $F(X)$ on $(A, B)$, and if a reasonable increase in N does not produce an acceptable $P(X)$, then sometimes a function $V(X)$ can be found such that $F(X)/V(X)$ *can* be estimated by a function $P(X)$ of the form (8.4.1); then an estimate to $F(X)$ is given by $V(X) * P(X)$.

**Example 5.** [An estimate for $F(X)/V(X)$]. Choose the form

(8.4.10)     $P(X) = V(X) * \sum A(K) * U(K, X), K \in //0, N//$.

And, corresponding to (8.4.2), choose

$$(8.4.11) \qquad \int W(T) * \big(F(T)/V(T) - \sum A(K) * U(K, T), K \in //0, N//, \big),$$

$$\text{over } T \in (A, B),$$

$$= \text{minimum.}$$

Then, the coefficients $A(K)$, $K \in //0, N//$, in (8.4.10) satisfying (8.4.11) are given by [compare (8.4.5)]

$$(8.4.12) \qquad A(K) = \int W(T) * \big(F(T)/V(T)\big) * U(K, T), \text{ over } T \in (A, B), /$$

$$\int W(T) * U(K, T) ** 2, \text{ over } T \in (A, B),$$

where the $U(K, X)$, $K \in //0, N//$, are orthogonal over $(A, B)$ relative to $W(X)$.

### SUGGESTED READING

1. Cheney, E. W. (1966): *Introduction to Approximation Theory*. McGraw-Hill Book Company. New York.
2. Davis, P. J. (1963): *Interpolation and Approximation*. Blaisdell Publishing Co., New York.
3. Hildebrand, F. B. (1956): *Introduction to Numerical Analysis*. McGraw-Hill Book Company, New York.

# 9 NUMERICAL DIFFERENTIATION

## 9.1. MOTIVATION. LAGRANGE FORMULAS

If we wish to estimate $F'(X)$ at a point $XX$ in terms of *known* values $F'(X(J))$, $J \in //0, N//$, then we could apply the methods of Chapter 7 (interpolation) and Chapter 8 (least-squares) to a table of $F'(X)$. For example, if $F'(X)$ has all the nice properties that we assumed $F(X)$ had in order to write (7.2.5) and (7.4.12), then we may write the estimate

$$(9.1.1a) \quad F'(X) \doteq \sum F'(X(J)) * LC(N, J; X), J \in //0, N//, \equiv PP(N; X)$$

with truncation error

$$(9.1.1b) \quad E(N; X) = F'(X) - PP(N; X)$$
$$= POLP(X) * DER ** (N + 1)F'(Z)/(N + 1)!$$
$$\text{for some } Z \text{ in } I(N),$$
$$= POLP(X) * DER ** (N + 2)F(Z)/(N + 1)!$$
$$\text{for some } Z \text{ in } I(N).$$

*Note.* Owing to the factor $DER ** (N + 2)F(Z)$, this last form for $E(N; X)$ may *look* better than some corresponding forms given below, but remember that values of $F'(X)$, not $F(X)$, are involved in the estimate $PP(N; X)$.

The estimate (9.1.1a) depends on the choice for $F'(X)$ [implicitly on $F(X)$] and the grid $X(J)$, $J \in //0, N//$.

We shall write a differentiation *formula*

$$(9.1.1c) \qquad F'(X) = PP(N;X) + E(N;X),$$

and the corresponding *operator*

$$(9.1.1d) \qquad T(F, GRID) \equiv F'(X) - PP(N;X).$$

The symbols $T(F, GRID)$ and $T(F, H)$ will also be used to denote truncation error for a formula. We say that a formula is of *degree* M for a specified grid, written $DEG(T) = M$, if $T(F, GRID) \equiv 0$, on the interval of interest, for $F(X)$ *any* polynomial of degree M *or less*, and $T(F, GRID) \not\equiv 0$ for $F(X)$ equal *some* polynomial of degree $M + 1$. Clearly, the formula corresponding to the estimate (9.1.1a) is of degree *at least* $N + 1$. Can you show $DEG(T) = N + 1$?

In this chapter we discuss briefly two other methods for obtaining formulas to estimate derivatives in terms of known values of $F(X)$ and/or known values of derivatives of $F(X)$. The first method consists in *picking a formula* that the user has reason to believe may give a usable estimate to the required derivative. The second method (§9.3) consists in *picking a form for the formula* and requiring that a set of conditions be satisfied—entirely analogous to the method used to get certain interpolation formulas in §7.3. This leads to a linear system which defines the coefficients of the form.

Useful representations of truncation error $T(F, GRID)$ for differentiation formulas defined by these methods are rare—except when the formula is equivalent to differentiating a Lagrange Polynomial, and even then only *at* grid points [see (9.1.3)]. However, in §9.2 assuming a uniform grid, we present examples of a general method for obtaining (sometimes useful) representations of truncation error for formulas defined by these methods.

For a uniform grid, representations of truncation error, written $T(F, H)$, are usually functions of higher derivatives of $F(X)$ at mysterious points times powers of the mesh length H. The constant coefficient and the power of H are the primary measures of the quality of a formula, since the nature of the derivatives involved is usually unknown. Of course, if $DER ** (N + 1)F(Z)$ is a factor of $T(F, H)$, then $T(F, H) \equiv 0$ for $F(X)$ any polynomial of degree $M \leq N$, so $DEG(T) \geq N$. The *exponent* of the highest power of H which is a factor of the truncation error is called the *order* of the formula. The name *order* is suggested by the assertion that the truncation error $T(F, H)$ of a formula of order P is at most of the order $H ** P$, written $T(F, H) = ORDB(H ** P)$. When we are not using a uniform grid, the *degree* of the formula, $DEG(T)$, is often used as a measure of its quality.

The remainder of this section is presented as a brief discussion of three classes of differentiation formulas which might be picked: derivatives of least-square polynomials, divided differences, and Lagrange Differentiation Formulas. Also, see the Exercises at the end of this section.

Our discussion of derivatives of least-square polynomials is indeed brief. The same arguments that lead us to use least-square estimates for F(X) are probably good enough to cause us to use the derivative of these least-square estimates to estimate F'(X). In particular, we do not want all the local maxima and minima that usually result when we "force" an interpolation polynomial through the specified points. Unfortunately, representations [like (9.1.1b)] of the truncation error for least-square estimates [of F(X) or F'(X)] are usually not available.

In §7.4 we showed, (7.4.17), that if F(X) has N + 1 continuous derivatives on an interval I(N), where I(N) is the smallest interval containing the distinct grid points X(J), J ∈ //0, N//, then for each XX in I(N), and XX not a grid point, *there exists* a Z in I(N) such that

(9.1.2)     [X(0), · · · , X(N), XX]F = DER ∗∗ (N + 1)F(Z)/(N + 1)!.

It may happen for some Z in I(N) that (9.1.2) does *not* hold for any XX in I(N). For example, if F(X) = X ∗∗ 3, N = 1, X(0) = 0, and X(1) = 1, so that I(N) = [0, 1], then

[X(0), X(1), XX]F = XX + 1, and DER ∗∗ (2)F(Z)/2! = 3 ∗ Z.

Thus, if Z ∈ (2/3, 1], then there is *no* XX ∈ [0, 1] so that (9.1.2) is satisfied. That is, given a Z, we may not be able to find an appropriate XX so that the divided difference in (9.1.2) gives the desired derivative at Z. Nevertheless, as indicated in (7.4.18), we sometimes *pick* divided differences to estimate derivatives. In §9.2 we indicate a method for computing the truncation error of such estimates.

As suggested in fundamental Problem 3 of §6.4, estimates to F'(X) may be obtained by differentiating polynomial estimates to F(X). Since a Lagrange Interpolation Polynomial P(N; X) usually *cuts* the function being estimated at the interpolation points (X(J), F(J)), J ∈ //0, N//, see Figure 7.1.1, then P'(N; X) is not likely to be a good estimate to F'(X) near the interpolation points. However, we may be able to use a representation of the truncation error of this estimate to F'(X) at the grid points as a bound on the error near the grid points.

The truncation error of the estimate to F(X) by the Lagrange Interpolation Polynomial P(N; X) characterized by (7.4.1) may be written (7.4.12)

$$E(N; X) = F(X) - P(N; X)$$
$$= POLP(X) * DER ** (N + 1)F(Z(X))/(N + 1)!.$$

Then

(9.1.3)    $E'(N; X) = F'(X) - P'(N; X)$
$$= POLP(X) * DER(DER ** (N + 1)F(Z(X)))/(N + 1)!$$
$$+ DER ** (N + 1)F(Z(X)) * DER(POLP(X))/(N + 1)!.$$

A knowledge of $Z(X)$ is required to compute the derivative in the first term of $E'(N; X)$. But since $POLP(X(J)) = 0, J \in //0, N//$, then *at each grid point* $X(J)$

(9.1.4a)   $E'(N; X(J))$
$$= DER ** (N + 1)F(Z(X(J)))$$
$$* (PROD(X(J) - X(K)), K \in //0, N//, \text{and } K \neq J,)/(N + 1)!.$$

And, if we have a uniform grid with $X(K) = X(0) + H * K, K \in //0, N//$, then we have *at* $X(J)$

(9.1.4b)   $E'(N; X(J)) = DER ** (N + 1)F(Z(X(J)))$
$$* (-1) ** (N - J) * J! * H ** N/(N + 1)!.$$

Again, we may estimate $|E'(N; X(J))|$ by getting bounds on the derivative factor. The sum $|E'(N; X(J))| + |E'(N; X(J + 1))|$ is probably an upper bound for the truncation error $E'(N; X)$ on the interval $[X(J), X(J + 1)]$. Similarly, $2 * MAX|E'(N; X(J))|$, over $J \in //0, N//$, is probably an upper bound for $E'(N; X)$ on $I(N)$. The *degree* of the formula $F'(X) = P'(N; X) + E'(N; X)$ is N. With a uniform grid, the *order* of the formula is N.

We shall list, for a uniform grid with mesh H, some *Lagrange Differentiation Formulas* (derivatives of Lagrange Polynomials *at* grid points) with truncation error given by (9.1.4b). The formulas are presented here as a linear combination of ordinates, obtained by evaluating at $X(J)$ the derivative of (7.4.2) where $P(N; X)$ is given in the form (7.3.9). As usual, we write $F(K)$ for $F(X(K))$, and $Z(J)$ for $Z(X(J))$.

(9.1.5a)      $F'(J) = \sum F(K) * DER(LC(N, K; X(J))), K \in //0, N//,$
$$+ E'(N; X(J))$$

and $E'(N; X(J))$ is (9.1.4b). Since $H ** N$ is a factor of $E'(N; X(J))$, the *order* of the formula (9.1.5a) is N. The formula (9.1.5a) has the form

(9.1.5b)     $F'(J) = \sum F(K) * A(K, H), K \in //0, N//, + T(F, H),$

where the $A(K, H)$ depend only on the assumed (fixed) uniform grid and the fixed $X(J)$, and the truncation error $T(F, H)$ depends only on H and the choice of function whose derivative is being estimated at $X(J)$.

**Example.** If $N = 2$ and $J = 0$, then (9.1.5a) becomes

$$F'(0) = F(0) * DER \big((X - X(1)) * (X - X(2))/$$
$$\big((X(0) - X(1)) * (X(0) - X(2))\big)\big), \text{ at } X = X(0),$$
$$+ F(1) * DER\big((X - X(0)) * (X - X(2))/$$
$$\big((X(1) - X(0)) * (X(1) - X(2))\big)\big), \text{ at } X = X(0),$$
$$+ F(2) * DER\big((X - X(0)) * (X - X(1))/$$
$$\big((X(2) - X(0)) * (X(2) - X(1))\big)\big), \text{ at } X = X(0),$$
$$+ F'''(Z(0)) * (X(0) - X(1)) * (X(0) - X(2))/3!$$
$$= F(0) * \big((X(0) - X(1)) + (X(0) - X(2))\big)/$$
$$\big((X(0) - X(1)) * (X(0) - X(2))\big)$$
$$+ F(1) * (X(0) - X(2))/\big((X(1) - X(0)) * (X(1) - X(2))\big)$$
$$+ F(2) * (X(0) - X(1))/\big((X(2) - X(0)) * (X(2) - X(1))\big)$$
$$+ F'''(Z(0)) * (X(0) - X(1)) * (X(0) - X(2))/3!$$
$$= F(0) * (-3 * H)/(2 * H ** 2) + F(1) * (-2 * H)/(-H ** 2)$$
$$+ F(2) * (-H)/(2 * H ** 2) + F'''(Z(0)) * (2 * H ** 2)/3!.$$

Our differentiation formula with truncation error as indicated [obtained by differentiating the Lagrange Polynomial which passes through the three points $(X(J), F(J))$, $J \in //0, 2//$, and evaluating the derived polynomial at $X(0)$] has the form

$$F'(0) = 1/(2 * H) * \big(-3 * F(0) + 4 * F(1) - F(2)\big)$$
$$+ (1/3) * H ** 2 * F'''(Z(0)).$$

This is the first entry in Table 9.1.1 Each of the formulas is of *order* N, and of *degree* N.

**Table 9.1.1** LAGRANGE DIFFERENTIATION FORMULAS

$F'(J) = \sum F(K) * A(K, H), K \in //0, N//, +T(F, H)$.
The $T(F, H)$ are defined by (9.1.4b).

### N = 2. Three Points.

$F'(0) = 1/(2 * H) * (-3 * F(0) + 4 * F(1) - F(2)) + H ** 2/3 * DER ** (3)F(Z(0))$.
$F'(1) = 1/(2 * H) * (-F(0) + F(2)) - H ** 2/6 * DER ** (3)F(Z(1))$.
$F'(2) = 1/(2 * H) * (F(0) - 4 * F(1) + 3 * F(2)) + H ** 2/3 * DER ** (3)F(Z(2))$.

### N = 3. Four Points.

$F'(0) = 1/(6 * H) * (-11 * F(0) + 18 * F(1) - 9 * F(2) + 2 * F(3))$
$\quad - H ** 3/4 * DER ** (4)F(Z(0))$.
$F'(1) = 1/(6 * H) * (-2 * F(0) - 3 * F(1) + 6 * F(2) - F(3))$
$\quad + H ** 3/12 * DER ** (4)F(Z(1))$.
$F'(2) = 1/(6 * H) * (F(0) - 6 * F(1) + 3 * F(2) + 2 * F(3))$
$\quad - H ** 3/12 * DER ** (4)F(Z(2))$.
$F'(3) = 1/(6 * H) * (-2 * F(0) + 9 * F(1) - 18 * F(2) + 11 * F(3))$
$\quad + H ** 3/4 * DER ** (4)F(Z(3))$.

### N = 4. Five Points.

$F'(0) = 1/(12 * H) * (-25 * F(0) + 48 * F(1) - 36 * F(2) + 16 * F(3) - 3 * F(4))$
$\quad + H ** 4/5 * DER ** (5)F(Z(0))$.
$F'(1) = 1/(12 * H) * (-3 * F(0) - 10 * F(1) + 18 * F(2) - 6 * F(3) + F(4))$
$\quad - H ** 4/20 * DER ** (5)F(Z(1))$.
$F'(2) = 1/(12 * H) * (F(0) - 8 * F(1) + 8 * F(3) - F(4))$
$\quad + H ** 4/30 * DER ** (5)F(Z(2))$.
$F'(3) = 1/(12 * H) * (-F(0) + 6 * F(1) - 18 * F(2) + 10 * F(3) + 3 * F(4))$
$\quad - H ** 4/20 * DER ** (5) F(Z(3))$.
$F'(4) = 1/(12 * H) * (3 * F(0) - 16 * F(1) + 36 * F(2) - 48 * F(3) + 25 * F(4))$
$\quad + H ** 4/5 * DER ** (5)F(Z(4))$.

When $N = 2 * M$, the Lagrange Formula for $F'(M)$ does not involve $F(M)$ explicitly. This formula involves N ordinates but has a truncation error term which we would expect only when $N + 1$ ordinates are involved. Also, the coefficient of $H ** N * DER ** (N + 1)F(Z)$ is *smallest* in this case. Thus, these *central formulas are preferred* to other Lagrange Differentiation Formulas which involve N ordinates [except of course at the beginning or end of a table of $F(X)$ where some ordinates needed in the central formula are not available].

We could have obtained equivalent formulas represented as linear combinations of forward, backward, or central differences of $F(X)$ by differentiating $P(N; X)$ in the forms (7.3.4), (7.3.7), or if $N = 2 * M$ (7.3.32b), respectively. For example, using (7.3.4),

(9.1.6)      $F'(J) = \sum \Delta ** (K)F(0) * DER\,(BINCO(S, K))$

$* DER\,(S(X)),\ K \in //0, N//,\ \text{at } S = J,$

$+ E'\,(N; X(J)),$

where $DER\,(S(X)) \equiv 1/H.$

1. Execute an analysis similar to that which led to (9.1.3) and (9.1.4a, b) to obtain a Taylor Polynomial estimate to $F'(X(J))$, where $C \neq X(J)$. Does the corresponding truncation error term simplify, as where (9.1.3) became (9.1.4a)?

   *Hint.* Differentiate (2.2.2b) with (2.2.1) substituted. Compare Example 5 of §9.3, below. [They are the same estimate if $J = 1$ and $C = X(0)$, but notice the very different representations for T(F, H). That is, compare your form for T(F, H) with (9.3.11a), and in general with (9.3.11b).]

2. Argue that $P'(N; XX, C)$ is probably a good estimate to $F'(XX)$ for XX close to C, and $N \geq 1$. Why don't we use it?

   *Answer.* We probably would if XX were close to C and if the *required* derivatives at C were available; they usually are not available when F(X) is a table.

### 9.2. TRUNCATION ERROR USING TAYLOR'S FORMULA

In this section we indicate by examples a method for deriving representations of the truncation error for expressions (possibly defined empirically) which might be used to estimate derivatives. The basic tool for this method is Taylor's Formula, (2.2.2), with $X = X(J)$ and $C = X(K)$,

(9.2.1)     $F(X(J)) = P(N; X(J), X(K)) + R(N; X(J), X(K))$

$= \sum DER ** (M)F(X(K)) * (X(J) - X(K)) ** M/M!,$

$M \in //0, N//,$

$+ DER ** (N + 1)F(Z(J))$

$* (X(J) - X(K)) ** (N + 1)/(N + 1)!,$

where $Z(J) = Z(X(J))$ is known only to be between X(J) and X(K).

We assume that a uniform grid with mesh H is used, and that a formula has been *picked* to estimate a derivative *at* a grid point. The basic idea of the method is to *replace in the estimate* values of $F(X)$ and its derivatives at grid points with equivalent values given by Taylor's Formula to obtain

$$(9.2.2) \qquad \text{(Estimate)} = \text{(Function being estimated)}$$
$$- \text{(Truncation error)}.$$

Of course, we want the expression for the truncation error to (i) have a factor $H ** P$ with P as large as possible, and (ii) have the lowest order derivative involved to be as high as possible.

**Example 1.** Find the truncation error for the estimate

$$(9.2.3) \qquad F'\big(X(0)\big) \doteq [X(0), X(1)]F = \Delta F(0)/H = \big(F(1) - F(0)\big)/H.$$

We want to write the divided difference in the form

$$(9.2.4) \qquad \big(F(1) - F(0)\big)/H = F'(0) - T(F, H).$$

First, observe that we want $F'(0)$, so expand $F(1)$ about $X(0)$ using (9.2.1) with $N = 1, K = 0,$ and $J = 1$

$$F(1) = F(0) + H * F'(0) + .5 * H ** 2 * F''\big(Z(1)\big).$$

We substitute this in the left member of (9.2.4) to obtain

$$\big(F(1) - F(0)\big)/H = \big((F(0) + H * F'(0) + .5 * H ** 2 * F''(Z(1))\big) - F(0)\big)/H$$
$$= F'(0) + .5 * H * F''\big(Z(1)\big).$$

Thus the truncation error for the estimation of $F'(0)$ by the first divided difference $[X(0), X(1)]F$ is

$$(9.2.5) \qquad T(F, H) = F'(0) - \big(F(1) - F(0)\big)/H = -.5 * H * F''\big(Z(1)\big).$$

The formula has *order* 1 and *degree* 1. Clearly, in this trivial case, (9.2.5) could be obtained by solving for $-.5 * H * F''\big(Z(1)\big)$ in the above representation of $F(1)$ by Taylor's Formula.

*Note.* We use $T(F, H)$ to denote the truncation error for an estimate "at a specific point". The *form* for $T(F, H)$ does not depend on the particular point at which an estimate is applied—but depends on the *relative* positions of the points involved in the estimate. For example, the estimate

$$F'(K) \doteq \big(F(K + 1) - F(K)\big)/H$$

corresponds to the formula

$$F'(K) = \big(F(K + 1) - F(K)\big)/H + T(F, H)$$

with truncation error

$$T(F, H) = F'(K) - \big(F(K + 1) - F(K)\big)/H$$
$$= -.5 * H * F''\big(Z(K)\big).$$

With $K = 0$, compare (9.2.3), (9.2.4), and (9.2.5). We often refer to statements for truncation error, like (9.2.5), as "the formula," when they involve the estimating function explicitly. We will usually pick a specific $K$ at which the estimate is applied whenever notation for an analysis is simplified.

**Example 2.** Find the truncation error for the estimate (this corresponds to the second Lagrange Formula in Table 9.1.1)

$$(9.2.6) \qquad F'(1) \doteq \big(F(2) - F(0)\big)/(2 * H).$$

The estimate (9.2.6) involves only two ordinates, but the formula has *order* 2 and *degree* 2. Here we write Taylor's Formula, (9.2.1) with $K = 1$,

$$F(2) = F(1) + H * F'(1) + .5 * H ** 2 * F''(1) + H ** 3/6 * F'''\big(Z(2)\big)$$

$$F(0) = F(1) - H * F'(1) + .5 * H ** 2 * F''(1) - H ** 3/6 * F'''\big(Z(0)\big).$$

On substitution in the right side of (9.2.6) we get

$$\big(F(2) - F(0)\big)/(2 * H) = F'(1) + H ** 2/6 * \big(F'''\big(Z(2)\big) + F'''\big(Z(0)\big)\big)/2.$$

Thus, if $F'''(X)$ is continuous between $Z\big(X(2)\big)$ and $Z\big(X(0)\big)$, then the truncation error for the estimate (9.2.6) is

$$(9.2.7) \qquad T(F, H) = F'(1) - \big(F(2) - F(0)\big)/(2 * H) = -H ** 2/6 * F'''(P),$$

for some $P$ between $Z\big(X(2)\big)$ and $Z\big(X(0)\big)$. This is the form of the truncation error in the corresponding Lagrange Formula. The representations of the truncation error for Lagrange Formulas in Table 9.1.1 are not always so easily obtained by this method, as is seen in the following example.

**Example 3.** Find the truncation error for the estimate (the first Lagrange Formula in Table 9.1.1)

$$(9.2.8) \qquad F'(0) \doteq \big(-3 * F(0) + 4 * F(1) - F(2)\big)/(2 * H).$$

Write

$$F(0) = F(0)$$

$$F(1) = F(0) + H * F'(0) + .5 * H ** 2 * F''(0) + H ** 3/6 * F'''\big(Z(1)\big)$$

$$F(2) = F(0) + 2 * H * F'(0) + 2 * H ** 2 * F''(0) + 8 * H ** 3/6 * F'''\big(Z(2)\big),$$

and compute

$$-3 * F(0) + 4 * F(1) - F(2)$$
$$= 2 * H * F'(0) + 2 * H ** 3/3 * \big(F'''\big(Z(1)\big) - 2 * F'''\big(Z(2)\big)\big),$$

so that the truncation error for the estimate (9.2.8) is

$$(9.2.9) \qquad T(F, H) = F'(0) - \big(-3 * F(0) + 4 * F(1) - F(2)\big)/(2 * H)$$
$$= H ** 2/3 * \big(2 * F'''\big(Z(2)\big) - F'''\big(Z(1)\big)\big).$$

It is not obvious that this is equivalent to the representation of the truncation error for the corresponding Lagrange Formula. However, from (9.2.9) we see the formula has *order* 2 and *degree* 2.

**Example 4.** Find the truncation error for the estimate [compare (9.1.2)]

(9.2.10)      $F''(1) \doteq 2 * [X(0), X(1), X(2)]F = \Delta ** (2)F(0)/H ** 2$

                $= (F(2) - 2 * F(1) + F(0))/H ** 2.$

Write

     $F(0) = F(1) - H * F'(1) + .5 * H ** 2 * F''(1) - H ** 3/6 * F'''(Z(0))$

     $F(1) = F(1)$

     $F(2) = F(1) + H * F'(1) + .5 * H ** 2 * F''(1) + H ** 3/6 * F'''(Z(2)),$

and compute

     $F(2) - 2 * F(1) + F(0) = H ** 2 * F''(1) - H ** 3/6 *(F'''(Z(0)) - F'''(Z(2))),$

so that the truncation error for the estimate (9.2.10) is

(9.2.11)      $T(F, H) = F''(1) - (F(2) - 2 * F(1) + F(0))/H ** 2$

                $= H/6 * (F'''(Z(0)) - F'''(Z(2))).$

The formula has *order* 1 and *degree* at least 2. [We could expand $F'''(Z(2))$ about $Z(0)$, etc.]

## EXERCISES

**1.** For each of the estimates in Examples 1 through 4 write a corresponding estimate *applied at* X(K).

*Hint.* Use the Note after Example 1.

**2.** For each estimate you obtained in Exercise 1 write the corresponding truncation error terms, $T(F, H)$.

### 9.3. DIFFERENTIATION FORMULAS BY THE METHOD OF UNDETERMINED COEFFICIENTS

In the first part of §7.3 we discussed a method (called *undetermined coefficients*) for computing the coefficients of an assumed form for an interpolation function by solving a linear system defined by requiring that the assumed form satisfy a specified set of conditions. For example, the coefficients in the polynomial (7.3.3) were obtained by solving the linear system defined by the requirement that polynomial form (7.3.2) satisfy conditions (7.3.1).

In this section we indicate by examples how the method of undetermined coefficients can be applied to obtain differentiation formulas.

**Example 1.** The Lagrange Differentiation Formulas (Table 9.1.1) for any specified uniform grid may be written (9.1.5b)

(9.3.1)     $T(F, H) = F'(J) - \sum F(K) * A(K, H), K \in //0, N//,$

where, since the degree of the formula is N,

(9.3.2)     $T(P, H) = P'(X(J)) - \sum P(X(K)) * A(K, H), K \in //0, N//, = 0$

for *any* polynomial $P(X)$ of degree N or less. In particular, $T(P, H) = 0$ for P each of the polynomials

$$1, X - X(J), (X - X(J)) ** 2, (X - X(J)) ** 3, \cdots, (X - X(J)) ** N.$$

Conversely, from the linearity of $T(F, H)$ in F and $F'$, if

(9.3.3)     $T((X - X(J)) ** M, H) = 0,$ for each $M \in //0, N//,$

then $T(P, H) = 0$ for P any polynomial of degree N or less. Therefore, $T(P, H) = 0$ for P the Lagrange Polynomial which agrees with $F(X)$ at the $N + 1$ grid points involved in (9.3.1). So, the *form*[1] (9.3.1) with coefficients $A(K, H), K \in //0, N//,$ determined so that the conditions (9.3.3) are satisfied *is* a Lagrange Differentiation Formula with truncation error (9.1.4a, b). The conditions (9.3.3) define a linear system which has a unique solution with components the cofficients $A(K, H), K \in //0, N//,$ in the form (9.3.1). We choose the polynomials $1, X - X(J), (X - X(J)) ** 2,$ etc., so that the coefficients in the linear system (9.3.3) will be functions of H. The existence and uniqueness of coefficients in (9.3.1) satisfying (9.3.3) is clear if we pick P each of the polynomials $1, X, X ** 2, \cdots, X ** N,$ so that $T(X ** M, H) = 0,$ $M \in //0, N//,$ is a linear system with matrix of coefficients having determinant the nonsingular Vandermonde Determinant.

**Example 2.** Using the method of Example 1 derive the second formula of Table 9.1.1. Pick the form (9.3.1)

(9.3.4a)     $T(F, H) = F'(1) - (A0 * F(0) + A1 * F(1) + A2 * F(2)).$

The conditions (9.3.3) become [using $F = 1, X - X(1),$ and $(X - X(1)) ** 2$]

$$T(1, H) = 0 - (A0 * 1 + A1 * 1 + A2 * 1) = 0$$

(9.3.4b)     $T(X - X(1), H) = 1 - (A0 * (X(0) - X(1)) + A1 * (X(1) - X(1))$
$$+ A2 * (X(2) - X(1))) = 0$$

$$T((X - X(1)) ** 2, H) = 2 * (X(1) - X(1)) - (A0 * (X(0) - X(1)) ** 2$$
$$+ A1 * (X(1) - X(1)) ** 2$$
$$+ A2 * (X(2) - X(1)) ** 2) = 0.$$

This linear system may be written

$$A0 + A1 + A2 = 0$$
$$- H * A0 \qquad + H * A2 = 1$$
$$H ** 2 * A0 + H ** 2 * A2 = 0$$

---

[1]In this context $T(F, H)$ is a *linear functional* with domain DOM a set of functions F, and range RNG a set of numbers. See §6.2.

with unique solution $(A0, A1, A2) = \left(-1/(2 * H), 0, 1/(2 * H)\right)$ so that (9.3.4a) becomes

(9.3.4c)          $T(F, H) = F'(1) - 1/(2 * H) * \left(-F(0) + F(2)\right).$

*Note.* If we had chosen

(9.3.5)          $T(F, H) = F'(1) - \left(A0 * F(0) + A1 * F(2)\right),$

then (9.3.3) becomes [using $F = 1, X - X(1)$]

$$A0 + \quad A1 = 0$$
$$-H * A0 + H * A1 = 1,$$

which has solution $(A0, A1) = \left(-1/(2 * H), 1/(2 * H)\right)$, again defining (9.3.4c). Since there are two undetermined coefficients in (9.3.5), we would expect the truncation error, (9.1.4b), to be a constant times $H * F''(Z(1))$. But, as seen in Example 2 of §9.2, the truncation error actually is $-H ** 2/6 * F'''(Z(1))$, as we would expect from the three-coefficient form (9.3.4a).

In the following examples we indicate how the method of Example 1 may be extended to obtain differentiation formulas that are equivalent to differentiating interpolation functions other than Lagrange Polynomials.

**Example 3.** Suppose one has reason to believe that the derivative of the interpolation polynomial P(X) characterized by

(9.3.6a)          $P\left(X(J)\right) = F(J), J \in //0, 1//$, and $P'\left(X(0)\right) = F'(0)$

will give a usable estimate to $F'(X)$ at $X(1)$. We may compute the coefficients of $F(0), F(1)$, and $F'(0)$ in the formula

(9.3.6b)          $T(F, H) = F'(1) - \left(A * F(0) + B * F(1) + C * F'(0)\right)$

by a method similar to that of Example 1. We require that (9.3.6b) be *exact*[2] for any polynomial of degree two or less. In particular, we require that

(9.3.6c)          $T\left((X - X(1)) ** M, H\right) = 0$, for each $M \in //0, 2//$.

That is,

$$T(1, H) = 0 - (A * 1 + B * 1 + C * 0) = 0$$
$$T\left(X - X(1), H\right) = 1 - \left(A * (X(0) - X(1)) + B * (X(1) - X(1))\right.$$
$$\left. + C * 1\right) = 0$$
$$T\left((X - X(1)) **2, H\right) = 2 * (X(1) - X(1)) - \left(A * (X(0) - X(1)) ** 2\right.$$
$$+ B * (X(1) - X(1)) ** 2$$
$$\left. + C * 2 * (X(0) - X(1))\right) = 0,$$

or

$$
\begin{bmatrix} 1 & 1 & 0 \\ -H & 0 & 1 \\ H**2 & 0 & -2*H \end{bmatrix} * \begin{bmatrix} A \\ B \\ C \end{bmatrix} = \begin{bmatrix} 0 \\ 1 \\ 0 \end{bmatrix},
$$

which has solution TRAN[A  B  C] = TRAN[−2/H  2/H  −1]. Thus, the differentiation formula

(9.3.7a)     $F'(1) = -2/H * F(0) + 2/H * F(1) - F'(0) + T(F, H)$

is exact [T(F, H) = 0] whenever F(X) is *any* polynomial of degree two or less. In particular, (9.3.7a) is exact for the interpolation polynomial P(X) characterized by (9.3.6a). We now find a representation of the truncation error for (9.3.7a) using the method of §9.2. We write

$$F(0) = F(1) - H * F'(1) + H ** 2/2 * F''(1) - H ** 3/6 * F'''(Z(0))$$

$$F(1) = F(1)$$

$$F'(0) = F'(1) - H * F''(1) + H ** 2/2 * F'''(Z1(0))$$

and compute

$$-2/H * F(0) + 2/H * F(1) - F'(0) = F'(1) - H ** 2/6$$
$$* \big(3 * F'''(Z1(0)) - 2 * F'''(Z(0))\big).$$

Thus, the truncation error for the formula (9.3.7a) is

(9.3.7b)     $T(F, H) = F'(1) - \big(-2/H * F(0) + 2/H * F(1) - F'(0)\big)$
$$= H ** 2/6 * \big(3 * F'''(Q) - 2 * F'''(R)\big),$$

where Q and R are generally unknown numbers between X(0) and X(1). From (9.3.7b) it is again clear that T(F, H) = 0 if F(X) is any polynomial of degree two or less. The formula (9.3.7a) has *order* 2 and *degree* 2.

**Example 4.** Find the coefficients in the estimate

(9.3.8a)     $F''(1) \doteq A * F'(0) + B * F'(1) + C * F''(0)$

so that the corresponding formula is exact for F'(X) any polynomial of degree two or less. Obviously the coefficients here are exactly those of the formula (9.3.7a). The truncation error for (9.3.8a) is [compare (9.3.7b)]

(9.3.8b)     $T(F, H) = F''(1) - \big(-2/H * F'(0) + 2/H * F'(1) - F''(0)\big)$
$$= H ** 2/6 * \big(3 * DER ** (4)F(Q) - 2 * DER ** (4)F(R)\big).$$

Here, the *order* of the formula is 2, while the *degree in F* is 3 *and* the *degree in F'* is 2.

*Note.* If we had tried to define the coefficients of (9.3.8a) by requiring that

$$T\big((X - X(1)) ** M, H\big) = 0, \text{ for each } M \in //0, 2//,$$

then we would have obtained only two equations in the three unknowns A, B, and C. The equation corresponding to M = 0 is 0 = 0. To determine the coefficients uniquely we need another equation which may be obtained by adding the condition $T\big((X - X(1)) ** 3, H\big) = 0$.

**Example 5.** Find the coefficients in the estimate

(9.3.9) $$F'(1) \doteq A * F(0) + B * F'(0) + C * F''(0)$$

so that the corresponding formula is exact for any polynomial of degree two or less. We write

$$T(F, H) = F'(1) - \big(A * F(0) + B * F'(0) + C * F''(0)\big)$$

and require that

$$T\big((X - X(1)) ** M, H\big) = 0, \text{ for each } M \in //0, 2//.$$

That is,

$$\begin{bmatrix} 1 & 0 & 0 \\ -H & 1 & 0 \\ H ** 2 & -2 * H & 2 \end{bmatrix} * \begin{bmatrix} A \\ B \\ C \end{bmatrix} = \begin{bmatrix} 0 \\ 1 \\ 0 \end{bmatrix},$$

which has solution TRAN [A B C] = TRAN [0 1 H]. The differentiation formula corresponding to (9.3.9) is then

(9.3.10) $$F'(1) = F'(0) + H * F''(0) + T(F, H).$$

Since the formula must be exact for the second degree Taylor Polynomial $P(2; X, X(0))$, which agrees with $F(X)$, $F'(X)$, and $F''(X)$ at $X(0)$, then the estimating function in (9.3.10) is $P'(2; X(1), X(0))$. But $P'(2; X(1), X(0))$ for $F(X)$ is just $P(1; X(1), X(0))$ for $F'(X)$, which has truncation error

(9.3.11a) $$T(F, H) = R(1; X(1), X(0)) = F'(1) - \big(F'(0) + H * F''(0)\big)$$

$$= H ** 2 * F'''\big(Z(1)\big)/2!.$$

In general, if $N \geq K$, then DER $** (K)P(N; X(1), X(0))$ for $F(X)$ is just $P(N - K; X(1), X(0))$ for DER $** (K)F(X)$, and we have the formula

(9.3.11b) $$T(F, H) = \text{DER} ** (K)F(1)$$

$$- \big(P(N - K; X(1), X(0)) \text{ for DER } ** (K)F(X)\big)$$

$$= R(N - K; X(1), X(0)) \text{ for DER } ** (K)F(X)$$

$$= H ** (N - K + 1)/(N - K + 1)!$$

$$* \text{DER} ** (N + 1)F\big(Z(1)\big).$$

The *order* of the formula is $(N - K + 1)$, while its degree in F is always N.

### SUGGESTED READING

1. Milne, W.E. (1949): *Numerical Calculus.* Princeton University Press. Princeton, N.J.

2. Hildebrand, F.B. (1956): *Introduction to Numerical Analysis.* McGraw-Hill Book Company, New York.

# 10 NUMERICAL INTEGRATION

## 10.1. MOTIVATION. LAGRANGE FORMULAS

Two important problems involving numerical integration require methods for the estimation of the definite integral

$$(10.1.1) \qquad DI(F; A, B) \equiv \int F(X), \text{ over } X \in (A, B),$$

and the indefinite integral

$$(10.1.2) \qquad II(F, Z) \equiv \int F(X), \text{ over } X \in (A, Z).$$

We sometimes use the symbol $DI(F; A, B)$ in an analysis to simplify notation.

Most numerical integration formulas are obtained by replacing $F(X)$ by an interpolation polynomial $P(X)$ with truncation error $E(X) = F(X) - P(X)$, and performing the indicated integration.[1] For example. we write the *formula*

---

[1]For other formulas see [5]—for example, see page 166.

(10.1.3a)     $DI(F; A, B) \equiv \int F(X)$, over $X \in (A, B)$,

$$= \int (P(X) + E(X)), \text{ over } X \in (A, B),$$

$$= DI(P; A, B) + DI(E; A, B)$$

$$= \text{(The estimate)} + \text{(Truncation error)},$$

and we write the truncation error for the estimate in the form

(10.1.3b)     $T(F, GRID) = DI(E; A, B)$

$$= \int (F(X) - P(X)), \text{ over } X \in (A, B),$$

$$= DI(F; A, B) - DI(P; A, B).$$

A rather general form for such formulas is given in (10.3.3), when we discuss a theorem that defines the truncation error for many of our useful formulas. The coefficients of the form are usually obtained by the method of undetermined coefficients discussed in §10.5.

The remainder of this section is a rather long-winded discussion of some properties of estimates and the associated truncation error defined using $P(X) = P(N; X)$, the Lagrange Interpolation Polynomial. Terms introduced here are explained briefly when they occur in later sections, thus the reader may choose to skip from Example 1, below, to §10.2.

When $P(X)$ is the Lagrange Polynomial $P(N; X)$ characterized by

(10.1.4)     $P(N; X(J)) = F(X(J)), J \in //0, N//$,

and when $F(X)$ has $N + 1$ continuous derivatives on the smallest interval $I(N)$ containing $X$ and the distinct grid points $X(J), J \in //0, N//$, then (7.4.12)

(10.1.5)     $E(N; X) = F(X) - P(N; X)$

$$= POLP(X) * DER ** (N + 1)F(Z(X))/(N + 1)!.$$

With $P(N; X)$ given by (7.3.9), then (10.1.3a) defines the *Lagrange Integration Formula* [we write $F(K)$ for $F(X(K))$]

(10.1.6a)    $DI(F; A, B) \equiv \int F(X)$, over $X \in (A, B)$,

$$= \int (P(N; X) + E(N; X)), \text{ over } X \in (A, B),$$

$$= \int (\sum F(K) * LC(N, K; X), K \in //0, N//, ), \text{ over } X \in (A, B),$$

$$+ \int POLP(X) * DER ** (N + 1)F(Z(X))/(N + 1)!, \text{ over } X \in (A, B),$$

$$= \sum F(K) * DI(LC(N, K; X); A, B), K \in //0, N//, + T(F, GRID)$$

$$= \sum F(K) * B(K), K \in //0, N//, + T(F, GRID).$$

The coefficients B(K) are integrals of Lagrange Coefficients that depend only on the relative positions of the grid points. With a uniform grid, we sometimes write B(K, H),

When the variable of integration is changed by a transformation of the form

$$X = XX(T) = C * T + D, \text{ with } C \neq 0$$

so that A1, B1, and a grid T(J), J $\in //0, N//$, are defined by T(J) = (X(J) − D)/C, etc., then

$$B(K) = DI(LC(N, K; X); A, B)$$
$$= C * DI(LC(N, K; XX(T)); A1, B1)$$
$$\equiv C * BB(K),$$

where the BB(K) are integrals over (A1, B1) of the Lagrange Coefficients for the grid T(J), J $\in //0, N//$. Also (10.1.6a) becomes

(10.1.6b)    $DI(F; A, B) = DI(F(XX(T)) * XX'(T); A1, B1)$
$$= \sum F(XX(T(K))) * B(K), K \in //0, N//,$$
$$+ T(F, GRID)$$
[since XX(T(K)) = X(K)] $= \sum F(K) * C * BB(K), K \in //0, N//,$
$$+ T(F, GRID)$$
$$= C * \sum F(K) * BB(K), K \in //0, N//,$$
$$+ T(F, GRID).$$

The truncation error is the same expression throughout (10.1.6a) and (10.1.6b):

$$T(F, GRID) = DI(POLP(X) * DER ** (N + 1)F(Z(X)) ; A, B)/$$
$$(N + 1)!.$$

*Note.* Sometimes we include the independent variable in the symbol DI, for clarity.

The BB(K) have been *tabulated* for certain choices of A1, B1, and grid $T(J), J \in //0, N//$. For example, see Tables 10.2.1, 2, 3, 4 of §10.2, where the grid is assumed uniform. Also, see Example 1 in §10.4, where the not-necessarily-uniform grid is assumed to be the set of zeros of a polynomial of degree $N + 1$.

The form (10.1.6b) is useful when we *have* one set of coefficients, say the BB(K), that defines an estimate to the integral of F(X) over an interval (A1, B1) using a specified grid, and we *want to use this formula* to estimate an integral over another interval, say (A, B).

**Example 1.** *Given* the formula

$$DI(F; A1, B1) = \int F(T), \text{ over } T \in (A1, B1),$$

$$= \sum F(T(K)) * BB(K), K \in //0, N//, + T(F, GRID).$$

We are looking to *find* the corresponding formula for $\int G(X)$, over $X \in (A, B)$. The change of variable

$$X = XX(T) = C * T + D, \text{ with } C \neq 0$$

such that $XX(A1) = A$ and $XX(B1) = B$ is

$$X = XX(T) = (B - A)/(B1 - A1) * T + (B1 * A - A1 * B)/(B1 - A1),$$

so $XX'(T) = (B - A)/(B1 - A1)$, and the new grid is $X(J) = XX(T(J)), J \in //0, N//.$

Thus, (10.1.6b),

$$\int G(X), \text{ over } X \in (A, B), = \int G(XX(T)) *(B - A)/(B1 - A1),$$

$$\text{over } T \in (A1, B1),$$

$$= (B - A)/(B1 - A1) * \int G(XX(T)),$$

$$\text{over } T \in (A1, B1).$$

Now, using the given formula,

$$\int G(X), \text{ over } X \in (A, B), = (B - A)/(B1 - A1) * \sum G(X(K)) * BB(K),$$

$$K \in //0, N//, + T(G, \text{GRID}).$$

That is, to use the given formula to estimate $\int G(X)$, over $X \in (A, B)$, we: (i) define the change of variable $X = XX(T)$; (ii) define the new grid $X(J) = XX(T(J))$, $J \in //0$, $N//$; (iii) compute the values $G(X(J)) = G(J), J \in //0, N//$, and then we compute the estimate

$$\int G(X), \text{ over } X \in (A, B), \doteq (B - A)/(B1 - A1) * \sum G(K) * BB(K),$$

$$K \in //0, N//.$$

With this notation, the *tabulated* formulas of §10.2 may be used in the form, with grid $T(J) = T(0) + J * H, J \in //0, N//$,

$$DI(G; A, B) \equiv \int G(X), \text{ over } X \in (A, B), = \int F(T), \text{ over } T \in (T(P), T(Q)),$$

$$= DI(F; T(P), T(Q))$$

$$= \sum F(K) * BB(K), K \in //0, N//, + T(F, H)$$

$$= (B - A)/(T(Q) - T(P)) * \sum G(K) * BB(K), K \in //0, N//,$$

$$+ T(F, H).$$

In most of the applications of these formulas in this text we have $A = T(P)$ and $B = T(Q)$, so the estimate may be used "as is"—without the factor $(B - A)/(B1 - A1)$.

*Note.* (10.4.7) is a case where we generally are *not* able to *pick* $A = T(P)$, $B = T(Q)$, and a uniform grid.

When the grid is uniform and $X = X(0) + H * S$, then the Lagrange Integration Formulas (10.1.6a) may be written [using (7.3.13), $A1 = (A - X(0))/H$, and $B1 = (B - X(0))/H$]

(10.1.6c)    $DI(F; A, B) = \sum F(K) * DI(LC(N, K; S) * H; A1, B1),$

$$K \in //0, N//, + T(F, H)$$

$$= \sum F(K) * BB(K, H), K \in //0, N//, + T(F, H)$$

or, using (7.3.4)    $= \sum \Delta ** (K)F(0) * DI(BINCO(S, K) * H; A1, B1)$

$$+ T(F, H)$$

$$= \sum \Delta ** (K)F(0) * BC(K, H), K \in //0, N//,$$

$$+ T(F, H).$$

Notice that H appears only as a factor in the BB(K, H) and in the BC(K, H). Representations of (10.1.6a) in terms of central and backward differences may be obtained using (7.3.32b) with $N = 2 * M$, and (7.3.7) respectively. In this text we restrict our discussion of Lagrange Integration Formulas to the representation (10.1.6a) in terms of *ordinates*.

If in (10.1.6a) the interval (A, B) does not contain a grid point, then POLP(X) does not change sign in [A, B], so the second law of the mean for integrals[2] may be applied to the truncation error term in (10.1.6a) to obtain

$$(10.1.7) \quad T(F, GRID) = DI(F; A, B) - \sum F(K) * B(K), \ K \in //0, N//,$$
$$= DER ** (N + 1)F(P)/(N + 1)! * DI(POLP; A, B),$$

where P is known only to be between A and B. When (A, B) contains a grid point, the truncation error cannot be obtained in this way. However we are able to obtain a *bound* for the truncation error term in (10.1.6a). Since |POLP(X)| is nonnegative, even if (A, B) does contain grid points, then we may apply the second law of the mean for integrals to obtain ($A \leq B$)

$$(10.1.8) \quad |T(F, GRID)|$$
$$= |DI(POLP(X) * DER ** (N + 1)F(Z(X)); A, B)|/(N + 1)!$$
$$\leq DI(|POLP(X)| * |DER ** (N + 1)F(Z(X))|; A, B)/(N + 1)!$$
$$= |DER ** (N + 1)F(Z(P))|/(N + 1)! * DI(|POLP|; A, B).$$

The theory for obtaining usable representations of the truncation error term in (10.1.6a) is incomplete. In §10.2, where the grid is assumed uniform, we list an *explicit* representation (10.2.3) of the truncation error for the whole class of Newton-Cotes Formulas. A few of these are listed in Table 10.2.1. Even though grid points may be contained in (A, B), the representation (10.2.3) has a form similar to (10.1.7). In §10.3 we state a theorem that does not require a uniform grid, and that may be applied to obtain the truncation error terms listed with each formula in any of the four tables in §10.2. In §10.3 we also present examples to indicate how the method of §9.2 may be applied to obtain representations of the truncation error for some numerical integration formulas.

---

[2]The *second law of the mean for integrals:* If F(X) and G(X) are continuous on [A, B] and if $G(X) \geq 0$, or if $G(X) \leq 0$, on [A, B], then there exists a Z in [A, B] such that

$$DI(F * G; A, B) = F(Z) * DI(G; A, B).$$

For F any polynomial of degree N or less, the truncation error term in (10.1.6a) is zero, and the formula is said to be *exact* for any such F. Thus, the degree of the formula (10.1.6a) is *at least* N, but the degree depends on the choice of grid and the limits of integration. The degree of the Lagrange Integration Formula (10.1.6a) that involves N + 1 ordinates *cannot exceed* 2 ∗ N + 1. For, if we choose F(X) = POLP(X) ∗∗ 2, which is a polynomial of degree 2 ∗ N + 2 with F(X(K)) = F(K) = 0 for each K ∈ //0, N//, [so that the estimate in (10.1.6a) is identically zero], then the truncation error term in (10.1.6a) is (A < B).

$$T(POLP ** 2, GRID) = DI(F; A, B) - 0 = DI(POLP ** 2; A, B) > 0.$$

That is, T(F, GRID) ≠ 0 for at least one polynomial of degree 2 ∗ N + 2. The formula has an associated *order* when a uniform grid is used.

In §10.4 we discuss a numerical integration formula (*Gaussian Quadrature*) which has the form [W(X) ≥ 0]

$$\int W(X) * F(X), \text{ over } X \in (A, B), \ = \sum F(K) * B(K), K \in //0, N//,$$

$$+ T(F, GRID),$$

[with W(X) ≡ 1, compare (10.1.6a)], where the grid points X(J), J ∈ //0, N//, are *chosen* so that T(F, GRID) = 0 for F any polynomial of degree 2 ∗ N + 1 or less. That is, the *degree* of this Gaussian Quadrature Formula is 2 ∗ N + 1, the highest degree possible for a formula of the form (10.1.6a).

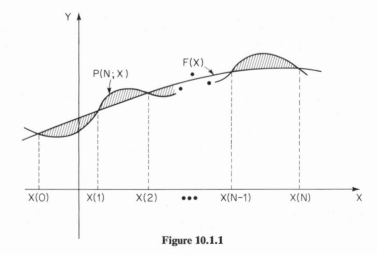

**Figure 10.1.1**

As suggested in §9.1, and now in Figure 10.1.1, the Lagrange Polynomial $P(N; X)$ characterized by (10.1.4) probably *cuts* $F(X)$ at the interpolation points. Thus, the estimate $F'(X) \doteq P'(N; X)$ is suspect, expecially at grid points. However, in numerical integration we are not so discouraged by the possibility of $P(N; X)$ cutting $F(X)$ at grid points. For, when the limits of integration are chosen so that A is near $X(0)$ and B(or X) is close to $X(N)$, then we can hope that the truncation error on subintervals (*add* shaded area below $F(X)$ in Figure 10.1.1, etc.) will tend to *cancel* one another over the interval (A, B). We might guess that a formula involving an even number of subintervals is preferred.

The truncation error terms in certain Lagrange Integration Formulas using $N + 1$ ordinates will be seen (see the Tables in §10.2) to involve a *higher* power of H than did Lagrange Differentiation Formulas using the same number of ordinates (see Table 9.1.1). Recall, when $N = 2*M$ the central formulas were recommended, since an ordinate was missing from the differentiation formula. In Table 10.2.1, the corresponding integration formula $(N = 2 * M)$ has $N + 1$ ordinates involved, but the truncation error term involves a *higher* power of H than would normally be expected. In Tables 10.2.3 and 10.2.4, certain formulas do have an ordinate missing.

If both limits of integration are grid points involved in (10.1.4), then the formula is said to be *closed*. If both A and B are grid points, and either A or B is a grid point outside I(N), then the formula is called *open*. When only A or only B is outside I(N), then the formula is sometimes called *half-open*.

Open formulas are often used to estimate the indefinite integral, (10.1.2), when computing numerical solutions of differential equations.

**Example 2.** Given the table $\big(X(J), Y(J)\big)$, $J \in //0, N//$, where $Y(J) = G\big(X(J)\big)$, and $Y(X) = G(X)$ is a solution of the differential equation

$$Y'(X) = F\big(X, Y(X)\big).$$

We may compute an estimate $YY(N + 1)$ to $Y(N + 1) = G\big(X(N + 1)\big)$ by using the half-open Lagrange Integration Formula (10.1.6a) with $B = X(N + 1)$ and $A = X(0)$ (compare Table 10.2.3).

$$(10.1.9a) \qquad Y(N + 1) - Y(0) = \int Y'(X), \text{ over } X \in \big(X(0), X(N + 1)\big),$$

$$= \int F\big(X, Y(X)\big), \text{ over } X \in \big(X(0), X(N + 1)\big),$$

$$= \sum F\big(X(K), Y(K)\big) * B(K), K \in //0, N//,$$

$$+ T(F, \text{GRID}).$$

That is, define the estimate

$$(10.1.9b) \qquad Y(N + 1) \doteq Y(0) + \sum F\big(X(K), Y(K)\big) * B(K), K \in //0, N//,$$
$$\equiv YY(N + 1).$$

If we place $\big(X(N + 1), YY(N + 1)\big)$ in the above table, and "pretend" that we have the table $\big(X(J), Y(J)\big), J \in //0, N + 1//$, then we may compute an estimate $YY(N + 2)$ to $Y(N + 2) = G\big(X(N + 2)\big)$ by defining a formula like (10.1.9b) using $B = X(N+2)$, $A = X(1)$, and the tabulated points $\big(X(J), Y(J)\big), J \in //1, N + 1//$. Similarly, we can get an estimate $YY(N + 3)$, etc., and thus generate a finite set of finite estimates to elements of the function $G(X)$ which is the solution of the differential equation. (This generated set is called a *numerical solution* of the differential equation.) If the grid involved in (10.1.9b) is uniform, one set of coefficients $B(K), K \in //0, N//$, is sufficient to define the following generalization of (10.1.9b).

$$(10.1.9c) \qquad Y(N + 1 + P) \doteq Y(P) + \sum F\big(X(K), Y(K)\big) * B(K), K \in //P, P + N//,$$
$$\equiv YY(N + 1 + P),$$

where the estimates $YY(N + 1 + P)$ become $Y(N + 1 + P)$ in the table as they are computed. The *given* $\big(X(J), Y(J)\big), J \in //0, N//$, are called the *starting-values* of the numerical solution.

## 10.2. NEWTON-COTES (CLOSED) FORMULAS. SOME OPEN FORMULAS

In this section we list some Lagrange Integration Formulas with a representation of truncation error where the grid is assumed to be uniform with mesh H, namely, $X(J) = X(0) + H * J, J \in //0, N//$. The limits of integration are grid points. These Lagrange Formulas are classified: (i) closed, if the interval of integration [A, B] is a subset of [X(0), X(N)], i.e., $X(0) \leq A \leq B \leq X(N)$; (ii) open, if $A < X(0) < X(N) < B$; and (iii) half-open, if either $A < X(0) \leq B \leq X(N)$ or $X(0) \leq A \leq X(N) < B$. The *Newton-Cotes Formulas* are the Lagrange Integration Formulas with $A = X(0)$ and $B = X(N)$.

Under the change of variable $X = X(0) + H * S$, the grid becomes $S(J) = J, J \in //0, N//$, the Lagrange coefficients (7.3.11) become (7.3.13)

$$LC(N, K; X) = LC(N, K; S)$$
$$= PROD(S - J), J \in //0, N//, \text{ and } J \neq K, /$$
$$(PROD(K - J), J \in //0, N//, \text{ and } J \neq K, ),$$

and in (10.1.6a)

$$\text{POLP}(X(0) + H * S) = \text{PROD}((X(0) + H * S) - (X(0) + H * J)),$$
$$J \in //0, N//,$$
$$= H ** (N + 1) * \text{PROD}(S - J), J \in //0, N//.$$

Then the Lagrange Integration Formula given in (10.1.6a) may be written, with $A1 = (A - X(0))/H$ and $B1 = (B - X(0))/H$,

$$(10.2.1) \qquad \text{DI}(F; A, B) \equiv \int F(X), \text{ over } X \in (A, B),$$
$$= \sum F(K) * \text{DI}(\text{LC}(N, K; S) * H; A1, B1), K \in //0, N//,$$
$$+ H ** (N + 1)/(N + 1)!$$
$$* \text{DI}(\text{PROD}(S - J), J \in //0, N//, *\text{DER} **(N + 1)F(Z(S)) * H; A1, B1).$$

The factor H in the integrand is due to the change of variable of integration to S. The truncation error term has this factor, so the *order* of the formula (10.2.1) is at least $N + 2$. The *degree* of the formula is at least N. (We say *at least* since the limits of integration have not been specified.)

If there are no grid points in the interval (A, B), then the truncation error in (10.2.1) may be written (using the second law of the mean for integrals)

$$(10.2.2) \qquad T(F, H) = \text{DI}(F; A, B) - \sum F(K) * H * \text{DI}(\text{LC}(N, K; S);$$
$$A1, B1), K \in //0, N//,$$
$$= H ** (N + 2)/(N + 1)! * \text{DER} ** (N + 1)F(P)$$
$$* \text{DI}(\text{PROD}(S - J), J \in //0, N//, ; A1, B1),$$

where P is only known to be in the smallest interval containing A, B, and $X(J), J \in //0, N//$. In this case the integral in $T(F, H)$ is not zero, so the formula (10.2.1) has order exactly $N + 2$ and degree exactly N.

It can be shown by a method essentially different from that used to obtain (10.2.2) that the truncation error for the closed *Newton-Cotes Formulas*, (10.2.1) with $A = X(0)$ and $B = X(N)$, may be written, for some P in [A, B],

$$(10.2.3) \qquad T(F, H) = \text{DI}(F, X(0), X(N))$$
$$- \sum F(K) * H * \text{DI}(\text{LC}(N, K; S); 0, N), K \in //0, N//,$$
(if N is odd) $\quad = H ** (N + 2)/(N + 1)! * \text{DER} ** (N + 1)F(P)$
$$* \text{DI}(\text{PROD}(S - J), J \in //0, N//, ; 0, N)$$
(if N is even) $\quad = H ** (N + 3)/(N + 2)! * \text{DER} ** (N + 2)F(P)$
$$* \text{DI}((S - .5 * H)*\text{PROD}(S - J), J \in //0, N//, ; 0, N).$$

Thus, the Newton-Cotes Formula

(10.2.4)     $DI(F; X(0), X(N)) \equiv \int F(X)$, over $X \in (X(0), X(N))$,

$$= \sum F(K) * H * DI(LC(N, K; S); 0, N),$$
$$K \in //0, N//, + T(F, H)$$
$$= \sum F(K) * B(K, H), K \in //0, N//, + T(F, H)$$

is of order $N + 2$, and of degree $N$ when $N$ is *odd*. And, when $N$ is *even*, then (10.2.4) is of order $N + 3$ and of degree $N + 1$. Whether order or degree of the formula is used as a measure of the quality of the formula, *the case N-even is preferred*. If $N$ is even, then an even number of subintervals of length $H$ are involved in the formula (recall a previous remark concerning canceling areas in Figure 10.1.1).

In Table 10.2.1 we list some Newton-Cotes Formulas with the correspond-

**Table 10.2.1** NEWTON-COTES (CLOSED) INTEGRATION FORMULAS

$DI(F; X(0), X(N)) \equiv \int F(X)$, over $X \in (X(0), X(N))$,
$$= \sum F(K) * B(K, H), K \in //0, N//, + T(F, H).$$
The $T(F, H)$ are defined by (10.2.3).

Trapezoidal Rule

$DI(F; X(0), X(1)) = H/2 * (F(0) + F(1)) - H ** 3/12 * F''(Z1).$

Simpson's Rule

$DI(F; X(0), X(2)) = H/3 * (F(0) + 4 * F(1) + F(2)) - H ** 5/90 * DER ** (4)F(Z2).$

Newton's Three-Eighths Rule

$DI(F; X(0), X(3)) = 3 * H/8 * (F(0) + 3 * F(1) + 3 * F(2) + F(3))$
$\qquad - 3 * H ** 5/80 * DER ** (4)F(Z3).$
$DI(F; X(0), X(4)) = 4 * H/90 * (7 * F(0) + 32 * F(1) + 12 * F(2) + 32 * F(3) + 7 * F(4))$
$\qquad - 8 * H ** 7/945 * DER ** (6)F(Z4).$
$DI(F; X(0), X(5)) = 5 * H/288 * (19 * F(0) + 75 * F(1) + 50 * F(2) + 50 * F(3)$
$\qquad + 75 * F(4) + 19 * F(5)) - 275 * H ** 7/12,096 * DER ** (6)F(Z5).$
$DI(F; X(0), X(6)) = 6 * H/840 * (41 * F(0) + 216 * F(1) + 27 * F(2) + 272 * F(3)$
$\qquad + 27 * F(4) + 216 * F(5) + 41 * F(6))$
$\qquad - 9 * H ** 9/1400 * DER ** (8)F(Z6).$
$DI(F; X(0), X(7)) = 7 * H/17280 * (751 * F(0) + 3577 * F(1) + 1323 * F(2)$
$\qquad + 2989 * F(3) + 2989 * F(4) + 1323 * F(5) + 3577 * F(6) + 751 * F(7))$
$\qquad - 8183 * H ** 9/518,400 * DER ** (8)F(Z7).$
$DI(F; X(0), X(8)) = 8 * H/28350 * (989 * F(0) + 5888 * F(1) - 928 * F(2)$
$\qquad + 10496 * F(3) - 4540 * F(4) + 10496 * F(5) - 928 * F(6) + 5888 * F(7)$
$\qquad + 989 * F(8)) - 2368 * H ** 11/467,775 * DER ** (10)F(Z8).$

ing truncation error term defined by (10.2.3). This representation for T(F, H) can also be obtained by applying the Theorem of §10.3.

The range of the coefficients of the F(K) in Newton-Cotes Formulas increases radically as N increases, and when N = 8, or when N ≥ 10, some coefficients are negative. In the interest of minimizing the effect of round-off errors *the only Newton-Cotes Formulas that are recommended are those with* N ≤ 4.

**Example.** Given the table $(X(J), F(J)), J \in //0, 9//$. It is required to estimate

$$DI(F; X(0), X(9)) \equiv \int F(X), \text{ over } X \in (X(0), X(9)),$$

to at least the order and degree of accuracy of Simpson's Rule. We would *not* use one Newton-Cotes Formula involving the 10 ordinates. (The order would be 11, which is greater than the required order 5 of Simpson's Rule, but some of the coefficients are almost twenty times as large as other coefficients involved in the formula). We *prefer* to use formulas of as low order, involving as few ordinates, and with range of coefficients as small as the situation permits. In this particular case we would probably use Simpson's Rule in the form

$$DI(F; X(0), X(6)) = DI(F; X(0), X(2)) + DI(F; X(2), X(4)) + DI(F; X(4), X(6))$$
$$= H/3 * (F(0) + 4 * F(1) + F(2)) - H ** 5/90 * DER ** (4)F(Z1)$$
$$+ H/3 * (F(2) + 4 * F(3) + F(4)) - H ** 5/90 * DER ** (4)F(Z2)$$
$$+ H/3 * (F(4) + 4 * F(5) + F(6)) - H ** 5/90 * DER ** (4)F(Z3)$$
$$= H/3 * (F(0) + 4 * F(1) + 2 * F(2) + 4 * F(3) + 2 * F(4) + 4 * F(5) + F(6))$$
$$- 3 * H ** 5/90 * DER ** (4)F(Z4),$$

and Newton's Three-Eighths Rule in the form

$$DI(F; X(6), X(9)) = 3 * H/8 * (F(6) + 3 * F(7) + 3 * F(8) + F(9))$$
$$- 3 * H ** 5/80 * DER ** (4)F(Z5)$$

to obtain the estimate

$$(10.2.5) \quad DI(F; X(0), X(9)) \doteq H/3 * (F(0) + 4 * F(1) + 2 * F(2) + 4 * F(3) + 2 * F(4)$$
$$+ 4 * F(5) + F(6))$$
$$+ 3 * H/8 * (F(6) + 3 * F(7) + 3 * F(8) + F(9)),$$

which has the required order 5 and degree 3.

In Table 10.2.2 we list a few *open* Lagrange Formulas (with the corresponding truncation error term obtained by applying the Theorem of §10.3). Again, those formulas that involve an even number of subintervals are *preferred*, since they are of a higher order and degree than we would expect for a formula involving its number of ordinates. The formula in Table 10.2.1 which involves K ordinates and the formula in Table 10.2.2 which involves K ordinates are integrals of Lagrange Polynomials of degree K − 1 involving the respective sets of ordinates. The coefficients are different because the limits of integration are different. We are not surprised that the constant coefficient of the truncation error for the open formula is larger than the constant coefficient of the corresponding closed formula, since the open formula involves extrapolation.

**Table 10.2.2** SOME OPEN LAGRANGE FORMULAS

$$DI(F; X(0), X(N + 1)) \equiv \int F(X), \text{ over } X \in (X(0), X(N + 1)),$$
$$\equiv \sum F(K) * B(K, H), K \in //1, N//, + T(F, H).$$

The T(F, H) are obtained by applying the Theorem of §10.3.

$$DI(F; X(0), X(2)) = 2 * H * F(1) + H ** 3/3 * F''(Z1).$$
$$DI(F; X(0), X(3)) = 3 * H/2 * (F(1) + F(2)) + H ** 3/4 * F''(Z2).$$
$$DI(F; X(0), X(4)) = 4 * H/3 * (2 * F(1) - F(2) + 2 * F(3))$$
$$+ 28 * H ** 5/90 * DER ** (4)F(Z3).$$
$$DI(F; X(0), X(5)) = 5 * H/24 * (11 * F(1) + F(2) + F(3) + 11 * F(4))$$
$$+ 95 * H ** 5/144 * DER ** (4)F(Z4).$$
$$DI(F; X(0), X(6)) = 6 * H/20 * (11 * F(1) - 14 * F(2) + 26 * F(3)$$
$$- 14 * F(4) + 11 * F(5))$$
$$+ 41 * H ** 7/140 * DER ** (6)F(Z5).$$

In Table 10.2.3 we list a few *half-open* Lagrange Formulas (with the corresponding truncation error term obtained by applying the Theorem of §10.3). These formulas are called *forward* half-open because only the upper limit of integration is outside I(N). The second, third, and fourth formulas have an ordinate missing, and are preferred. The second and fourth formulas in Table 10.2.3 are the same as the first and third formulas in Table 10.2.2. The truncation error terms are the same since the Theorem in §10.3 is applicable, and the truncation error then depends only on the coefficients in the formula and the limits of integration. When one of these formulas is in Table 10.2.2 we are pleased to find that the order of the formula is so high. When it is in Table 10.2.3 we are pleased to find that a coefficient is zero.

In Table 10.2.4. we list some Lagrange Formulas with only the lower limit of integration outside I(N). Compare corresponding formulas in Table 10.2.3.

**Table 10.2.3** SOME HALF-OPEN (FORWARD) LAGRANGE FORMULAS

$$DI(F; X(0), X(N + 1)) \equiv \int F(X), \text{ over } X \in (X(0), X(N + 1)),$$
$$\equiv \sum F(K) * B(K, H), K \in //0, N//, + T(F, H).$$

The $T(F, H)$ are obtained by applying the Theorem of §10.3.

Euler's Forward Formula

$DI(F; X(0), X(1)) = H * F(0) + H ** 2/2 * F'(Z1).$
$DI(F; X(0), X(2)) = 2 * H * F(1) + H ** 3/3 * F''(Z2).$
$DI(F; X(0), X(3)) = 3 * H/4 * (F(0) + 3 * F(2)) + 3 * H ** 4/8 * F'''(Z3).$
$DI(F; X(0), X(4)) = 4 * H/3 * (2 * F(1) - F(2) + 2 * F(3))$
$\qquad\qquad + 28 * H ** 5/90 * DER ** (4)F(Z4).$

**Table 10.2.4** SOME HALF-OPEN (BACKWARD) LAGRANGE FORMULAS

$$DI(F; X(0), X(N)) \equiv \int F(X), \text{ over } X \in (X(0), X(N)),$$
$$\equiv \sum F(K) * B(K, H), K \in //1, N//, + T(F, H).$$

The $T(F, H)$ are obtained by applying the Theorem of §10.3.

Euler's Backward Formula

$DI(F; X(0), X(1)) = H * F(1) - H ** 2/2 * F'(Z1).$
$DI(F; X(0), X(2)) = 2 * H * F(1) + H ** 3/3 * F''(Z2).$
$DI(F; X(0), X(3)) = 3 * H/4 * (3 * F(1) + F(3)) - 3 * H ** 4/8 * F'''(Z3).$
$DI(F; X(0), X(4)) = 4 * H/3 * (2 * F(1) - F(2) + 2 * F(3))$
$\qquad\qquad + 28 * H ** 5/90 * DER ** (4)F(Z4).$

Recall Example 1 of §10.1 where we discussed a change of variable that permits the use of these formulas to estimate

$$DI(F; A, B) \equiv \int F(X), \text{ over } X \in (A, B).$$

**EXERCISES**

1. Pick a formula from any of the tables of this section.

   (a) *Write* explicitly the Lagrange Polynomial, including the LC(N, K; X), which is involved in the integration formula you chose.

   (b) *Compute* the B(K, H) for your formula.

   (c) If you chose a Newton-Cotes Formula, *compute* T(F, H) for it.

   *Note.* Do not despair! We shall find (in §10.5) that the B(K, H) are "relatively" easy to find by the method of undetermined coefficients, and it is not difficult to *apply* (10.3.6) to obtain T(F, H).

**2.** Make a *sketch* corresponding to Figure 10.1.1, for the estimate (10.2.5) obtained in the Example of this section.

*Hint.* The P(X) which is integrated to define the estimate consists of arcs of three parabolas and an arc of a cubic polynomial.

**3.** Define an estimate to $DI(F; X(0), X(9))$ using only Euler's Forward Formula. Give a sketch analogous to that required in Exercise 2.

*Note.* The line segments defining P(X) are probably separated, so that P(X) is not a polygon.

**4.** Same as Exercise 3, but use Euler's Backward Formula.

### 10.3. TRUNCATION ERROR

Most numerical integration formulas are obtained by integrating an interpolation polynomial P(X) of the form

$$(10.3.1) \qquad P(X) = \sum \big(F(K) * CO(K, X) + F'(K) * C1(K, X)$$
$$+ \cdots + DER ** (M)F(K) * CM(K, X)\big), K \in //0, N//.$$

The coefficients $CO(K, X), \ldots, CM(K, X)$ are polynomials in X, where many of these polynomials may be identically zero [i.e., *missing* in the form (10.3.1)]. Compare the Lagrange Polynomial, (7.3.9). the Hermite Polynomial, (7.3.22a), and the form (7.3.27a).

The numerical integration formula then has the form

$$(10.3.2) \qquad DI(F; A, B) \equiv \int F(X), \text{ over } X \in (A, B),$$

$$= DI(P; A, B) + T(F, GRID)$$

$$= \sum (F(K) * DI(CO(K, X); A, B)$$
$$+ F'(K) * DI(C1(K, X); A, B) + \cdots$$
$$+ DER ** (M)F(K) * DI(CM(K, X); A,B)),$$
$$K \in //0, N//, + T(F, GRID)$$

$$= \sum (F(K) * BO(K) + F'(K) * B1(K)$$
$$+ \cdots + DER **(M)F(K) * BM(K)),$$
$$K \in //0, N//, + T(F, GRID),$$

where many of the (constant) coefficients $BO(K), \ldots, BM(K)$, may be zero. Of course, these coefficients are functions of H, if the grid is uniform.

With $P(X)$ in the form (10.3.1), the truncation error for the formula (10.3.2) is

$$T(F, GRID) = DI(F; A, B) - DI(P; A, B).$$

And, $T(F, GRID)$ may be considered a *linear operator*—linear in $F$ and its derivatives [defined at grid points $X(J), J \in //0, N//, ]$. The *degree of the operator* is defined to be the degree of the formula (10.3.2). That is, the degree of the operator is $D$ if

$$T(X ** K, GRID) = 0 \text{ for each } K \in //0, D//,$$
$$\text{and } T(X ** (D + 1), GRID) \neq 0.$$

The maze from here to the Theorem of this section is used in Example 2 to show that a specific operator satisfies the hypotheses of the Theorem, so the truncation error for the corresponding formula is defined by (10.3.6).

It can be shown that when $T(F, GRID)$ is a linear operator of degree $D$ which does not involve derivatives of $F(X)$ of order exceeding $D - 1$, then

$$(10.3.3) \quad T(F, GRID) = DI(F; A, B) - \Sigma \left( F(K) * B0(K) + F'(K) * B1(K) \right.$$
$$+ \cdots + DER ** (D - 1)F(K) * BDM1(K) \big),$$
$$K \in //0, N//,$$
$$= \int DER ** (D + 1)F(S) * G(S), \text{ over } S \in (A1, B1),$$

where $A < B$, and

$$A1 = MIN(A, X(J), J \in //0, N//, )$$
$$B1 = MAX(B, X(J), J \in //0, N//, )$$
$$G(S) = TX(W(X, S, D), GRID)/D!.$$

$TX(W(X, S, D), GRID)$ is $T(F, GRID)$ applied to $F = W(X, S, D)$ considered a function of $X$,

$$W(X, S, M) = (X - S) ** M, \text{ if } X \geq S, M > 0$$
$$W(X, S, M) = 0, \text{ if } X \leq S, M > 0$$
$$W(X, S, 0) = 1, \text{ if } X \geq S$$
$$W(X, S, 0) = 0, \text{ if } X < S.$$

$$DER ** (K)W(X, S, D) \equiv PAR ** (K, , )W(X, S, D)$$
$$= PROD(D - J), J \in //0, K - 1//,$$
$$* W(X, S, D - K).$$

$$\text{DI(W(X, S, D); A, B)} \equiv \int \text{W(X, S, D)}, \text{ over } X \in (A, B),$$

$$= (\text{W(B, S, D} + 1) - \text{W(A, S, D} + 1))/(D + 1).$$

Thus, G(S) has the form

(10.3.4)    $\text{G(S)} = 1/\text{D!} * (\text{DI(W(X, S, D); A, B)}$

$$- \sum \text{B0(K)} * \text{W(X(K), S, D)}, K \in //0, N//,$$

$$- \sum \text{B1(K)} * \text{DER} ** (1)\text{W(X(K), S, D)}, K \in //0, N//,$$

$$- \cdots - \sum \text{BDM1(K)}$$

$$* \text{DER} ** (D - 1)\text{W(X(K), S, D)}, K \in //0, N//, )$$

$$= 1/\text{D!} * ((\text{W(B, S, D} + 1) - \text{W(A, S, D} + 1))/(D + 1)$$

$$- \sum \text{B0(K)} * \text{W(X(K), S, D)}, K \in //0, N//,$$

$$- \sum \text{B1(K)} * D * \text{W(X(K), S, D} - 1), K \in //0, N//,$$

$$- \cdots - \sum \text{BDM1(K)} * \text{D!} * \text{W(X(K), S, 1)},$$

$$K \in //0, N//, ).$$

G(S) is continuous where segments of G(S) between adjacent elements of the set {A, B, X(J), J $\in$ //0, N//, } are polynomials of degree not exceeding D + 1. If A < B, then G(S) = 0 for B1 < S, since then all the polynomials in (10.3.4) are zero. And G(S) = 0 for S < A1, since T(F, GRID) has degree D. If the formula that defines the operator T(F, GRID) is symmetric about a grid point, then G(S) is also symmetric about that grid point. For example, Simpson's Rule is symmetric about the point X(1), so G(S) is symmetric about S = X(1).

The operator T(F, GRID) is *definite* if G(S) does not change sign, otherwise the operator is *indefinite*.

*Note.* G(S) depends only on the operator T—not on the argument function F.

If $F(X) = X ** (D + 1)/(D + 1)!$, so that $\text{DER} ** (D + 1)F = 1$, then (10.3.3) becomes

(10.3.5)    $\text{T(F, GRID)} = \text{T(X} ** (D + 1)/(D + 1)!, \text{GRID)}$

$$= \int \text{G(S)}, \text{ over } S \in (A1, B1).$$

If the operator T(F, GRID) is definite, and if $\text{DER} ** (D + 1)F(X)$ is continuous, then the second law of the mean for integrals may be applied to (10.3.3) to get

$$T(F, GRID) = DER ** (D + 1)F(Z) * \int G(S), \text{ over } S \in (A1, B1).$$

Now apply (10.3.5) to obtain the following formula to *compute* $T(F, GRID)$.

**Theorem.** If the linear operator $T(F, GRID)$ is *definite* and has *degree* D, then

$$(10.3.6) \qquad T(F, GRID) = DER ** (D + 1)F(Z)/(D + 1)!$$
$$* T(X ** (D + 1), GRID),$$

where Z is known only to be between the smallest and the largest values of X involved in $T(F, GRID)$.

It is known that all Newton-Cotes Formulas of the type listed in Table 10.2.1, and all open formulas of the type listed in Table 10.2.2, define definite operators. For other formulas it is necessary to compute the polynomial segments of $G(S)$, (10.3.4), to determine whether or not $G(S)$ changes sign. When a formula is found to define an indefinite operator, we are sometimes content with a bound like (10.1.8), but we can still get a representation of $T(F, GRID)$ (e.g., see [1]). Many of the important formulas used in the numerical solution of differential equations are definite, so that $T(F, GRID)$ may be obtained by the relatively simple formula (10.3.6).

**Example 1.** Compute the truncation error term for Simpson's Rule (the second formula in Table 10.2.1) which defines the definite linear operator

$$(10.3.7) \qquad T(F, H) = \int F(X), \text{ over } X \in (X(0), X(2)),$$
$$- H/3 * (F(0) + 4 * F(1) + F(2)).$$

We find $T(X ** M, H) = 0$ for each $M \in //0, 3//$, and

$$T(X ** 4, H) = DI(X ** 4; X(0), X(2))$$
$$- H/3 * (X(0) ** 4 + 4 * X(1) ** 4 + X(2) ** 4)$$
$$= ((X(0) + 2 * H) ** 5 - X(0) ** 5)/5$$
$$- H/3 * (X(0) ** 4 + 4 * (X(0) + H) ** 4$$
$$+ (X(0) + 2 * H) ** 4)$$
$$= 32 * H ** 5/5 - 20 * H ** 5/3$$
$$= - 4 * H ** 5/15.$$

Thus, the degree of the operator (10.3.7) is $D = 3$, and the truncation error for Simpson's Rule is (10.3.6)

$$T(F, H) = DER ** (3 + 1)F(Z)/(3 + 1)! * T(X ** (3 + 1), H)$$
$$= DER ** (4)F(Z)/4! * (-4 * H ** 5/15)$$
$$= -H ** 5/90 * DER ** (4)F(Z).$$

**Example 2.** Show that the operator defined by the third formula in Table 10.2.3 is *definite*, so that the truncation error term may be obtained by the method, (10.3.6), used in Example 1.

$$(10.3.8) \qquad T(F, H) = \int F(X), \text{ over } X \in (X(0), X(3)),$$
$$- 3 * H/4 * (F(0) + 3 * F(2)).$$

In this case, compare (10.3.3), $A = X(0)$, $B = X(3) = X(0) + 3 * H$, $N = 2$, $B0(0) = 3 * H/4$, $B0(1) = 0$, $B0(2) = 9 * H/4$, and all $B1(K) = \cdots = BDM1(K) = 0$. We push a pencil to conclude that the operator (10.3.8) has degree $D = 2$. We may without loss of generality choose $X(0) = 0$, so that

$$A1 = A = 0, B1 = B = 3 * H, \text{ and } X(J) = H * J, J \in //0, 3//.$$

Then

$$G(S) = 1/D! * TX(W(X, S, D), GRID)$$
$$= 1/2! * TX(W(X, S, 2), H)$$
$$= 1/2! * (DI(W(X, S, 2); X(0), X(3))$$
$$- 3 * H/4 * (W(X(0), S, 2) + 3 * W(X(2), S, 2)))$$

by (10.3.4)
$$= 1/2! * ((W(3 * H, S, 3) - W(0, S, 3))/3$$
$$- 3 * H/4 * W(0, S, 2) - 9 * H/4 * W(2 * H, S, 2)).$$

We determine that $G(S)$ does not change sign on the interval $[A1, B1] = [0, 3 * H]$ by showing that $G(S)$ has the same sign, or is zero, on the subintervals $0 \leq S \leq H$, $H \leq S \leq 2 * H$, and $2 * H \leq S \leq 3 * H$.

**Case I.** If $0 \leq S \leq H$, then

$$W(3 * H, S, M) = (3 * H - S) ** M, \text{ since } X = 3 * H > S$$
$$W(0, S, M) = 0, \text{ since } X = 0 \leq S$$
$$W(2 * H, S, M) = (2 * H - S) ** M, \text{ since } X = 2 * H > S$$

so that

$$G(S) = 1/2! * \big(((3 * H - S) ** 3 - 0)/3 - 3 * H/4 * 0$$
$$- 9 * H/4 * (2 * H - S) ** 2\big)$$
$$= S ** 2/4! * (9 * H - 4 * S) \geq 0, \text{ for } 0 \leq S \leq H.$$

**Case II.** If $H \leq S \leq 2 * H$, then

$$W(3 * H, S, M) = (3 * H - S) ** M, \text{ since } X = 3 * H > S$$
$$W(0, S, M) = 0, \text{ since } X = 0 < S$$
$$W(2 * H, S, M) = (2 * H - S) ** M, \text{ since } X = 2 * H \geq S$$

so that

$$G(S) = S ** 2/4! * (9 * H - 4 * S) > 0, \text{ for } H \leq S \leq 2 * H.$$

**Case III.** If $2 * H \leq S \leq 3 * H$, then

$$W(3 * H, S, M) = (3 * H - S) ** M, \text{ since } X = 3 * H \geq S$$
$$W(0, S, M) = 0, \text{ since } X = 0 < S$$
$$W(2 * H, S, M) = 0, \text{ since } X = 2 * H \leq S$$

so that

$$G(S) = (3 * H - S) ** 3/3! \geq 0, \text{ for } 2 * H \leq S \leq 3 * H.$$

Thus, $G(S)$ is nonnegative on $0 \leq S \leq 3 * H$, see Figure 10.3.1. If $S \geq 3 * H$, then each $W(X, S, M) = 0$ so $G(S) = 0$; and, if $S \leq 0$, then $G(S) = TX\big((X - S) ** 2, H\big)/2!$, and since $T(F, H)$ is of degree 2, then $G(S) = 0$.

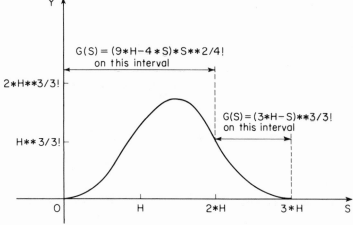

**Figure 10.3.1**

The methods of §9.2 may be used to obtain certain integration formulas and a representation of the truncation error.

**Example 3.** Euler's Forward Formula (the first entry in Table 10.2.3) may be obtained directly from Taylor's Formula

$$Y(1) = Y(0) + H * Y'(0) + H ** 2/2 * Y''(Z)$$

by writing

$$Y(1) - Y(0) = DI(Y'; X(0), X(1)) = H * Y'(0) + H ** 2/2 * Y''(Z).$$

Then, in the last equality replace $Y'$ by $F$ to obtain

$$\int F(X), \text{ over } X \in (X(0), X(1)), = H * F(0) + H ** 2/2 * F'(Z).$$

**Example 4.** The second formula in Table 10.2.3 may be obtained from

$$Y(2) = Y(1) + H * Y'(1) + H ** 2/2 * Y''(1) + H ** 3/6 * Y'''(Z1)$$
$$Y(0) = Y(1) - H * Y'(1) + H ** 2/2 * Y''(1) - H ** 3/6 * Y'''(Z2)$$

by writing

$$Y(2) - Y(0) = \int Y'(X), \text{ over } X \in (X(0), X(2)),$$
$$= 2 * H * Y'(1) + H ** 3/6 * (Y'''(Z1) + Y'''(Z2)).$$

Then, replace $Y'$ by $F$, etc. to obtain

$$\int F(X), \text{ over } X \in (X(0), X(2)), = 2 * H * F(1) + H ** 3/3 * F''(Z3).$$

**Example 5.** More ingenuity is required to obtain the Trapezoidal Rule of Table 10.2.1.

$$\int F(X), \text{ over } X \in (X(0), X(1)), = H/2 * (F(0) + F(1))$$
$$- H ** 3/12 * F''(Z).$$

Here, we compute $Y(1)$ expanded about $X(0)$ minus $Y(0)$ expanded about $X(1)$ to obtain

$$Y(1) - Y(0) = H/2 * (Y'(0) + Y'(1)) + H ** 2/4 * (Y''(0) - Y''(1))$$
$$+ H ** 3/6 * (Y'''(Z0) + Y'''(Z1)).$$

We replace $Y''(1)$ by $Y''(0) + H * Y'''(Z2)$ to get

$$\int Y'(X), \text{ over } X \in (X(0), X(1)), = Y(1) - Y(0)$$
$$= H/2 * (Y'(0) + Y'(1)) + H ** 2/4 * (-H * Y'''(Z2))$$
$$+ H ** 3/6 * (Y'''(Z0) + Y'''(Z1))$$
$$= H/2 * (Y'(0) + Y'(1))$$
$$+ H ** 3/12 * (2 * Y'''(Z0) + 2 * Y'''(Z1) - 3 * Y'''(Z2)).$$

Then, replacing $Y'$ by F, we get the Trapezoidal Rule with another representation of the truncation error. Here, too, we see that the order of the formula is 3 and that the degree is 2.

### 10.4. GAUSSIAN QUADRATURE

The important *Gaussian Quadrature* Formulas have the form

(10.4.1)     $DI(W * F; A, B) \equiv \int W(X) * F(X), \text{ over } X \in (A, B),$
$$= \sum F(K) * A(K), K \in //0, N//,$$
$$+ T(F, GRID),$$

and have *degree* $2 * N + 1$. They are obtained by an extension of the method used in §10.1 to obtain the Lagrange Integration Formula (10.1.6a). Several classes of Gaussian Quadrature Formulas are in use. Each class of formulas is characterized by a particular *choice* of weighting function $W(X)$ and limits of integration A, B. The weighting function is required not to change sign in (A, B), but here we assume $W(X) > 0$ in (A, B). Some particular choices for $W(X)$, A, and B, and the name for the associated Gaussian Quadrature Formula are indicated in Table 10.4.1. Recall Figure 8.4.1.

#### Table 10.4.1

| W(X) | A | B | Name |
|:---:|:---:|:---:|:---|
| 1 | $-1$ | 1 | Legendre-Gauss |
| $EXP(-X)$ | 0 | $\infty$ | Laguerre-Gauss |
| $EXP(-X ** 2)$ | $-\infty$ | $\infty$ | Hermite-Gauss |
| $1/SQRT(1 - X ** 2)$ | $-1$ | 1 | Chebyshev-Gauss |

The method used to define (10.4.1) assumes in

(10.4.2)     $DI(W * F; A, B) = DI(W * P; A, B) + DI(W * E; A, B),$

compare (10.1.3a), that we choose for P(X) the Hermite Polynomial, (7.3.22a),

(10.4.3)     $P(X) = \sum F(K) * HH(K, X), K \in //0, N//,$
                $+ \sum F'(K) * H(K, X), K \in //0, N//,$

characterized by (7.3.22b)

$$P(X(K)) = F(X(K)) \equiv F(K), K \in //0, N//,$$
$$P'(X(K)) = F'(X(K)) \equiv F'(K), K \in //0, N//,$$

where the grid points $X(J), J \in //0, N//,$ are *chosen* to be the $N + 1$ zeros (*nodes*) of a polynomial of degree $N + 1$. These node-defining polynomials are elements of the family of polynomials orthogonal over $(A, B)$ relative to the weighting function $W(X)$ [see (8.4.3)]. The nodes are known to be distinct and lie in $(A, B)$. With the nodes chosen as grid points, it can be shown that for each K

$$DI(W(X) * H(K, X); A, B) = 0$$

so that (10.4.2) becomes

(10.4.4a)     $DI(W * F; A, B) = DI(W * P; A, B) + T(F, GRID)$
                $= \sum F(K) * DI(W(X) * HH(K, X); A, B),$
                $\qquad K \in //0, N//,$
                $+ \sum F'(K) * DI(W(X) * H(K, X); A, B),$
                $\qquad K \in //0, N//, + T(F, GRID)$
                $= \sum F(K) * DI(W(X) * HH(K, X); A, B),$
                $\qquad K \in //0, N//, + T(F, GRID)$
                $= \sum F(K) * A(K), K \in //0, N//,$
                $+ T(F, GRID).$

*This is the Gaussian Quadrature Formula* (10.4.1) with truncation error term [defined in (10.4.6) below]. The coefficients

$$A(K) = DI(W(X) * HH(K, X); A, B)$$

are called *Christoffel Numbers*. They depend only on the chosen nodes and are all positive. Since the HH(K, X), (7.3.25), depend only on the relative positions of the grid points, when the independent variable in (10.4.1), or (10.4.4a), is changed using the linear transformation

$$X = XX(T) = C * T + D, \text{ with } C \neq 0$$

so that XX(A1) = A, XX(B1) = B, and XX(T(J)) = X(J), J ∈ //0, N//, then each

$$A(K) = DI(W(X) * HH(K, X); A, B)$$
$$= DI(W(XX(T)) * HH(K, XX(T)) * XX'(T); A1, B1)$$
$$= C * DI(W(XX(T)) * HH(K, XX(T)); A1, B1)$$
$$= C * AA(K),$$

where the AA(K) are the *Christoffel Numbers* corresponding to the *weighting function* W(XX(T)), *limits of integration* A1, B1, and the *nodes* T(J), J ∈ //0, N//, which are zeros of the polynomial P(N + 1, T) orthogonal over (A1, B1) relative to the weighting function W(XX(T)). The integral involving H(K, X) still vanishes after the change of variable. Thus (10.4.4a) becomes [We write $F(XX(T(K))) = F(X(K)) \equiv F(K)$.]

$$(10.4.4b) \quad DI(W * F; A, B) = DI(W(XX(T)) * F(XX(T)) * XX'(T); A1, B1)$$
$$= \sum F(K) * A(K), K \in //0, N//,$$
$$+ T(F, GRID)$$
$$= C * \sum F(K) * AA(K), K \in //0, N//,$$
$$+ T(F, GRID).$$

This form is often used when the Christoffel Numbers AA(K) are available while the A(K) are not. Recall Example 1 of §10.1.

The nodes and Christoffel Numbers have been tabulated for certain much-used choices for W(X), A, and B (see [2]). Then, the estimate in (10.4.1) is obtained simply by evaluating F(X) at the nodes and computing the inner product indicated.

Gaussian Quadrature Formulas are *recommended* only when F(X) is given in a form so that the points (X(J), F(J)), J ∈ //0, N//, may be specified. (Of course, this is usually *not* the case when this table is determined by a physical experiment.)

The truncation error for the Hermite Polynomial is, (7.4.23),

(10.4.5)    E(X) = F(X) − P(X)

= POLP(X) ∗∗ 2 ∗ DER ∗∗ (2 ∗ N + 2)F(Z)/(2 ∗ N + 2)!,

where Z(X) is in [A, B] when X is. The truncation error for the Gaussian Quadrature Formula (10.4.1), or (10.4.4a), is then

(10.4.6)    T(F, GRID) = DI(W ∗ F; A, B) − ∑ F(K) ∗ A(K), K ∈ //0, N//,

= DI(W(X) ∗ POLP(X) ∗∗ 2 ∗ DER

∗∗ (2 ∗ N + 2)F(Z(X))/(2 ∗ N + 2)!; A, B)

= DER ∗∗ (2 ∗ N + 2)F(P)/(2 ∗ N + 2)!

∗ DI(W ∗ POLP ∗∗ 2; A, B),

for some P in [A, B].

*Note.* We assumed W(X) > 0 and DER ∗∗ (2 ∗ N + 2)F(X) continuous on (A, B) so that we could apply the second law of the mean for integrals.

Since the last integral in (10.4.6) is not zero, the *degree* of the Gaussian Quadrature Formula is *exactly* 2 ∗ N + 1. If W(X) ≡ 1, then the corresponding Gaussian Quadrature Formula (10.4.1) is the Lagrange Formula (10.1.6a) with *maximal degree*.

Probably the most-used Gaussian Quadrature Formula is the Legendre-Gauss Formula with W(X) ≡ 1, A = − 1, and B = 1. When the limits of integration of the integral being estimated are *not* A = − 1 and B = 1, then a change of variable in the given integral is executed using (compare Example 1 of §10.1)

X = XX(T) = .5 ∗ (B − A) ∗ T + .5 ∗ (A + B)

to obtain the estimate in (10.4.4b)

(10.4.7)    DI(F; A, B) = DI(F(XX(T)) ∗ XX′(T); −1, 1)

≐ .5 ∗ (B − A) ∗ ∑ F(K) ∗ AA(K), K ∈ //0, N//.

The *nodes* T(J), J ∈ //0, N//, are the zeros of the Legendre Polynomial PL (N + 1, T) defined by the recursion relation (8.4.7)

$$PL(K + 1, T) = (2 * K + 1)/(K + 1) * T * PL(K, T)$$
$$- K/(K + 1) * PL(K - 1, T),$$
$$PL(0, T) \equiv 1, \quad PL(1, T) = T.$$

The *Christoffel Numbers*

(10.4.8) $$AA(K) = DI(HH(K, T); -1, 1),$$

corresponding to these nodes, are independent of F(X), A, and B, so they may be computed once and for all. In this case, the nodes and corresponding Christoffel Numbers (for several values of N) are available in published tables (see [2]). The F(X), A, and B involved in the original integral are used to define the coefficients of the Christoffel Numbers in the (inner product) estimate, (10.4.7).

**Example 1.** Find the Legendre-Gauss Quadrature Formula with N = 2 for the estimate, compare (10.4.7),

$$DI(F; -1, 1) \doteq \sum F(K) * A(K), K \in //0, 2//.$$

The *nodes* are the zeros of the Legendre polynomial PL(N + 1, X),

$$PL(3, X) = .5 * (5 * X ** 3 - 3 * X).$$

$$X(0) = - SQRT(3/5), X(1) = 0, X(2) = SQRT(3/5).$$

The Christoffel numbers for these nodes are (10.4.8)

$$A(K) = DI(HH(K, X); -1, 1), K \in //0, 2//.$$

In particular, using (7.3.25),

$$A(0) = DI((A0 * X + B0) * (X - X(1)) ** 2 * (X - X(2)) ** 2/$$
$$((X(0) - X(1)) ** 2 * (X(0) - X(2)) ** 2); -1, 1),$$

where

$$A0 = -2 * (1/(X(0) - X(1)) + 1/(X(0) - X(2))) = SQRT(15),$$

and

$$B0 = 1 - A0 * X(0) = 4,$$

so that

$$A(0) = 25/36 * DI\big((SQRT(15) * X ** 3 - 2 * X ** 2$$
$$- SQRT(15) * X + 12/5) * X ** 2; -1, 1\big)$$
$$= 5/9.$$

Similarly.

$$A(1) = 8/9, \text{ and } A(2) = 5/9.$$

Thus the required Legendre-Gauss Quadrature Formula is

$$DI(F; -1, 1) = 5/9 * F(0) + 8/9 * F(1) + 5/9 * F(2) + T(F, GRID),$$

where X(0), X(1), and X(2) are the nodes listed above. Of course, we would not normally compute the nodes and Christoffel Numbers, but would find them already tabulated.

**Example 2.** Find the Chebyshev-Gauss Quadrature Formula for the estimate

$$DI\big(1/SQRT(1 - X ** 2) * F(X); -1, 1\big) \doteq \sum F(K) * A(K), K \in //0, N//.$$

The *nodes* are the zeros (Chebyshev Abscissas), (7.4.14),

$$X(J) = COS\big((2 * J + 1) * \pi/(2 * N + 2)\big), J \in //0, N//,$$

of the Chebyshev Polynomial T(N + 1; X) defined by the recursion relation

$$T(K; X) = 2 * X * T(K - 1; X) - T(K - 2; X),$$
$$T(0; X) \equiv 1, T(1; X) = X.$$

The *Christoffel numbers* in this case are known to be all equal

$$A(K) = DI\big(1/SQRT(1 - X ** 2) * HH(K, X); -1, 1\big) = \pi/(N + 1).$$

Thus the required Chebyshev-Gauss Quadrature Formula is

$$DI(W * F; -1, 1) = \int 1/SQRT(1 - X ** 2) * F(X), \text{ over } X \in (-1, 1),$$
$$= \pi/(N + 1) * \sum F(K), K \in //0, N//, + T(F, GRID),$$

where the X(K) are the Chebyshev Abscissas.

### 10.5. INTEGRATION FORMULAS BY THE METHOD OF UNDETERMINED COEFFICIENTS

In §7.3 and in §9.3 the method of undetermined coefficients was applied to specified forms to obtain interpolation and differentiation formulas.

In this section we indicate how the method of undetermined coefficients may be applied to the *specified form*, compare (10.3.2),

$$(10.5.1) \quad DI(F; A, B) = \sum F(K) * B0(K), K \in //0, N//,$$
$$+ \sum F'(K) * B1(K), K \in //0, N//, + \cdots$$
$$+ \sum DER ** (M)F(K) * BM(K), K \in //0, N//,$$
$$+ T(F, GRID),$$

where some of the coefficients B0(K), B1(K), . . . , BM(K), may be defined to be zero, to obtain numerical integration formulas of a *specified degree* D[> M].

The method consists of the following steps.

**1.** Define the operator

$$(10.5.2) \quad T(F, GRID) = DI(F; A, B) - \sum F(K)*B0(K), K \in //0, N//,$$
$$- \sum F'(K) * B1(K), K \in //0, N//, - \cdots$$
$$- \sum DER ** (D - 1)F(K)$$
$$* BDM1(K), K \in //0, N//,$$

corresponding to the specified form (10.5.1), where it is assumed that when a particular derivative at a particular grid point, say DER ** (M)F(1), is involved explicitly in (10.5.2), then F(1), F'(1), . . . , and DER ** (M − 1)F(1) are also involved explicity in (10.5.2).

**2.** When the specified *degree* for the required formula is D, then the operator (10.5.2) involves exactly D + 1 of the coefficients in the set B0(J), B1(J), . . . , BDM1(J), J ∈ //0, N//.

**3.** Require that the operator (10.5.2) have degree D. Specifically, we require

$$(10.5.3a) \quad T(X ** M, GRID) = 0. \text{ for each } M \in //0, D//,$$

or, for some convenient X0

(10.5.3b)    $T((X - X0) ** M, GRID) = 0$, for each $M \in //0, D//$.

**4.** Solve the linear system defined by (10.5.3a) for the coefficients [specified in (2)] that define the required formula (10.5.1).

The truncation error for a formula defined by this method may be obtained by applying the Theorem of §10.3 if the $G(S)$, (10.3.4), for the assumed grid and limits of integration does not change sign.

**Example 1.** For the uniform grid $X(J) = -H + H * J, J \in //0, 2//$, find A0 $(= B0(0))$, A1 $(= B0(1))$, A2 $(= B0(2))$, and B0 $(= B1(0))$, so that the operator, (10.5.2),

(10.5.4)     $T(F, GRID) = DI(F; X(0), X(2)) - A0 * F(0) - A1 * F(1)$

$$- A2 * F(2) - B0 * F'(0)$$

has degree $D = 3$. The system (10.5.3a) becomes

$$T(1, H) = DI(1; -H, H) - A0 * 1 - A1 * 1 - A2 * 1 - B0 * 0 = 0$$
$$T(X, H) = DI(X; -H, H) - A0 * X(0) - A1 * X(1) - A2 * X(2)$$
$$- B0 * 1 = 0$$
$$T(X ** 2, H) = DI(X ** 2; -H, H) - A0 * X(0) ** 2 - A1 * X(1) ** 2$$
$$- A2 * X(2) ** 2 - B0 * 2 * X(0) = 0$$
$$T(X ** 3, H) = DI(X ** 3; -H, H) - A0 * X(0) ** 3 - A1 * X(1) ** 3$$
$$- A2 * X(2) ** 3 - B0 * 3 * X(0) ** 2 = 0.$$

The corresponding linear system may be written

| | | | |
|---|---|---|---|
| A0 + A1 | + A2 | | = 2 * H |
| - H * A0 | + H * A2 | + B0 = 0 | |
| H ** 2 * A0 | + H ** 2 * A2 | - 2 * H * B0 = 2 * H ** 3/3 | |
| - H ** 3 * A0 | + H ** 3 * A2 | + 3 * H ** 2 * B0 = 0, | |

and has solution $(A0, A1, A2, B0) = (H/3, 4 * H/3, H/3, 0)$. The formula (10.5.1) corresponding to (10.5.4) is Simpson's Rule

$$DI(F; -H, H) = H/3 * (F(-H) + 4 * F(0) + F(H)) + T(F, H).$$

*Note.* Simpson's Rule could have been obtained by this method if we replaced the term $B0 * F'(0)$ with $AM1 * F(-1)$, $A3 * F(3)$, $B1 * F'(1)$, or $B2 * F'(2)$.

**Example 2.** For the uniform grid $X(J) = H * J, J \in //0, 3//$, find the formula (10.5.1) corresponding to the operator

$$(10.5.5) \quad T(F, H) = DI\big(F, X(0), X(3)\big) - A0 * F(0) - A1 * F(1) - A2 * F(2)$$
$$= DI(F; 0, 3 * H) - A0 * F(0) - A1 * F(H) - A2 * F(2 * H),$$

which is required to have degree $D = 2$. Then, (10.5.3a) becomes

$$T(1, H) = DI(1; 0, 3 * H) - A0 * 1 - A1 * 1 - A2 * 1 = 0$$
$$T(X, H) = DI(X; 0, 3 * H) - A0 * 0 - A1 * H - A2 * 2 * H = 0$$
$$T(X ** 2, H) = DI(X ** 2; 0, 3 * H) - A0 * 0 - A1 * H ** 2$$
$$- A2*(2*H) ** 2 = 0,$$

which has solution $(A0, A1, A2) = (3 * H/4, 0, 9 * H/4)$. The corresponding formula (10.5.1) is

$$DI(F; 0, 3 * H) = 3 * H/4 * \big(F(0) + 3 * F(2 * H)\big) + T(F, H).$$

This is the third formula in Table 10.2.3.

The method of undetermined coefficients is particularly useful when we have reason to believe that a usable estimate of the required integral may be obtained as a linear function of $F(X)$ *and* certain of its derivatives at grid points, so that none of the formulas in the tables of §10.2 may be used.

**Example 3.** For the uniform grid $X(J) = H * J, J \in //0, 3//$, find the formula (10.5.1) of degree $D = 3$ corresponding to the operator

$$(10.5.6a) \quad T(F, H) = DI\big(F; X(0), X(1)\big) - A0 * F(0) - A1 * F(1)$$
$$- A3 * F(3) - B3 * F'(3).$$

The conditions (10.5.3a) become

$$T(1, H) = DI(1; 0, H) - A0 * 1 - A1 * 1 - A3 * 1 - B3 * 0 = 0$$
$$T(X, H) = DI(X; 0, H) - A0 * 0 - A1 * H - A3 * 3 * H - B3 * 1 = 0$$
$$T(X ** 2, H) = DI(X ** 2; 0, H) - A0 * 0 - A1 * H ** 2$$
$$- A3 * (3 * H) ** 2 - B3 * 6 * H = 0$$
$$T(X ** 3, H) = DI(X ** 3; 0, H) - A0 * 0 - A1 * H ** 3$$
$$- A3 *(3 * H) ** 3 - B3 * 27 * H ** 2 = 0,$$

which has solution

$(A0, A1, A3, B3) = (172 * H/432, 297 * H/432, -37 * H/432, 5 * H ** 2/72)$.

Thus the required formula (10.5.1) corresponding to (10.5.6a) is

$$(10.5.6b) \quad DI(F; X(0), X(1)) = H/432 * (172 * F(0) + 297 * F(1) - 37 * F(3))$$
$$+ 5 * H ** 2/72 * F'(3) + T(F, GRID).$$

The form (10.5.6a) was chosen here to demonstrate that terms like $A2 * F(2)$ could be left out.

## EXERCISES

**1.** Derive a formula to demonstrate that if *only* derivatives are involved in the assumed form, then we do not get an equation involving the coefficients from the condition $T(1, GRID) = 0$.

**2.** Show by example that it *can happen* that an assumed form for $T(F, GRID)$ involving $F'(M)$ but not involving $F(M)$ has (10.5.3a) define a linear system with a unique solution.

## SUGGESTED READING

1. Hamming, R. W. (1962): *Numerical Methods for Scientists and Engineers.* McGraw-Hill Book Company New York. (Page 150.)

2. *Handbook of Mathematical Functions with Formulas, Graphs, and Mathematical Tables* (1964) National Bureau of Standards Applied Mathematics Series 55.

3. Hildebrand, F. B. (1956): *Introduction to Numerical Analysis.* McGraw-Hill Book Company, New York.

4. Davis, P. J. (1963): *Interpolation and Approximation.* Blaisdell Publishing Co. New York.

5. Davis, P. J. and P. Rabinowitz. (1967): *Numerical Integration.* Blaisdell Publishing Co. New York.

# 11 DIFFERENCE EQUATIONS

## 11.1. MOTIVATION. PARTICULAR SOLUTIONS

It would be natural to define a difference equation to be an equation involving differences of a function at grid points. For example,

$$(11.1.1a) \qquad \Delta ** (2)F(0) + 3 * \nabla F(1) - 4 * EF(2) = 0$$

is an equation involving the forward difference operator $\Delta$, the backward difference operator $\nabla$, and the shifting operator E. Here a much more restrictive definition is used [see (11.1.3)]. We will use tables of the form $(X(J), F(X(J))), J \in // P, Q //$, where the grid is *uniform*. This may be a subset of a larger table. We may refer to this table as $F(J), J \in // P, Q //$.

A theory of difference equations in which all the operators $\Delta, \nabla, \delta$, $\mu$, and E discussed in Chapter 6 are allowed to enter in a general way seems hopeless. However, a theory for a particular class of equations involving the operators $\Delta, \nabla$, and E exists. Since $\Delta = E - I$ and $\nabla = I - INV(E)$, where $INV(E)F(K) = F(K - 1)$, this theory is in fact the one that considers equations involving *only* the operator E. In the above example,

$$(11.1.1b) \quad \Delta ** (2)F(0) + 3 * \nabla F(1) - 4 * EF(2)$$
$$= (E ** (2) - 2 * E + I)F(0) + 3 * (I - INV(E))F(1) - 4 * EF(2)$$
$$= E ** (2)F(0) - 2 * EF(0) + IF(0) + 3 * IF(1) - 3 * INV(E)F(1) - 4 * EF(2)$$
$$= E ** (2)F(0) - 2 * EF(0) + IF(0) + 3 * EF(0) - 3 * IF(0) - 4 * E ** (3)F(0)$$
$$= (-4 * E ** (3) + E **(2) + E - 2 * I)F(0)$$
$$\equiv PHI(E)F(0).$$

315

Thus, the equation involving all three operators is equivalent to an equation involving just the shifting operator E. That is, elements of a table $F(J), J \in // 0, 3 //$, satisfy

$$\Delta ** (2)F(0) + 3 * \nabla F(1) - 4 * EF(2) = 0$$

if and only if they satisfy

$$PHI(E)F(0) \equiv (-4 * E **(3) + E ** (2) + E - 2 * I)F(0)$$
$$= -4 * F(3) + F(2) + F(1) - 2 * F(0) = 0.$$

In general, every finite linear combination of terms like $\Delta ** (M)F(K)$, $\nabla ** (M)F(K)$, and $E ** (M)F(K)$ with coefficients independent of the function F can be written, for some integers P and Q, in the form

(11.1.1c) $\qquad PHI(E)F(P) = \sum A(K) * F(K), K \in // P, Q //,$

where $PHI(E)$ is a polynomial in E with coefficients independent of the function F. The reader should choose a specific linear combination of ordinates, and show that the chosen expression can be written in several ways as a linear combination of the differences $\Delta$, $\nabla$, and E.

Except in §11.2, the operator notation will be suppressed, and we *define* a difference equation to be any equation involving a finite set of ordinates. For example, we may consider $X(N)$ and $X(N + 1)$ as ordinates so that Newton's Method [compare (3.2.1)]

(11.1.2a) $\qquad X(N + 1) - X(N) + F(X(N))/F'(X(N)) = 0$

is a difference equation. The expressions $F(X(N))$ and $F'(X(N))$ may be complicated functions of $X(N)$. We define a table $(J, X(J)), J \in // 0, \infty //$, where every pair of consecutive elements of the table satisfies (11.1.2a), and call the table a *solution* of the difference equation (11.1.2a). In this example we are interested in the character of the set of computed ordinates, and hope that $LIM(X(K)) = XX$, as K App $\infty$, and hope that $F(XX) = 0$.

Motivated by applications considered below, we usually denote ordinates by $Y(K)$. We will be interested in *linear* difference equations [compare (11.1.1c)],

(11.1.2b) $\qquad \sum A(K) * Y(K), K \in // P, Q //, = B,$

where the $A(K)$ and $B$ are not functions of the ordinates $Y(K)$. Note that (11.1.2a) is generally not a linear difference equation. Also we will consider linear difference equations in *two indices,* see Example 6 in this section,

(11.1.2c)     $\sum\sum A(J, K) * U(J, K), J \in // P1, Q1 //, K \in // P2, Q2 //, = B,$

where the $A(J, K)$ and $B$ are not functions of the ordinates $U(J, K)$. We always hope that our computed solution to the difference equation has properties that prompted our choice of difference equation.

In this section we discuss two important sources of difference equations and some methods for computing particular solutions of linear difference equations. The method of Example 2 may lead to particular solutions of nonlinear difference equations. In §11.2, we discuss a method for finding general solutions of linear difference equations with constant coefficients. When the difference equation is represented in terms of the operator E, or ordinates, the method of §11.2 is reminiscent of a well-known method for solving linear differential equations with constant coefficients.

An equation of the form (here, N is treated like an independent variable and $A(M; N)$ is read: A sub M of N)

(11.1.3)     $A(M; N) * Y(N) + A(M - 1; N) * Y(N - 1) + \cdots$

$+ A(0; N) * Y(N - M) = B(N),$

or, $\sum A(M - K; N) * Y(N - K), K \in // 0, M //, = B(N),$

where $A(M; N) \neq 0$ and $A(0; N) \neq 0$ for each N in an *index set* I, is called a *linear difference equation of order* M (in one index). If the $A(K; N), K \in //0, M//,$ are constants, then (11.1.3) is said to have *constant coefficients.* If $B(N) \equiv 0$, then the difference equation is called *homogeneous.* If the index set is

(11.1.4)          $I = \{N | N \text{ is an integer, } N \geq M\} \equiv // M, \infty //,$

then a *particular solution* of the difference equation (11.1.3) with index set (11.1.4) is a sequence of numbers, real or complex,

(11.1.5)          $Y(0), Y(1), Y(2), \ldots, Y(M), Y(M + 1), \ldots,$

where each set of $M + 1$ *consecutive* elements

$$Y(N), Y(N - 1), Y(N - 2), \ldots, Y(N - M)$$

satisfies (11.1.3) with the appropriate coefficients $A(M; N)$, $A(M - 1; N), \ldots, A(0; N)$, and $B(N)$.

> *Note.* Here we assume that the *order* M is a positive integer. To get a particular solution (11.1.5) beginning with a negative index we need only choose the index set $I = // M1, \infty //$, with $M1 < M$. Unless stated to the contrary, we assume $I = // M, \infty //$.

Every homogeneous linear difference equation has at least one solution: $Y(J) = 0, J \in // 0, \infty //$, called the *trivial solution*. In the examples of this chapter we indicate how nontrivial particular solutions of difference equations may be obtained.

**Example 1.** Equation (11.1.3) with $M = 3$, $A(3; N) \equiv -4$, $A(2; N) \equiv 1$, $A(1; N) \equiv 1$, $A(0; N) \equiv -2$, and $B(N) \equiv 0$ becomes

$$-4 * Y(N) + Y(N - 1) + Y(N - 2) - 2 * Y(N - 3) = 0,$$

a linear homogeneous difference equation of order 3 with constant coefficients. If the index set is

$$I = // 3, \infty //,$$

then a particular solution of the difference equation is a sequence

$$Y(J), J \in // 0, \infty //,$$

with the property that $Y(J), J \in // 0, 3 //$, is a solution of the equation (for $N = 3$)

$$-4 * Y(3) + Y(2) + Y(1) - 2 * Y(0) = 0,$$

and $Y(J), J \in // 1, 4 //$, is a solution (for $N = 4$) of

$$-4 * Y(4) + Y(3) + Y(2) - 2 * Y(1) = 0,$$

and if $N = K$ in I, then $Y(J), J \in // K - 3, K //$, is a solution of the equation

$$-4 * Y(K) + Y(K - 1) + Y(K - 2) - 2 * Y(K - 3) = 0.$$

The reader should verify, by substitution of appropriate elements of the sequence into the above equations, that the elements listed in the following table belong to a particular solution of this particular difference equation.

| J | 0 | 1 | 2 | 3 | 4 | 5 | ⋯ |
|---|---|---|---|---|---|---|---|
| Y(J) | 1 | 1 | 1 | 0 | −1/4 | −9/16 | ⋯ |

*Note.* If the index set had been $I = \{N|N = 3\}$, then the difference equation would be simply

$$-4 * Y(3) + Y(2) + Y(1) - 2 * Y(0) = 0,$$

and a particular solution would be one quadruple $Y(0), Y(1), Y(2), Y(3)$.

If the elements of (11.1.5) may be obtained by evaluating an explicit function of N, then (11.1.5) may be written

(11.1.6)          $Y(J) = YY(J), J \in // \, 0, \infty \, //.$

Sometimes we are only interested in solutions of (11.1.3) for *finite index sets*. For example, if

(11.1.7)          $I = \{N|N \in // \, M, M + P \, //\} \equiv // \, M, M + P \, //,$

then a particular solution of (11.1.3) is written

(11.1.8)          $Y(0), Y(1), \ldots, Y(M), Y(M + 1), \ldots, Y(M + P),$

or

$$Y(J) = YY(J), J \in // \, 0, M + P \, //.$$

A subset of a particular solution of (11.1.3) must be *specified* (implicitly or explicitly) to determine completely that particular solution. This specified subset is called a *table of starting-values* for the particular solution. When *computing* particular solutions of (11.1.3), the table of starting-values must contain M elements. Various tables of starting-values for one particular solution may be specified, depending on the method being used to solve the difference equation.

A difference equation together with a specified table of starting-values is called a *difference equation problem*.

**Example 2.** Since the coefficients A(K; N), K $\in$ // 0, M //, and B(N) are presumed known, A(M; N) $\neq$ 0, and A(0; N) $\neq$ 0, for each N in I, (11.1.4), then a particular solution (11.1.5) of (11.1.3) is obtained if we choose as starting-values *any* M *consecutive* elements of that particular solution. With starting-values Y(J), J $\in$ // 0, M $-$ 1 //, solve (11.1.3) for Y(N) to define, for N $\in$ // M, $\infty$ //,

(11.1.9a)      Y(N) = 1/A(M; N) $*$ (B(N)

$$- \sum A(M - K; N) * Y(N - K), K \in // 1, M //,).$$

With Q $>$ M, and starting-values Y(J), J $\in$ // Q $-$ M, Q $-$ 1 //, define, for N $\in$ // Q $-$ 1, $-1$, M //,

(11.1.9b)      Y(N $-$ M) = 1/A(0; N) $*$ (B(N)

$$- \sum A(M - K; N) * Y(N - K), K \in // 0, M - 1 //,)$$

and, for N $\in$ // Q, $\infty$ //,

(11.1.9c)      Y(N) = 1/A(M; N) $*$ (B(N)

$$- \sum A(M - K; N) * Y(N - K), K \in //1, M //,).$$

Specifically, with M = 2, A(2; N) $\equiv$ 1, A(1; N) = N, A(0; N) = $-2 * N ** 2$, and B(N) $\equiv$ 0, then (11.1.3) becomes

$$Y(N) + N * Y(N - 1) - 2 * N ** 2 * Y(N - 2) = 0.$$

With index set I = // 2, 5 //, and starting-values Y(0) = 1, Y(1) = 1, then the particular solution is given in the following table.

| | Given | | From (11.1.9a) | | | |
|---|---|---|---|---|---|---|
| J | 0 | 1 | 2 | 3 | 4 | 5 |
| Y(J) | 1 | 1 | 6 | 0 | 192 | $-960$ |

How would you compute the particular solution if the starting-values were Y(2) and Y(3)?

**Example 3.** Two particular solutions of the second order linear homogeneous difference equation with constant coefficients, [the reader should relate this to (11.1.3)]

(11.1.10a)      Y(N) $- 3 * Y(N - 1) + 2 * Y(N - 2) = 0,$

with the index set I = {N|N is any integer}, are

$$Y(N) = YY(N) = 2 ** N, \text{ and } Y(N) = YY(N) = 1 ** N.$$

That is, for every integer N,

$$2 ** N - 3 * 2 ** (N - 1) + 2 * 2 ** (N - 2) \equiv 0,$$

and

$$1 ** N - 3 * 1 ** (N - 1) + 2 * 1 ** (N - 2) \equiv 0.$$

The linearity in the Y(K) of the homogeneous difference equation (11.1.10a) implies (with A and B arbitrary constants)

(11.1.10b)          $$Y(N) = YY(N) = A * 2 ** N + B * 1 ** N$$

is also a solution. If Y(P) = YP and Y(Q) = YQ, P ≠ Q, are elements for any particular solution of (11.1.10a) with the index set I, then the particular solution corresponding to the table of starting-values Y(P) = YP, Y(Q) = YQ is defined by (11.1.10b), where A and B are elements of the solution of the linear system

$$Y(P) = YY(P) = A * 2 ** P + B * 1 ** P = YP$$
$$Y(Q) = YY(Q) = A * 2 ** Q + B * 1 ** Q = YQ.$$

That is, the particular solution of (11.1.10a) with the index set I and starting-values Y(P) = YP, Y(Q) = YQ is

(11.1.10c)   $$Y(N) = YY(N)$$
$$= (YP - YQ)/(2 ** P - 2 ** Q) * 2 ** N$$
$$+ (YQ * 2 ** P - YP * 2 ** Q)/(2 ** P - 2 ** Q) * 1 ** N.$$

In §11.2 we discuss a method for obtaining *general solutions* of linear difference equations with constant coefficients. In this example, (11.1.10b) is a general solution of (11.1.10a). The *order* of the difference equation is 2, and the solution (11.1.10b) involves 2 essential arbitrary constants. The reader should, for a specific finite index set and two starting-values, use the method of Example 2 to (construct a table) solve (11.1.10a); then he should use the method of this example to compute (11.1.10c), and should verify the table just computed.

**Example 4.** We might obtain a numerical solution (compare Example 2 of §10.1) of the differential equation problem

(11.1.11a)     $Y''(X) = Y(X)$, $X \in [0, 1]$, $Y(0) = A$, $Y(1) = B$

in the following way. On the interval $[0, 1]$ choose the grid

$$X(J) = H * J, J \in //\, 0, M\, //, \text{ with } H = 1/M,$$

so that $X(0) = 0$ and $X(M) = 1$. Choose the estimate (9.2.10)

(11.1.11b)     $\big(Y(K + 1) - 2 * Y(K) + Y(K - 1)\big)/H ** 2 \doteq Y''(K)$.

Suppose that M is chosen so large that $H = 1/M$ is so small that when the elements $Y\big(X(J)\big) \equiv Y(J)$, $J \in //\, K - 1, K + 1\, //$, of the range of the solution $Y(X)$ of (11.1.11a) are substituted in the left member of the estimate (11.1.11b) we obtain a number which is usable as an estimate to $Y''(K)$ and to $Y(K)$. This is just another criterion for choosing H, but it does emphasize the fact that estimates like (11.1.11b) are only used to *motivate a choice of difference equation*. In practice, we would probably try to choose H so small that the truncation error term associated with estimates like (11.1.11b) would be "sufficiently small"—even though these error terms involve higher derivatives at mysterious points. We do *not* claim that a difference equation defined using such an H will have a particular solution which corresponds to a useful estimate to $Y(X)$. The estimate, compare (11.1.11b) and note (11.1.11a),

$$\big(Y(N) - 2 * Y(N - 1) + Y(N - 2)\big)/H ** 2 \doteq Y(N - 1)$$

*suggests* the second order linear homogeneous difference equation with constant co-efficients

$$\big(Y(N) - 2 * Y(N - 1) + Y(N - 2)\big)/H ** 2 = Y(N - 1),$$

or

(11.1.11c)     $Y(N) - (2 + H ** 2) * Y(N - 1) + Y(N - 2) = 0$,

with the index set $I = //\, 2, M\, //$, and starting-values $Y(0) = A$, $Y(M) = B$. The requirement that (11.1.11c) be satisfied for the $M - 1$ elements of the index set defines a linear system.

| Index | Equation |
|:---:|:---|
| 2 | $Y(2) - (2 + H ** 2) * Y(1) + Y(0) = 0$ |
| 3 | $Y(3) - (2 + H ** 2) * Y(2) + Y(1) = 0$ |
| 4 | $Y(4) - (2 + H ** 2) * Y(3) + Y(2) = 0$ |
| ⋮ | ⋮ |
| M | $Y(M) - (2 + H ** 2) * Y(M - 1) + Y(M - 2) = 0$. |

This is $M - 1$ equations in the $M - 1$ unknowns $Y(J)$, $J \in //1, M - 1//$. The corresponding matrix equation is

(11.1.11d)

$$
\begin{bmatrix}
2 + H**2 & -1 & 0 & \cdots & 0 & 0 \\
-1 & 2 + H**2 & -1 & \cdots & 0 & 0 \\
0 & -1 & 2 + H**2 & \cdots & 0 & 0 \\
\vdots & \vdots & \vdots & \ddots & \vdots & \vdots \\
0 & 0 & 0 & \cdots & 2 + H**2 & -1 \\
0 & 0 & 0 & \cdots & -1 & 2 + H**2
\end{bmatrix}
*
\begin{bmatrix}
Y(1) \\
Y(2) \\
Y(3) \\
\vdots \\
Y(M-2) \\
Y(M-1)
\end{bmatrix}
=
\begin{bmatrix}
Y(0) \\
0 \\
0 \\
\vdots \\
0 \\
Y(M)
\end{bmatrix},
$$

which has a matrix of coefficients that is symmetric and dominant diagonal. Since M is usually large, iteration methods are often used to solve (11.1.11d). In the present case (11.1.11c) has a unique particular solution for each choice of starting-values $Y(0) = A$, $Y(M) = B$. This particular solution

| J | 0 | 1 | 2 | $\cdots$ | M − 1 | M |
|---|---|---|---|---|---|---|
| Y(J) | A | Y(1) | Y(2) | $\cdots$ | Y(M − 1) | B |

of (11.1.11c) is used to define the set

Numerical Solution of (11.1.11a)

| J | 0 | 1 | 2 | $\cdots$ | M − 1 | M |
|---|---|---|---|---|---|---|
| X(J) | 0 | 1/M | 2/M | $\cdots$ | (M − 1)/M | 1 |
| Y(J) | A | Y(1) | Y(2) | $\cdots$ | Y(M − 1) | B |

which is considered a set of finite *estimates* to elements

| X | 0 | 1/M | 2/M | $\cdots$ | (M − 1)/M | 1 |
|---|---|---|---|---|---|---|
| Y(X) | A | Y(1/M) | Y(2/M) | $\cdots$ | Y((M − 1)/M) | B |

of $Y(X)$, the solution of (11.1.11a). Thus a particular solution of a difference equation may be used to define a numerical solution of a differential equation problem. In Chapter 12 we discuss some *guides* for choosing estimates such as

(11.1.11b) which *suggest* difference equations, and guides for choosing H and criteria for deciding when a numerical solution of a differential equation problem is acceptable. The reader should write explicitly the linear system corresponding to (11.1.11c) with index set $I = //2, 5//$. This is four equations in the four unknowns $Y(J), J \in //1, 4//$. Then write the equivalent matrix equation (11.1.11d).

The difference equation (11.1.3) with index set I, (11.1.4) or (11.1.7), and starting-values consecutive elements of a particular solution is called a *linear difference equation problem with consecutive starting-values*. The requirement that the difference equation hold for each element of the index set defines a linear system with a matrix of coefficients, corresponding to (11.1.11d), which is triangular *or* may be written as a $2by2$ partitioned diagonal matrix with diagonal elements triangular matrices. Thus the linear system may be solved directly by back-substitution. This is equivalent to (11.1.9a) *or* (11.1.9b, c), respectively, in Example 2 of this section.

A difference equation problem with consecutive starting-values will also be called an *initial-value difference equation problem*. The problems in Example 2, and Example 3 with P and Q consecutive integers, are initial-value problems. The problems in Example 3 with P and Q not consecutive integers, and Example 4, are *boundary-value difference equation problems*. The starting-values are *not* consecutive, and the corresponding particular solution can *not* be obtained directly from the difference equation as in Example 2.

The next example illustrates how numerical integration formulas of the types listed in the Tables of §10.2 may be used to obtain difference equations. The simple differential equation used here is the one used in Chapter 12 in a discussion of *stability* of methods for computing numerical solutions of ordinary differential equations. See also Example 3 and Example 4 of §11.2.

**Example 5.** Numerical solutions of the differential equation problem

(11.1.12a)     $Y'(X) = A * Y(X), \ X \in [0, 1], \ Y(0) = Y0, \ A = \text{constant}$

may be defined, as in Example 4, in terms of particular solutions of linear homogeneous difference equations, where the difference equations are obtained in the following way. On the interval [0, 1] choose the grid

$$X(J) = H * J, J \in // 0, M1 //, \text{ with } H = 1/M1,$$

so that $X(0) = 0$ and $X(M1) = 1$. Choose a numerical integration formula of the form [recall Example 2 of §10.1, compare (10.1.9c)]

$$(11.1.12b) \qquad Y(S) - Y(R) = \int Y'(X), \text{ over } X \in (X(R), X(S)),$$

$$= \int A * Y(X), \text{ over } X \in (X(R), X(S)),$$

$$\doteq A * \sum Y(K) * B(K, H), \ K \in // \ P, Q \ //,$$

where $R < S$, $P \le Q$, and $R, S, P,$ and $Q$ are elements of $//0, M1//$. The estimate (11.1.12b) is *motivation* for the choice of difference equation

$$(11.1.12c) \qquad Y(S) - Y(R) = A * \sum Y(K) * B(K, H), K \in // \ P, Q \ //.$$

Generally H appears only as a factor of the $B(K, H)$ [see (10.2.4)]. The *order* M of the difference equation (11.1.12c) is the maximum of numbers

$$S - R, Q - P, |P - R|, |Q - R|, |P - S|, \text{ and } |Q - S|.$$

A table of starting-values will have M elements—obtained by hook or by crook —usually including the given element $Y(0) = Y0$. In Chapter 12 we indicate how these starting-values might be obtained by evaluating certain Taylor Polynomials.

*Note.* If the differential equation problem is

$$Y'(X) = F(X, Y(X)), \ X \in [0, 1], \ Y(0) = Y0,$$

where $F(X, Y)$ is *not* a linear function of Y, then the corresponding difference equation

$$Y(S) - Y(R) = \sum F(X(K), Y(K)) * B(K, H), \ K \in // \ P, Q \ //,$$

is *not linear*. The method of Example 2 of this section, where the starting-values are consecutive elements of the particular solution, may define a particular solution of the nonlinear difference equation problem—giving a numerical solution of the nonlinear differential equation problem. Iteration processes like (12.1.6) are particularly useful in solving these non-linear difference equations.

Finally, we present two examples to illustrate a source of *linear difference equations in two indices* of the form [compare (11.1.3)],

(11.1.13)     $\sum$ A(N + J, M + P2; N, M) $*$ U(N + J, M + P2),

$\qquad$ J $\in$ // P1, Q1 //,

$\qquad$ + $\sum$ A(N + J, M + P2 + 1; N, M) $*$ U(N + J, M + P2 + 1),

$\qquad$ J $\in$ // P1, Q1 //,

$\qquad$ + $\cdots$

$\qquad$ + $\sum$ A(N + J, M + Q2; N, M) $*$ U(N + J, M + Q2),

$\qquad$ J $\in$ // P1, Q1 //,

$\qquad$ = B(N, M),

where P1 and P2 may be negative integers. Many of the coefficients A(R, S; N, M), and/or B(N, M), may be defined to be zero.

**Example 6.** An *estimate* to a subset of the solution U(X, T) of the partial differential equation

(11.1.14a)     PAR $**$ (2,)U(X, T) = PAR $**$ (,1)U(X, T),

which satisfies the specified boundary conditions

(11.1.14b)     U(0, T) = U(1, T) = 0, for T $\geq$ 0

(11.1.14c)     U(X, 0) = G(X), for 0 $\leq$ X $\leq$ 1,

will be defined in terms of a particular solution of a difference equation of the form (11.1.13). We extend the method used in Example 4 of this section. The region of interest is a semiinfinite strip and its boundary. Choose the grid points

$\qquad$ X(N) = H $*$ N, N $\in$ // 0, P //, on the interval 0 $\leq$ X $\leq$ 1

$\qquad$ T(M) = K $*$ M, M $\in$ // 0, $\infty$ //, on the T-axis,

so that X(0) = 0, X(P) = 1, and T(0) = 0 as indicated in Figure 11.1.1. The mesh lengths H (=1/P) and K are assumed chosen in some educated way, usually with 1 $\leq$ H/K $\leq$ 2.

$\qquad$ An estimate to a solution of the partial differential equation (11.1.14a) will be defined at the grid points

$\qquad\qquad$ (0, T(M)), for M $\in$ // 0, $\infty$ //,

Boundary grid points:     (X(N), 0), for N $\in$ // 0, P //,

$\qquad\qquad$ (1, T(M)), for M $\in$ // 0, $\infty$ //,

Interior grid points:     (X(N), T(M)), for N $\in$ // 1, P − 1 //, and M $\in$ // 1, $\infty$ //.

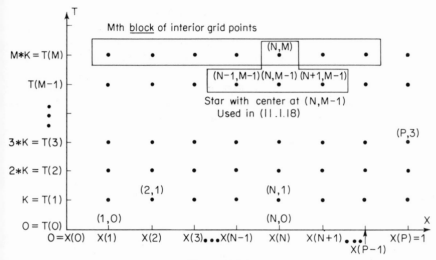

**Figure 11.1.1**

Let the (boundary or interior) grid point $(X(N), T(M))$ be assigned the *name* (N, M). Choose the estimates (9.2.10)

(11.1.15a)     PAR ** (2,)U$\big(X(N), T(M)\big)$

$\doteq \big(U\big(X(N + 1), T(M)\big) - 2 * U\big(X(N), T(M)\big) + U\big(X(N - 1), T(M)\big)\big)/H ** 2,$

and (9.2.3)

(11.1.15b)     PAR ** (,1)U$\big(X(N), T(M)\big) \doteq \big(U\big(X(N), T(M + 1)\big)$

$- U\big(X(N), T(M)\big)\big)/K.$

The suggestion that we might replace the partial derivatives in (11.1.14a) with the estimates (11.1.15a, b) is *motivation* for defining the linear difference equation in two indices

$$\big(U(N + 1, M) - 2 * U(N, M) + U(N - 1, M)\big)/H ** 2$$
$$= \big(U(N, M + 1) - U(N, M)\big)/K,$$

or

(11.1.16)     $K * U(N + 1, M) + (H ** 2 - 2 * K) * U(N, M)$

$+ K * U(N - 1, M) - H ** 2 * U(N, M + 1) = 0.$

*Note.* An element U(N, M) of a solution of the difference equation (11.1.16) is *generally not equal* U$\big(X(N), T(M)\big)$. However, we will use U(N, M) as an estimate to U$\big(X(N), T(M)\big)$.

The *grid points* in Figure 11.1.1 whose names are number pairs the components of which appear explicitly as a subscript of U in (11.1.16) are said to define the *star* for (11.1.16). Since $\big(X(N), T(M)\big)$ is the point *at which* the estimates (11.1.15a, b) were made, and the estimates were equated to obtain motivation for the difference equation (11.1.16), then we call $(N, M)$ the *center of the star,* and call (11.1.16) an *operator applied at* $(N, M)$. An index set associated with (11.1.16) is the set of $(N, M)$'s at which the operator is to be applied. In this example, $U(X, T)$ is *known* at the boundary grid points, so define

$$U(0, M) \equiv U\big(0, T(M)\big) = 0, \text{ for each } M \in // \, 0, \infty \, //,$$

(11.1.17)    $U(N, 0) \equiv U\big(X(N), 0\big) = G\big(X(N)\big), \text{ for each } N \in // \, 0, P \, //,$

$$U(P, M) \equiv U\big(1, T(M)\big) = 0, \text{ for each } M \in // \, 0, \infty \, //.$$

These form a *table of starting-values* for a particular solution of the linear difference equation (11.1.16). Since the operator (11.1.16) applied at $(N, M) = (1, 0)$ defines

$$K * U(2, 0) + (H ** 2 - 2 * K) * U(1, 0) + K * U(0, 0) - H ** 2 * U(1, 1) = 0,$$

and in this equation only $U(1, 1)$ is unknown, we may immediately compute $U(1, 1)$. Similarly, the operator (11.1.16) applied at $(N, M) = (N, 0)$, $N \in // \, 1, P-1 \, //$, defines a *system* of $P - 1$ equations in the unknowns $U(N, 1)$, $N \in // \, 1, P-1 \, //$, which may be solved sequentially as a simple back-substitution. For each $N \in // \, 1, P - 1 \, //$, we get

$$U(N, 1) = \big(K * U(N + 1, 0) + (H ** 2 - 2 * K) * U(N, 0)$$
$$+ K * U(N - 1, 0)\big)/H ** 2.$$

Thus, the particular solution of the difference equation (11.1.16) with starting-values (11.1.17) is known at the boundary grid points, (11.1.17), *and* at the first row (*block*) of interior grid points in Figure 11.1.1. Elements of this particular solution of (11.1.16) corresponding to the second block of interior grid points in Figure 11.1.1 are given for each $N \in // \, 1, P - 1 \, //$, by

$$U(N, 2) = \big(K * U(N + 1, 1) + (H ** 2 - 2 * K) * U(N, 1)$$
$$+ K * U(N - 1, 1)\big)/H ** 2.$$

In general, if we have completed the calculation for the $(M - 1)th$ block of interior grid points in Figure 11.1.1, then the elements of the particular solution of (11.1.16) corresponding to the $Mth$ block of interior grid points in Figure 11.1.1 are given for each $N \in // \, 1, P - 1 \, //$, by

(11.1.18)     $U(N, M) = (K * U(N + 1, M - 1))$
$+ (H ** 2 - 2 * K) * U(N, M - 1)$
$+ K * U(N - 1, M - 1))/H ** 2.$

The operator (11.1.18) involves the star with center at $(N, M - 1)$, and may be interpreted as the condition that the image of each interior grid point $(N, M)$ in the M*th* row of grid points in Figure 11.1.1 is equal to a linear combination of the (known) images of the grid points immediately below and to the right, below, and below and to the left of $(N, M)$. The boundary-values (11.1.17) with (11.1.18) executed for a *finite* number of blocks of interior grid points in Figure 11.1.1, a subset of a particular solution of (11.1.16),

| M | 0 | 0 | 0 | ··· | 0 | 1 | 1 | 1 | ··· | 1 | 1 | 2 | ··· |
|---|---|---|---|---|---|---|---|---|---|---|---|---|---|
| N | 0 | 1 | 2 | ··· | P | 0 | 1 | 2 | ··· | P − 1 | P | 0 | ··· |
| U(N, M) | * | * | * | * | * | * | U(1, 1) | U(2, 1) | ··· | U(P−1 ,1) | * | * | ··· |

\* Indicates given boundary value.

may be used to define a *numerical solution*

| M | 0 | 0 | ··· | 0 | 1 | 1 | 1 | ··· | 1 | 1 | 2 | ··· |
|---|---|---|---|---|---|---|---|---|---|---|---|---|
| N | 0 | 1 | ··· | P | 0 | 1 | 2 | ··· | P − 1 | P | 0 | ··· |
| T(M) | 0 | 0 | ··· | 0 | K | K | K | ··· | K | K | 2 * K | ··· |
| X(N) | 0 | H | ··· | 1 | 0 | H | 2 * H | ··· | (P − 1) * H | 1 | 0 | ··· |
| U(N, M) | * | * | ··· | * | * | U(1, 1) | U(2, 1) | ··· | U(P − 1, 1) | * | * | ··· |

Numerical Solution of (11.1.14a, b, c).

of the partial differential equation problem (11.1.14a, b, c). The reader should construct (fill-in) these tables for this example with   $P = 4$, $G(X) = X ** 2 - X$,   and three blocks of interior grid points. Make an appropriate sketch in Euclidean 3-space of a polyhedral estimate (with vertices corresponding to elements of the numerical solution) to the solution surface $Z = U(X, T)$. See Exercise 4.

*Hint.* Triangulate the domain by drawing one diagonal of each rectangle determined by the grid points in the X, T-plane.

**Example 7.**   The terminology and methods of Example 6 may be applied to define a numerical solution of the partial differential equation (Laplace's Equation)

(11.1.19a)          PAR ** (2,)U(X, T) + PAR ** (,2)U(X, T) = 0

with boundary-values of the solution U(X, T) specified on the unit square

(11.1.19b)
$$U(0, T) = G1(T), \text{ for } 0 \le T \le 1$$
$$U(X, 0) = G2(X), \text{ for } 0 \le X \le 1$$
$$U(1, T) = G3(T), \text{ for } 0 \le T \le 1$$
$$U(X, 1) = G4(X), \text{ for } 0 \le X \le 1.$$

If we choose the estimates (9.2.10)

$$PAR ** (2,)U\big(X(N), T(M)\big) \doteq \big(U\big(X(N + 1), T(M)\big) - 2 * U\big(X(N), T(M)\big)$$
$$+ U\big(X(N - 1), T(M)\big)\big)/H ** 2$$
$$PAR ** (,2)U\big(X(N), T(M)\big) \doteq \big(U\big(X(N), T(M + 1)\big) - 2 * U\big(X(N), T(M)\big)$$
$$+ U\big(X(N), T(M - 1)\big)\big)/K ** 2,$$

and choose a *square grid* with H = K = 1/P, then the linear difference equation in two indices "corresponding" to (11.1.19a) is

(11.1.20)     U(N + 1, M) + U(N - 1, M) + U(N, M + 1) + U(N, M - 1)
$$- 4 * U(N, M) = 0.$$

The *star* corresponding to (11.1.20) is the set of grid points with names (N + 1, M), (N − 1, M), (N, M + 1), (N, M − 1), and (N, M). The *center* of the star is the point whose name is (N, M). The operator (11.1.20) is said to define the image of the center of the star as the average of the images of the other points in the star. When the operator (11.1.20) is applied to each interior grid point, a linear system is obtained which can *not* be solved sequentially as in Example 6 (equivalent to a back-substitution); but, for this example, the system corresponding to (11.1.11d) is known to have a unique solution for the images of the interior grid points. The set containing these images of interior grid points and the boundary-values (11.1.19b) at boundary grid points may be used to define a numerical solution of the partial differential equation problem (11.1.19a, b). Sometimes the boundary-values of the solution U(X, T) of (11.1.19a) are specified on another contour (instead of the square in this example), and sometimes the linear system corresponding to (11.1.11d) has a matrix of coefficients that may be partitioned and solved as several (blocks) smaller linear systems. Iteration methods are particularly useful when computing solutions of the usually large linear system defined by applying operators like (11.1.20) at interior grid points. For certain choices of grid, several different operators may be used to define the linear system. For this example, with $P = 4$, the reader should make a sketch of the square grid with 9 interior grid points, write the linear system (9 equations in 9 unknowns) and corresponding matrix equation, and make an appropriate sketch of a polyhedral estimate to the solution surface $Z = U(X, T)$.

### EXERCISES

1. Show by substitution that $U(X, T) = SIN(X) * EXP(-T)$ is a solution of the differential equation (11.1.14a) and satisfies the boundary conditions $U(X, 0) = SIN(X)$ for $0 \leq X \leq \pi$, and $U(0, T) = U(\pi, T) = 0$ for $T \geq 0$.

2. Make a sketch in Euclidean 3-space of $Z = U(X, T)$, the solution in Exercise 1, to see that the surface is contained in the cylinder with directrix the simple closed curve (in the $T = 0$ plane) defined by $Z = SIN(X)$ for $0 \leq X \leq \pi$, and $Z = 0$ for $0 \leq X \leq \pi$.

3. Use the method of Example 6 to compute an estimate (numerical solution) to the solution in Exercise 1. Notice that unless H and K are chosen properly, we immediately find elements of the numerical solution on the "wrong" side of the plane $Z = 0$.

4. Use the method of Example 6 to estimate the solution of (11.1.14a, b, c) with $G(X) = X * (X - 1)$. The solution is

$$U(X, T) = \sum A(N) * SIN(N * \pi * X) * EXP(-T * (N * \pi) ** 2),$$
$$N \in //1, \infty//,$$

where

$$A(N) = \int G(X) * SIN(N * \pi * X), \text{ over } X \in (0, 1).$$

### 11.2. GENERAL SOLUTIONS. AN EXAMPLE DEMONSTRATING CONVERGENCE

In §11.1 we suggested that the *linear difference equation of order* M *with real constant coefficients* [compare (11.1.3)]

(11.2.1a)          A(M) * Y(N) + A(M − 1) * Y(N − 1) + ⋯

                                        + A(0) * Y(N − M) = B(N),

or in terms of the shifting operator E

(11.2.1b)          ($\sum$ A(M − K)*E ** (M − K), K ∈ //0, M//,)Y(N − M)

                   ≡ PHI(E)Y(N − M)

                   = B(N),

may be solved by methods analogous to the well-known theory for finding
general solutions of linear difference equations with real constant coefficients. A modern and rather complete discussion of this theory for the
finite difference equation (11.2.1a) is contained in [1]. A brief corresponding theory for differential equations

(11.2.2a)          A(M) * DER ** (M)Y(X) + ⋯ + A(1) * Y'(X)

                                        + A(0) * Y(X) = F(X),

or in terms of the differentiation operator D ≡ DER

(11.2.2b)   ($\sum$ A(K) * D ** (K), K ∈ //0, M//,)Y(X) ≡ PHI(D)Y(X) = F(X),

is given in [2].

In this section, we first outline that part of the theory of differential
equations which suggests the steps used below to find a *general solution* (a
solution involving M essential arbitrary constants) of the difference equation (11.2.1a) with B(N) ≡ 0. In Example 3 and Example 4 of this section we give an interpretation of convergence of these general solutions which
is used in Chapter 12 in a discussion of stability of methods for computing
numerical solutions of differential equations. In Example 5 we indicate
that the methods for finding general solutions of the differential equation
(11.2.2a) also suggest methods for finding general solutions of the non-
homogeneous difference equation (11.2.1a) with B(N) not identically
zero.

In the theory for linear differential equations with real constant coefficients we find the *general (complementary) solution* YC(X) *of the
reduced equation,* (11.2.2b) with right-hand side equal zero,

(11.2.3)                    PHI(D)YC(X) = 0,

and find a *particular solution* YP(X) *of the original equation* (11.2.2b)

(11.2.4)                    PHI(D)YP(X) = F(X).

Then, due to the linearity of PHI(D), a *general solution of the original equation* is

(11.2.5)                    Y(X) = YC(X) + YP(X).

For,

$$PHI(D)Y = PHI(D)(YC + YP) = PHI(D)YC + PHI(D)YP$$
$$= 0 + F(X) = F(X).$$

To *find* YC(X) we ask: For what values of Q is

(11.2.6)                    Y(X) = EXP(Q * X)

a solution of the reduced equation (11.2.3)? Since the coefficients of the D ** (K) in PHI(D) are constants, then Y(X) = EXP(Q * X) is a solution of (11.2.3) implies

$$PHI(D)EXP(Q * X) = PHI(Q) * EXP(Q * X) = 0$$

for each X in the interval of interest. And, since EXP(Q * X) is not zero for any finite X, then Y(X) = EXP(Q * X) is a solution of (11.2.3) implies

(11.2.7)        PHI(Q) $\equiv \sum$ A(K) * Q ** K, K $\in$ //0, M//, = 0.

The roots of the *auxiliary equation*, (11.2.7), are used to define the complementary solution YC(X) of (11.2.3). If the roots

$$Q1, Q2, \ldots, QM$$

of the auxiliary equation are distinct, then

(11.2.8a)        YC(X) = C(1) * EXP(Q1 * X) + C(2) * EXP(Q2 * X) + $\cdots$
$$+ C(M) * EXP(QM * X).$$

If the roots are distinct and Q1 and Q2 are conjugate complex numbers [I = SQRT($-1$), and the coefficients in (11.2.7) are presumed real], say Q1 = A1 + I * B1, and Q2 = A1 $-$ I * B1, then we may write (11.2.8a) as

(11.2.8b)  YC(X)

$$= EXP(A1 * X) * (CC(1) * COS(B1 * X) + CC(2) * SIN(B1 * X))$$
$$+ C(3) * EXP(Q3 * X) + \cdots + C(M) * EXP(QM * X),$$

where

$$CC(1) = C(1) + C(2), \text{ and } CC(2) = I * (C(1) - C(2)).$$

If Q1 has multiplicity P, then the contribution of these P roots to YC(X) may be written

(11.2.8c)

$$(C(1) * X ** (P - 1) + \cdots + C(P - 1) * X + C(P)) * EXP(Q1 * X).$$

A *particular solution* YP(X) is often obtained by the method of undetermined coefficients, where a *form* for YP(X) is chosen to be a linear combination of the different terms involved in the right-hand side of (11.2.4), F(X), and derivatives of F(X)—with certain terms multiplied by an appropriate power of X when some of these terms appear in the complementary solution YC(X) of (11.2.3).

We now outline the corresponding theory of *homogeneous* linear difference equations.

The reduced difference equation, (11.2.1a) with B(N) $\equiv$ 0,

(11.2.9)  PHI(E)Y(N $-$ M) = $\sum$ A(M $-$ K)*Y(N $-$ K), K $\in$ //0, M//, = 0

has a solution of the form

(11.2.10)  Y(N) = YY(N) = Q ** N

only if

$$PHI(E)Q ** (N - M) = \sum A(M - K) * Q ** (N - K), K \in //0, M//,$$
$$= (\sum A(M - K) * Q ** (M - K), K \in //0, M//,)$$
$$* Q ** (N - M) = 0.$$

We are interested in solutions of (11.2.9) other than the trivial solution $Y(N) \equiv 0$, so we assume $Q \neq 0$. Since $A(M) \neq 0$ and $A(0) \neq 0$, then this condition becomes [compare with (11.2.7)]

(11.2.11)      $PHI(Q) = \sum A(K) * Q ** K, K \in //0, M//, = 0.$

If the roots of the characteristic equation, (11.2.11), are denoted by

$$Q1, Q2, \ldots, QM$$

and are *distinct,* then the *general solution* $Y(N)$ of the linear *homogeneous* difference equation of order M with constant coefficients, (11.2.9), is

(11.2.12a)      $YC(N) = C(1) * Q1 ** N + C(2) * Q2 ** N + \cdots$
$$+ C(M) * QM ** N.$$

If the roots are distinct, and Q1 and Q2 are conjugate complex numbers,

$$Q1 = A1 + I * B1 = R * EXP(I * T)$$

and

$$Q2 = A1 - I * B1 = R * EXP(-I * T),$$

then (11.2.12a) may be written

(11.2.12b)    $YC(N) = R ** N * (CC(1)*COS(N * T) + CC(2) * SIN(N * T))$
$$+ C(3) * Q3 ** N + \cdots + C(M) * QM ** N,$$

where

$$CC(1) = C(1) + C(2), \text{ and } CC(2) = I * (C(1) - C(2)).$$

If the first P roots are real and equal, $Q1 = Q2 = \cdots = QP$, then the contribution of these roots to (11.2.12a) is

(11.2.12c)      $(C(1)*N**(P - 1) + \cdots + C(P - 1)*N + C(P))*Q1**N.$

In Example 5 of this section we indicate how the method of undetermined coefficients may be applied to find a particular solution YP(N) of a non-homogeneous difference equation.

**Example 1.** If the roots of the characteristic equation (11.2.11) with $M = 8$ are [A $\neq$ B, and I = SQRT($-1$)]

(11.2.13a)     A, A, A, B, R * EXP(I * T), R * EXP(I * T),

R * EXP($-$I * T), R * EXP($-$I * T),

then the general solution of the corresponding eighth-order linear homogeneous difference equation (11.2.9) is

(11.2.13b)     Y(N) = (C1 * N ** 2 + C2 * N + C3) * A ** N + C4 * B ** N

\+ (C5 * N + C6) * R ** N

\* (C7 * COS(N * T)+ C8 * SIN(N * T)).

Of course, the order in which the terms in (11.2.13b) are written is immaterial.

**Example 2.** See Example 3 of §11.1. The second-order linear homogeneous difference equation (11.1.10a)

(11.2.14)          Y(N) $-$ 3 * Y(N $-$ 1) + 2 * Y(N $-$ 2) = 0

has characteristic equation

Q ** 2 $-$ 3 * Q + 2 = 0

with roots Q1 = 1 and Q2 = 2. Thus, as was claimed in (11.1.10b),

Y(N) = C(1) * 1 ** N + C(2) * 2 ** N

is the general solution of (11.2.14).

**Example 3.** See Example 5 of §11.1. Numerical solutions of the differential equation problem (11.1.12a)

(11.2.15a)     Y'(X) = A * Y(X), X $\in$ [0, 1], Y(0) = Y0, A = constant

may be defined in terms of particular solutions of a linear homogeneous difference equation (11.1.12c)

(11.2.15b)     Y(S) $-$ Y(R) = A * $\sum$ Y(K) * B(K, H), K $\in$ //P, Q//, where the $B(K, H)$ are coefficients in a Lagrange Integration Formula (usually one of the types listed in the Tables of §10.2) involving several of the grid points $X(R), X(S)$, and $X(J), J \in //P, Q//$. If the integration formula is *Euler's Formula*, then the difference equation (11.2.15b) with $R = N, S = N + 1, P = Q = N$, becomes

$$Y(N + 1) - Y(N) = A * Y(N) * B(N, H) = A * H * Y(N),$$

or

(11.2.15c)          $Y(N + 1) - (1 + A * H) * Y(N) = 0.$

The corresponding characteristic equation is

$$Q - (1 + A * H) = 0;$$

also, the general solution of the difference equation (11.2.15c) is

(11.2.15d)          $Y(N) = C * (1 + A * H) ** N.$

The particular solution of (11.2.15c) with starting-value $Y(0) = Y0 [= Y(X(0))]$ is

(11.2.15e)          $Y(N) = Y0 * (1 + A * H) ** N.$

For this example we choose a positive integer M so that $H = 1/M$ is "sufficiently small," and define a *numerical solution* of (11.2.15a) to be

$$\{(X(N), Y(N)) \,|\, X(N) = H * N, Y(N) = Y0 * (1 + A * H) ** N, N \in //0, M//\}.$$

We are still *not* prepared to say how to choose H so that this numerical solution of the differential equation problem, (11.2.15a), is usable as an estimate to elements of the exact solution

(11.2.15f)          $Y(X) = Y0 * EXP(A * X).$

However, the particular analytic representation (11.2.15e) of $Y(N)$ does allow us to *begin* a study of *quality* of numerical solutions. We say

$$Y(N) = Y0 * (1 + A * H) ** N \; corresponds \; to \; Y(X) = Y0 * EXP(A * X)$$

in the following sense (compare pointwise convergence). For each choice of the integer M there is an associated numerical solution of (11.2.15a). Define the sequence of numerical solutions for $M = 2 ** K, K \in //0, \infty//$.

| M | Numerical Solution |
|---|---|
| 1 | $\{(0, Y0), (1, Y0 * (1 + A))\}$ |
| 2 | $\{(0, Y0), (.5, Y0 * (1 + .5 * A)), (1, Y0 * (1 + .5 * A) ** 2)\}$ |
| 4 | $\{(0, Y0), (.25, Y0 * (1 + .25 * A)), (.5, Y0 * (1 + .25 * A) ** 2),$ |
|   | $(.75, Y0 * (1 + .25 * A) ** 3), (1, Y0 * (1 + .25 * A) ** 4)\}$ |
| $\vdots$ | |
| $2 ** K$ | $\{(0, Y0), (2 ** (-K), Y0 * (1 + 2 ** (-K) * A)), \ldots,$ |
|   | $(1, Y0 * (1 + 2 ** (-K) * A) ** (2 ** K))\}$ |
| $\vdots$ | |

For increasing M, after an XX appears in a number pair of one numerical solution, say in $(X(P), Y(P))$ when $M = 2 ** K1$, then $(XX, Y(P * 2))$ is an element of the next numerical solution in the sequence [when $M = 2 ** (K1 + 1)$], and XX appears in a number pair of every subsequent numerical solution in the sequence of numerical solutions. Thus we obtain the following sequence of estimates to the element $(XX, Y0 * EXP(A * XX))$ of the solution (11.2.15f).

$$(XX, Y(P)), (XX, Y(P * 2)), (XX, Y(P * 4)), \ldots, (XX, Y(P * 2 ** J)), \ldots.$$

We naturally ask if $LIM(Y(P * 2 ** J)) = Y0 * EXP(A * XX)$, as J App $\infty$. Clearly, yes, if $P = 0$. In this example the answer for $P \neq 0$ is *yes*. For, if $XX = X(P) = H * P$, then $H = XX/P$ and

$$Y(P) = Y0 * (1 + A * H) ** P = Y0 * (1 + A * XX/P) ** P,$$

while if $XX = X(P * 2 ** J) = P * 2 ** J * H$, then $H = XX/(P * 2 ** J)$ and

$$Y(P * 2 ** J) = Y0 * (1 + A * H) ** (P * 2 ** J)$$
$$= Y0 * (1 + A * XX/(P * 2 ** J)) ** (P * 2 ** J).$$

Our sequence $Y(P)$, $Y(P * 2)$, $Y(P * 4), \ldots, Y(P * 2 ** J), \ldots$ is a *subsequence* of (another sequence, with $XX = H * N$)

$$Y(N) = Y0 * (1 + A * XX/N) ** N, N \in //1, \infty//,$$

which is known to converge as N App $\infty$. In particular

(11.2.15g) $\quad$ LIM $($Y0 $* (1 + A * XX/N) ** N) = $ Y0 $*$ EXP$(A * XX)$,

$$\text{as N App } \infty.$$

Thus, our sequence has the property

(11.2.15h) $\quad$ LIM $($Y$(P * 2 ** J)) = $ Y0 $*$ EXP$(A * XX)$, as J App $\infty$,

and we say (11.2.15e) *corresponds to* (11.2.15f) *at grid points.* If we had not insisted that $(1, $Y$(M))$ be an element of each numerical solution, then we could have chosen XX *any* point in [0, 1] and defined a sequence of numerical solutions where the N*th* numerical solution uses H $=$ XX/N, and XX $=$ H $*$ N stays fixed as N App $\infty$. In this case we define a new sequence of numerical solutions for each choice of XX, and say

$$\text{Y}(N) = \text{Y0} * (1 + A * H) ** N \; \textit{corresponds to} \; \text{Y}(X) = \text{Y0} * \text{EXP}(A * X)$$

in the sense of (11.2.15h).

**Example 4.** If in Example 3 the numerical integration formula used to define the difference equation (11.2.15b) is *Simpson's Rule* with R $=$ P $=$ N $-$ 1 and S $=$ Q $=$ N $+$ 1, then (11.2.15b) becomes

$$\text{Y}(N + 1) - \text{Y}(N - 1) = A * H/3 * \big(\text{Y}(N - 1) + 4 * \text{Y}(N) + \text{Y}(N + 1)\big),$$

or

(11.2.16a) $\quad (1 - A * H/3) * \text{Y}(N + 1) - 4 * A * H/3 * \text{Y}(N)$

$$- (1 + A * H/3) * \text{Y}(N - 1) = 0.$$

The corresponding characteristic equation is

(11.2.16b) $\quad (1 - A * H/3) * Q ** 2 - 4 * A * H/3 * Q - (1 + A * H/3) = 0,$

with roots [by the quadratic formula, binomial theorem, and

$1/(1 - X) = 1 + X + X ** 2 + \cdots]$

$$Q = \big(2 * A * H/3 \pm \text{SQRT}\big(1 + 3 * (A * H/3) ** 2\big)\big)/(1 - A * H/3)$$

$$= \big(2 * A * H/3 \pm \big(1 + 3/2 * (A * H/3) ** 2 - 9/8 * (A * H/3) ** 4$$

$$+ \cdots\big)\big)/(1 - A * H/3)$$

$$= \big(2 * A * H/3 \pm \big(1 + 3/2 * (A * H/3) ** 2 - \cdots\big)\big)$$

$$* \big(1 + A * H/3 + (A * H/3) ** 2 + \cdots\big).$$

or

(11.2.16c)
$$Q1 = 1 + A * H + .5 * (A * H) ** 2 + \cdots$$
$$Q2 = -1 + A * H/3 - (A * H) ** 2/18 + \cdots.$$

The general solution of (11.2.16a) is thus

(11.2.16d)　　　$$Y(N) = C1 * \left(1 + A * H + ORDB(H ** 2)\right) ** N$$
$$+ C2 * \left(-1 + A * H/3 + ORDB(H ** 2)\right) ** N.$$

The particular solution obtained from (11.2.16d) by setting $C1 = Y0$ and $C2 = 0$ *acts like* (11.2.15e) and, in the sense (11.2.15h) described in Example 3, *corresponds to* the solution of the differential equation problem (11.2.15a). The particular solution of the difference equation (11.2.16a) obtained by setting $C1 = 0$ and $C2 = -Y0$ *does not* correspond in the above sense to the solution of the differential equation problem (11.2.15a). Solutions of the difference equation (11.2.15b) which do not correspond, in the sense (11.2.15h) of Example 3, to the solution of the differential equation problem (11.2.15a) are called *parasitic solutions of the difference equation* (11.2.15b). Parasitic solutions occur when the order of the difference equation exceeds the order of the differential equation that gave rise to the difference equation.

**Example 5.** A general solution of the *nonhomogeneous* difference equation

(11.2.17a)　　　　$$Y(N) - 3 * Y(N - 1) + 2 * Y(N - 2) = N$$

is obtained by a method entirely analogous to the method used to obtain (11.2.5) as a general solution of (11.2.2b). The reduced difference equation

$$Y(N) - 3 * Y(N - 1) + 2 * Y(N - 2) = 0$$

has general solution (see Example 2)

(11.2.17b)　　　$$YC(N) = C1 * 1 ** N + C2 * 2 ** N = C1 + C2 * 2 ** N.$$

Since the right-hand side of (11.2.17a) is a polynomial of degree one in N, we *would* assume the *form* for a particular solution of (11.2.17a) to be

$$YP(N) = A * N + B,$$

*but* since the constant C1 is a term in the complementary solution (11.2.17b), *we choose the form*

(11.2.17c)　　　$$YP(N) = (A * N + B) * N = A * N ** 2 + B * N$$

for the particular solution, and determine the coefficients A and B so that (11.2.17c) satisfies (11.2.17a). We substitute (11.2.17c) into (11.2.17a) and equate coefficients to get

$$0 * N ** 2 - 2 * A * N + (5 * A - B) = N,$$

so that

$$-2 * A = 1 \quad \text{and} \quad 5 * A - B = 0.$$

Thus, A = $-1/2$ and B = $-5/2$. So

(11.2.17d) $\qquad$ YP(N) = $- N ** 2/2 - 5 * N/2$

is a *particular solution* of (11.2.17a). The reader should verify this by substitution. The *general solution* of (11.2.17a) is the sum of (11.2.17b) and (11.2.17d)

(11.2.17e) $\quad$ Y(N) = YC(N) + YP(N) = C1 + C2 * 2 ** N - N ** 2/2 - 5 * N/2.

*Note.* If the right-hand side of (11.2.17a) were

$$B(N) = N + N * 2 ** N + 3 ** N + N ** 2 * 5 ** N,$$

then we would choose the form for the particular solution to be

$$YP(N) = A1 * N ** 2 + A2 * N + (A3 * N ** 2 + A4 * N) * 2 ** N$$
$$+ A5 * 3 ** N + (A6 * N ** 2 + A7 * N + A8) * 5 ** N.$$

### SUGGESTED READING

1. Henrici, P. (1962): *Discrete Variable Methods in Ordinary Differential Equations.* John Wiley & Sons, Inc. New York. (Chapter 6.)

2. Spiegel, M. R. (1958): *Applied Differential Equations.* Prentice-Hall, Inc. Englewood Cliffs, N. J. (Chapter 4.)

3. Forsythe, G. E. and W. R. Wasow (1960): *Finite-Difference Methods for Partial Differential Equations.* John Wiley & Sons, Inc. New York.

4. Greenspan, D. (1965): *Introductory Numerical Analysis of Elliptic Boundary Value Problems.* Harper & Row, Publishers. New York.

# 12 NUMERICAL SOLUTION OF DIFFERENTIAL EQUATIONS

## 12.1. MOTIVATION

We begin with some geometric considerations. The equation FF(X, Y, Z) = 0 has solution set S: {(X, Y, Z)|FF(X, Y, Z) = 0}, the real elements of which are points on one or more surfaces in Euclidean 3-space. Estimates to elements of S may be obtained by choosing sets X(K), K ∈ // 0, N //, and Y(J), J ∈ // 0, M //, and Z(I), I ∈ // 0, P //, and then for each pair (X(K), Y(J)), (X(K), Z(I)), and (Y(J), Z(I)) compute corresponding Z's, Y's, and X's from FF(X(K), Y(J), Z) = 0, FF(X(K), Y, Z(I)) = 0, and FF(X, Y(J), Z(I)) = 0, respectively. For example, estimates to the Z's corresponding to (X(K), Y(J)) may be obtained by applying Newton's Method, and variations of it, to FF(X(K), Y(J), Z) = 0, an equation involving the single variable Z.

An important special case of an equation of the form FF(X, Y, Z) = 0 is Z = F(X, Y), where the function F(X, Y) and the first partial derivatives PAR ** (1,)F(X, Y) and PAR ** (,1)F(X, Y) are real, finite, single-valued, and continuous in the rectangle

$$R: \{(X, Y)| \; |X - X0| \le A, |Y - Y0| \le B\}.$$

We denote the patch of the surface Z = F(X, Y) corresponding to R by

$$\sum: Z = F(X, Y), \text{ for } (X, Y) \text{ in } R.$$

We now give a geometric interpretation, using $\sum$, for the solution of a corresponding special case of the differential equation $FF(X, Y, Y') = 0$.

If $F(X, Y)$ has in R the continuity properties listed above, then the *solution* in R of the differential equation problem

$$Y' = F(X, Y), \ Y(X0) = Y0$$

is a *function* $Y = G(X)$ satisfying $G(X0) = Y0$, and $G'(X) = F(X, G(X))$ for each $(X, G(X))$ in R. The curve $Y = G(X)$ in the X, Y-plane is the projection of a curve $\Gamma$: $Z = F(X, G(X))$ which is on the surface $\sum$: $Z = F(X, Y)$. The *slope* of the tangent at each point of the solution $Y = G(X)$ of the differential equation problem is the Z-coordinate of the corresponding point on $\Gamma$. The problem of finding a solution of the differential equation problem is then equivalent to the problem of finding a curve $\Gamma$ on the surface $\sum$, where the projection of $\Gamma$ in the X, Y-plane is a curve $Y = G(X)$ whose tangent at each point has slope equal to the Z-coordinate of the corresponding point on $\Gamma$. The reader should make a sketch in E3 indicating $\sum : Z = F(X, Y) \equiv C$ (a constant), and see that lines $Y = G(X) = C * X + D$ in the X,Y-plane have slope C and *correspond to* lines $\Gamma$ (with Z-coordinate equal to C) on the plane surface $\sum$. Notice that there is only one such line through any point $(X0, Y0, 0)$. A similar sketch involving the cylinder $\sum$ (generated by the curve $Z = X ** 2$), and curves $Y = G(X) = X ** 3/3 + D$ will prove instructive.

An estimate to a solution of the above differential equation problem may be obtained by the following *graphical method*. The associated sketch in Figure 12.1.1 is restricted to the X, Y-plane. A corresponding estimate

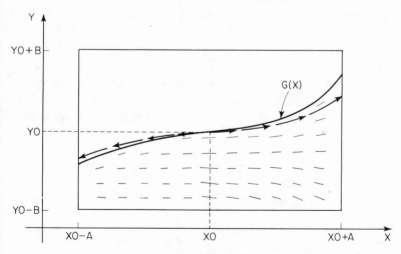

**Figure 12.1.1**

to $\Gamma$ may be obtained by constructing the obvious tangent line segments at points on $\sum$ that correspond to points chosen below in the X, Y-plane. Through the point (X0,Y0) construct a "short" line segment with slope F(X0, Y0). Choose points near[1] the ends of the segment just constructed, say a point $(X(-1), Y(-1))$ to the left of (X0, Y0), and $(X(1), Y(1))$ to the right of (X0, Y0). Construct a line segment beginning at $(X(-1), Y(-1))$ ( and extending a short distance to the left of $(X(-1),$ $Y(-1))$ with slope $F(X(-1), Y(-1))$. Similarly, construct a line segment beginning at $(X(1), Y(1))$ and extending a short distance to the right of $(X(1),$ $Y(1))$ with slope $F(X(1), Y(1))$. Similarly, choose points $(X(-2), Y(-2))$ and $(X(2), Y(2))$ near the ends of the line segments just constructed, and construct new short line segments from these chosen points to the left and to the right respectively, etc. Thus, we obtain a set of line segments in R that *may* give an indication of certain general features of the graph of the solution curve Y = G(X). Hopefully, the sketch indicates where the solution is increasing or decreasing, and gives estimates to where it has maxima, minima, and zeros.

Graphical methods are most often used to estimate the character of a *family* of solutions in a region [as opposed to the case above, where an estimate to one particular solution passing through (X0, Y0) was required]. In this case a grid $(X(K), Y(J)), K \in // 0, N //, J \in // 0, M //$, is chosen in R (just as we would if we were estimating elements of the surface $\sum$), and short line segments are constructed through these points with the slope of the line through $(X(K), Y(J))$ defined to be $F(X(K), Y(J))$ (see the lower third of Figure 12.1.1). If the grid is chosen sufficiently fine, we may be able to use "engineering judgement" to sketch-in usable estimates to solutions of the differential equation Y' = F(X, Y). Most often this method is used to get an estimate of the *stability of the differential equation* (how elements of the family of solutions become close or separate in R, see §12.2). Stability is often used as a guide in choosing a method of numerical solution and an order for the method. The reader should use this method to sketch the family of solutions to $Y'(X) = Y(X)$. That is, sketch-in $Y = A * EXP(X)$ for several values of A.

We turn now to some theoretical considerations and corresponding suggested numerical methods.

We have seen in the integral calculus that if F(X) is continuous in

---

[1]If the chosen points are *at* the ends of the segment(s), then the estimate to a solution of the differential equation problem is a polygon. Compare the polygon, (12.1.7b, c) with vertices defined by (12.1.7d), used by Henrici.

[A, B] and if $X0 \in$ [A, B], then the solution in [A, B] of the differential equation problem

(12.1.1)                    $Y'(X) = F(X), \ Y(X0) = Y0$

is a subset of the function

$$Y(X) - Y(X0) = \int Y'(T), \text{ over } T \in (X0, X),$$

namely

(12.1.2)      $Y(X) = Y0 + \int F(T)$, over $T \in (X0, X)$, for $X \in$ [A, B].

The graph of the particular solution of (12.1.1) satisfying $Y(X0) = Y0 = 0$ is a segment of a curve in the X, Y-plane passing through the point $(X, Y) = (X0, 0)$. Graphs of other particular solutions of (12.1.1) are just *translations* of this segment (up or down) so that it passes through

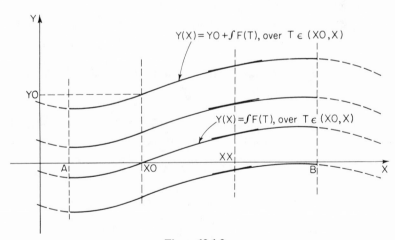

**Figure 12.1.2**

$(X, Y) = (X0, Y0)$ (see Figure 12.1.2). The slope of each of these curves at any point $XX \in$ [A, B] is $Y'(XX) = F(XX)$. The infinite strip $\{ (X, Y)|X \in$ [A, B], Y any real number $\}$ of the X, Y-plane is *simply covered* by the one parameter family of curves (12.1.2). That is, exactly *one* element of the family passes through any specified point $(X, Y) = (X0, Y0)$ in the strip. Thus, the differential equation problem (12.1.1) *has* a solution in the strip, and that solution is *unique*.

A numerical solution of (12.1.1) may be obtained by replacing the integral in (12.1.2) by one of the numerical integration formulas of the type considered in Chapter 10. The reader should execute the steps in Example 5 of §11.1 using the differential equation problem (12.1.1) instead of (11.1.12a).

The situation is more complicated for the differential equation problem

$$(12.1.3) \qquad Y'(X) = F(X, Y), \ Y(X0) = Y0.$$

We have the following theorem giving sufficient conditions for the existence and uniqueness of a solution to (12.1.3).

**Theorem.** H1: R is the region $\{(X, Y)| \ |X - X0| < A, |Y - Y0| < B\}$.

H2: F(X, Y) is real, finite, single-valued, and continuous in R.

H3: $|F(X, Y)| < M$ in R, where M is a constant.

H4: A Lipschitz Condition for F with respect to Y holds on R: there is a constant $L > 0$ such that
$|F(X, Y(J)) - F(X, Y(K))| \le L * |Y(J) - Y(K)|$
for each (X, Y(J)) and (X, Y(K)) in R.

C1: There exists a constant $H > 0$, and a *unique* function $Y = G(X)$, which satisfies (12.1.3)

$$G'(X) = F(X, G(X)), \text{ for each } X \in [X0, X0 + H],$$
$$G(X0) = Y0.$$

C2: The solution in conclusion C1 may be *extended* over a maximal interval of existence. For example, as shown in

**Figure 12.1.3**

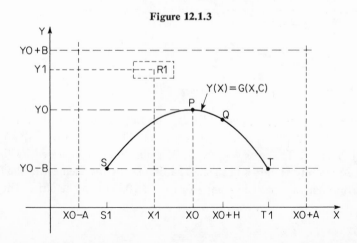

Figure 12.1.3, the solution arc PQ on [X0, X0 + H] may
be extended to the solution arc ST on [S1, T1].

Since any point (X1, Y1) in R is the center of a subregion R1: {(X, Y)|
|X − X1| < A1, |Y − Y1| < B1}, in which the hypotheses H2, H3, and
H4 hold, then the Theorem has the following generalization: The region
R is *simply covered* by a one parameter family of curves, solutions of
(12.1.3),

(12.1.4)        Y(X) = G(X, C),  C = C(X0, Y0),

where the parameter C generally is *not simply additive*. [The constant Y0
was additive in (12.1.2).] The parameter C has the same value at every
point on any particular solution Y = G(X), but two solutions are not
necessarily parallel.

The Theorem is usually proved by Picard's Method, also called the
method of *successive substitutions*. For example, see [1a], and [2].  In
this method, any point (X0, Y0) in R is *chosen* so that C = C(X0, Y0)
specifies a particular element of the family (12.1.4). A sequence of estimates to the solution

$$Y(X) = G(X, C)$$

of (12.1.3) is defined by the following iteration.

$$Y(0, X) \equiv Y(X0) = Y0$$

$$Y(1, X) = Y0 + \int F(T, Y0), \text{ over } T \in (X0, X),$$

$$Y(2, X) = Y0 + \int F(T, Y(1, T)), \text{ over } T \in (X0, X),$$

$$\vdots$$

(12.1.5)    $$Y(N + 1, X) = Y0 + \int F(T, Y(N, T)), \text{ over } T \in (X0, X),$$

$$\vdots$$

By construction, each element of this sequence satisfies Y(N, X0) = Y0.
An H satisfying 0 < H < A is *found* so that on the interval X0 ≤ X ≤
X0 + H, every element of the sequence Y(N, X), N ∈ //0, ∞//, satisfies
|Y(N, X) − Y0| < B. The sequence is then shown to converge uniformly on
[X0, X0 + H] to a function YY(X), which is continuous and differentiable
there. The function YY(X) is then shown to satisfy (12.1.3). Finally, YY(X)
is shown to be the only function with these properties on [X0, X0 + H], so
we write G(X, C), or simply G(X), for YY(X).

In particular, given H so that $0 < H < A$ and $|Y(N, X) - Y0| < B$ in $X0 \leq X \leq X0 + H$ for each N, and given any $D > 0$, no matter how small, there exists an integer N1, which depends only on H and D, such that whenever $N > N1$

$$|G(X, C) - Y(N, X)| < D, \text{ for each X in } [X0, X0 + H].$$

Geometrically, when $N > N1$, then the $Y(N, X)$ lie *inside* a strip about $G(X, C)$ of width $2 * D$. That is,

$$G(X, C) - D < Y(N, X) < G(X, C) + D, \text{ for each } X \in [X0, X0 + H],$$

as indicated in Figure 12.1.4. Recall that each $Y(N, X)$ satisfies $Y(N, X0) = Y0$.

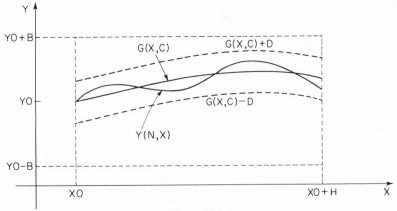

**Figure 12.1.4**

Picard's Method of successive substitutions for defining estimates to solution of differential equation problems has an analog in certain methods for estimating solutions of *nonlinear* difference equation problems. One important class of these difference equations is obtained by replacing the integral in (12.1.5) by a *closed* numerical integration formula, like Simpson's Rule, say, where only $Y(X)$ at the upper limit of integration is unknown. This is,

$$(12.1.6) \quad Y(N + 1, H) = Y(-H) + H / 3 * (F(-H, Y(N, -H)) + 4 * F(0, Y(N, 0)) + F(H, Y(N, H))),$$

where $Y(-H)$ and $Y(0)$ are known, and for each N we define $Y(N, -H) \equiv$ $Y(-H)$ and $Y(N, 0) \equiv Y(0)$. The iteration is then designed to produce a sequence $Y(J, H), J \in // 0, \infty //$, which (hopefully) converges to $Y(H)$. See the predictor-corrector method discussed in the Example of §12.4. The reader should *execute* the suggested replacement of the integral in (12.1.5) with the estimate in Simpson's Rule, and obtain the iteration formula (12.1.6).

Henrici [3a] has given a similar proof of this Theorem for the infinite strip R: $\{(X, Y)|X \in [A, B], -\infty < Y < +\infty\}$, where the sequence of differentiable functions (12.1.5) is replaced by a sequence of *polygons*. This proof is particularly satisfying to the numerical analyst, since a *numerical solution* of a differential equation is usually defined[2] to be a finite set (table) of finite estimates to elements of the solution of the differential equation. The elements of this table are usually computed solutions of difference equations. In each of the methods considered in this chapter, elements of a numerical solution may be considered vertices of a polygonal estimate to the solution of the differential equation. Elements of a numerical solution of a partial differential equation may be considered vertices of a polyhedron (see Examples 6 and 7 of §11.1).

The *polygons* used by Henrici are defined on the *whole interval* [A, B], as indicated in Figure 12.1.5. Define on the interval [A, B] the uniform grid

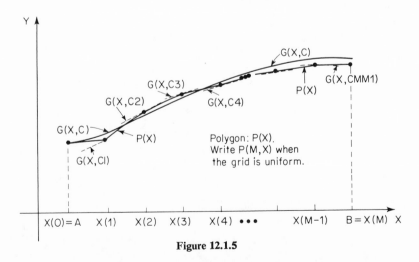

**Figure 12.1.5**

<hr />

[2]In some important numerical methods a table of coefficients $C(J), J \in //0, N //$, of a *specified form* $S(X) = \sum C(K) * U(K, X), K \in //0, N //$, are determined so that $S(X)$ is in some sense a "best" solution.

$$X(J) = A + H * J, J \in //0, M//, \text{ with } H = (B - A)/M$$

so that $X(0) = A$ and $X(M) = B$. The vertices of a polygonal estimate $P(X)$ to $G(X, C)$ will be defined at these grid points. The *left-most vertex* of the polygon is defined to be at $(X(0), G(X(0), C)) = (A, Y0)$. Counting from $(A, Y0)$, the *first segment* of the polygon $P(X)$ is defined to be a segment of the *tangent* to the solution $G(X, C)$ at $(A, Y0)$. Using Euler's Forward Formula in (12.1.5) (see Table 10.2.3),

(12.1.7a)   $G(X, C) - G(X(0), C) = \int F(T, G(T, C))$, over $T \in (X(0), X)$,

$$\doteq (X - X(0)) * F(X(0), G(X(0), C)),$$

we define the first segment

(12.1.7b)   $P(X) = Y0 + (X - X(0)) * F(A, Y0)$, for $X \in [X(0), X(1)]$.

The *second vertex* of the polygon $P(X)$ is at $(X(1), P(X(1)))$, the terminal end of this first segment. This second vertex, and possibly each of the vertices of $P(X)$ yet to be defined, is probably *not* on the solution $G(X, C)$, but it is in R. Therefore, it is on *some* solution $G(X, C1)$ of $Y'(X) = F(X, Y)$ (see Figure 12.1.5). The second segment of the polygon $P(X)$ is the segment of the tangent to $G(X, C1)$ at the second vertex $(X(1), P(X(1)))$

$$P(X) = P(X(1)) + (X - X(1)) * F(X(1), P(X(1))), \text{ for } X \in [X(1), X(2)].$$

And in general, the $(K + 1)th$ segment of the polygon $P(X)$ is the segment of the tangent to a solution $G(X, CK)$ at the $(K + 1)th$ vertex $(X(K), P(X(K)))$

(12.1.7c)   $P(X) = P(X(K)) + (X - X(K)) * F(X(K), P(X(K)))$,

$$\text{for } X \in [X(K), X(K + 1)],$$

and the $(K + 2)th$ vertex is at $(X(K + 1), P(X(K + 1)))$, etc., until the final vertex $(X(M), P(X(M)))$ is obtained. We write $P(M, X)$ for this $P(X)$, where $[A, B]$ is subdivided into M equal subintervals. Now, $P(M, X)$ is a polygonal estimate to the solution $G(X, C)$ of (12.1.3), where the vertices of $P(M, X)$ are defined at the grid points $X(J) = A + H * J, J \in //0, M//$, with $H = (B - A)/M$. The Y-coordinates of the *vertices* $(X(J), P(M, X(J))), J \in //0, M//$, are corresponding elements of the particular solution $Y(J), J \in //0, M//$, of the (generally, nonlinear) first order initial-value difference equation problem, H = (B — A)/M,

(12.1.7d)      Y(N) = Y(N — 1) + H ∗ F(X(N — 1), Y(N — 1)),

with index set I = //1, M//, and starting-value Y(0) = Y0. The difference equation is solved *sequentially* as indicated in Example 2 of §11.1.

Henrici considers the sequence

(12.1.7e)      P(1, X), P(2, X), P(4, X), P(8, X), . . . , P(2 ∗∗ N, X), . . .

of such polygons, and shows that they converge uniformly on [A, B] to the unique solution G(X, C) of (12.1.3). That is, if the mesh length H is required to become small as stated (M = 1, 2, 4, 8, . . . ), then, given any D > 0, there is an integer N1 such that whenever N > N1, then all the polygons P(2 ∗∗ N, X) lie inside a strip about G(X, C), as the Y(N, K) did in Figure 12.1.4. In particular, when N > N1, then the vertices of the polygon P(2 ∗∗ N, X) have the same X-coordinate as the odd vertices (first, third, etc.) of the polygon P(2 ∗∗ (N + 1), X), and the absolute value of the difference of the corresponding Y-coordinates is less than 2 ∗ D.

When we see that using Euler's Formula of order 2 insures the existence of such an N1, and since we usually use a numerical integration formula of higher order, we are encouraged (though *not assured* that such numerical solutions are acceptable) to use the following "rule of thumb."

A CRITERION FOR ACCEPTING A NUMERICAL SOLUTION

When computing numerical solutions of differential equation problems, we make an educated choice for mesh length H. We *check the choice of H* by repeating the calculation (for a few test cases if the program is to be used to solve a known class of problems) with H replaced by H/2. If the (first, third, fifth, etc.) elements of the latter solution agree with corresponding (first, second, third, etc.) elements of the first solution to an acceptable number of significant digits, then the original H may be used in the computer program. If the agreement is *not* acceptable, then compare the second calculation with a third one using H/4, etc. We should *be careful* not to repeat this process until round-off errors exceed the acceptable bound on the error (disagreement of corresponding elements in two consecutive calculations). Sometimes H can be *increased*. When a calculation using H agrees with the calculation using H/2 to *more* digits than are required, we compare the first calculation with one using 2 ∗ H, etc.

We will usually drop the reference to the polygon (which was useful in proving the above existence theorem), and revert to a description of numerical solutions of differential equations as *tables*—solutions of difference equations.

The methods of this chapter may be used to compute estimates to solutions of *higher order differential equations*. For example, the second order differential equation problem

(12.1.8)     $Y''(X) = F(X, Y, Y'), \; Y(X0) = Y0, \; Y'(X0) = YP0$

is *equivalent* to the pair of differential equation problems

(12.1.9a)          $V'(X) = U(X), \; V(X0) = Y0$

(12.1.9b)          $U'(X) = F(X, V, U), \; U(X0) = YP0.$

The method of successive substitutions may be applied to this *pair* of first order equations by computing in order

$$V(0, X) \equiv Y0$$

$$U(0, X) \equiv YP0$$

$$V(1, X) = Y0 + \int U(0, T), \text{ over } T \in (X0, X),$$

$$U(1, X) = YP0 + \int F(T, V(0, T), U(0, T)), \text{ over}$$

$$T \in (X0, X),$$

$$V(2, X) = Y0 + \int U(1, T), \text{ over } T \in (X0, X),$$

$$U(2, X) = YP0 + \int F(T, V(1, T), U(1, T)), \text{ over}$$

$$T \in (X0, X),$$

$$\vdots$$

(12.1.10a)     $V(N + 1, X) = Y0 + \int U(N, T), \text{ over } T \in (X0, X),$

(12.1.10b)     $U(N + 1, X) = YP0 + \int F(T, V(N, T), U(N, T)), \text{ over}$

$$T \in (X0, X),$$

$$\vdots$$

so that, hopefully, for each X in the interval of interest

$$\text{LIM } (V(N, X)) = G(X), \text{ as N App } \infty,$$

and

$$\text{LIM } (U(N, X)) = G'(X), \text{ as N App } \infty,$$

where $V = G(X)$ and $U = G'(X)$ are a simultaneous solution of (12.1.9a, b), and thus satisfy

$$G''(X) = F(X, G, G'), \quad G(X0) = Y0, \quad G'(X0) = YP0.$$

Most of the methods discussed below would be applied to compute elements of a *numerical solution* of (12.1.9a, b)

$$(G, G'): \{(X(K), G(K), G'(K)) | K \in //0, M //\}$$

*one step* at a time.

*Step 1.* Given $(G(0), G'(0))$, compute $(G(1), G'(1))$.

*Step 2.* Using $(G(0), G'(0))$ and $(G(1), G'(1))$, compute $(G(2), G'(2))$.

*Step 3.* etc.

Step 1 might be accomplished by setting the upper limit of integration in (12.1.10a, b) equal $X(1)$, and use a *closed formula* of the type discussed in Chapter 10 to estimate the definite integral. For example, if we use the Trapezoidal Rule (see Table 10.2.1), then we get the pair of estimates

$$V(N + 1, X(1)) = G(0) + \int U(N, T), \text{ over } T \in (X0, X(1)),$$
$$\doteq G(0) + (X(1) - X0)/2 * (U(N, X0) + U(N, X(1)))$$

$$U(N + 1, X(1)) = G'(0) + \int F(T, V(N, T), U(N, T)), \text{ over } T \in (X0, X(1)),$$
$$\doteq G'(0) + (X(1) - X0)/2 * \big(F(X0, V(N, X0), U(N, X0))$$
$$+ F(X(1), V(N, X(1)), U(N, X(1)))\big),$$

which suggest the pair of iteration formulas (for Step 1)

$$V(N + 1, X(1)) = G(0) + H/2 * (G'(0) + U(N, X(1)))$$
$$U(N + 1, X(1)) = G'(0) + H/2 * (F(X0, G(0), G'(0))$$
$$+ F(X(1), V(N, X(1)), U(N, X(1)))).$$

Now, with a first guess, e.g., choosing $V(0, X(1)) = G(0)$ and $U(0, X(1)) = G'(0)$, we define a sequence

$$(V(K, X(1)), U(K, X(1))), K \in //1, \infty //,$$

and *choose* one of its elements for $(G(1), G'(1))$. We hope that $(X(1), G(1), G'(1))$ is a usable estimate to $(X(1), G(X(1)), G'(X(1)))$, an element of the solution of (12.1.9a, b). For Step 2, set the upper limit of integration equal X(2), etc. What iteration formulas are used at Step K? The reader should also obtain the pair of iteration formulas for Step K corresponding to (12.1.6), using Simpson's Rule. How would you get the two required starting-values?

If an *open* numerical integration formula involving the P points $(X(J), G(J), G'(J))$, $J \in // N - P, N - 1 //$, is used with *each* of the differential equation problems (12.1.9a, b) (see Example 5 of §11.1), and if the appropriate starting-values have been computed, then elements $(G(K), G'(K))$ of a numerical solution of (12.1.9a, b) may be obtained *without iteration*. We use formulas of the form

(12.1.11a)     $V(N) = V(N - P) + \sum U(N - J) * B(J, H), J \in // 1, P //,$

(12.1.11b)     $U(N) = U(N - P) + \sum F(X(N - J), V(N - J), U(N - J))$
$$* B(J, H), J \in //1, P//.$$

Of course, we may find it permissible and convenient to use a numerical integration formula of lower order for one of the equations, (12.1.9a) or (12.1.9b), than is used for the other equation.

An N*th* order ordinary differential equation

(12.1.12a)     $DER ** (N)Y(X) = F(X, Y, Y', \ldots, DER ** (N - 1)Y)$

with all N side conditions specified at the *same* point $X = X0$

(12.1.12b)                    $Y(X0) = A(0),$ and
$$DER ** (K)Y(X0) = A(K), K \in //1, N - 1//,$$

is called an initial-value differential equation problem. In particular, all first-order ordinary differential equation problems are initial-value problems. Notice that the initial-value problem (12.1.8) is equivalent to the *system* (12.1.9a, b) of first-order problems.

An ordinary differential equation problem with at least two side conditions specified at *different* points is called a *boundary-value* differential equation problem. For example, with $X0 \neq X1$,

$$(12.1.13) \qquad Y''(X) = F(X, Y(X), Y'(X)), \quad Y(X0) = Y0, \quad Y(X1) = Y1$$

is a boundary-value problem. In Example 4 of §11.1 we obtained a numerical solution of a boundary-value second order differential equation problem (11.1.11a) by solving the matrix equation (11.1.11d).

The boundary-value problem (12.1.13) may also be solvable as a function of solutions of certain initial-value problems. For example, if the differential equation in (12.1.13) is *linear*

$$(12.1.14) \qquad Y''(X) + B(X) * Y'(X) + C(X) * Y(X) = 0,$$
$$Y(X0) = Y0, \quad Y(X1) = Y1,$$

then we may obtain a solution of (12.1.14) as a linear combination of solutions of two initial-value problems. Each problem has the form (12.1.8), which may be written as (12.1.9a, b), and solved numerically using (12.1.11a, b).

$$U''(X) + B(X) * U'(X) + C(X) * U(X) = 0,$$
$$U(X0) = Y0, \quad U'(X0) = S1,$$

where S1 is any slope for $U(X)$ at $X = X0$ chosen so that $U(X)$ is defined on the interval [X0, X1]. Also,

$$V''(X) + B(X) * V'(X) + C(X) * V(X) = 0,$$
$$V(X0) = 0, \quad V'(X0) = S2,$$

where S2 is any slope for $V(X)$ at $X = X0$ chosen so that $V(X)$ is defined on [X0, X1] and *not zero* at $X = X1$. The desired solution of (12.1.14) is then

$$Y(X) = U(X) + K * V(X),$$

where the constant K is determined so that $Y(X1) = Y1$.

As another example, if $F(X, Y, Y')$ in (12.1.13) is *not linear* in Y and $Y'$, then we may attempt a *hit or miss* method (motivated by the problem of shelling a target with a howitzer). From the point $(X0, Y0)$ *pick* a slope $Y'(X0) = S1$ and solve the corresponding initial-value problem. If the computed solution *misses* the point $(X1, Y1)$, then use some intelligent method of changing the slope $Y'(X0)$ to define a new initial-value problem that has solution that comes closer to $(X1, Y1)$, etc., until (hopefully) the point $(X1, Y1)$ is *hit*.

Numerical solutions of two boundary-value partial differential equation problems were considered in Examples 6 and 7 of §11.1. In Example 6 the associated linear system is solved, (11.1.18), one block at a time. In fact, each block can be solved sequentially, one equation at a time. In Example 7 the associated linear system is generally not solvable sequentially.

The numerical methods considered in this chapter are usually applied to obtain numerical solutions of initial-value problems, (12.1.12a, b), where higher-order differential equations are replaced by equivalent *systems* of first-order differential equations, as (12.1.8) is replaced by (12.1.9a, b). Thus, the problem here reduces to one of computing estimates to solutions of the differential equation problem (12.1.3)

$$Y'(X) = F(X, Y(X)), \quad Y(X0) = Y0.$$

### 12.2. STABILITY

The term *stable* is overworked in numerical analysis. The reader has survived too many encounters with the term *homogeneous*, so perhaps he can handle *stable* also. Various *types* of stability are considered here for three not-mutually-exclusive contexts: iteration processes to solve equations, a differential equation and its solutions, and (several types of stability for) numerical methods for solving differential equations. As a rule of thumb, *stability* exists when a small error is propagated as a *decreasing* error; *instability* exists when a small error is propagated as an *increasing* error.[1]

We have considered various iteration processes that produce sequences of estimates that hopefully converge to solutions of an equation. *An itera-*

---

[1] Recall that the terms "stable" and "condition" associated with matrices and linear systems given at the end of §4.6 did not involve iteration, but were concerned with propagated error in only one "operation."

*tion process* to compute a particular solution is *stable* (convergent) if a small error (presumed not zero) in any first guess near the solution is propagated through the iteration process into errors in the iterants where the sequence of errors in the iterants converges to zero; otherwise, the process is *unstable* (divergent). The stability of an iteration process is determined without considering the effects of round-off errors in the calculation.

**Example 1.** The method involving equation (3.5.2) with $G(X) = X$

$$(12.2.1) \qquad F(X) = X - P(X) = 0$$

is associated with the iteration process

$$(12.2.2) \qquad X(N + 1) = P\big(X(N)\big).$$

There may be several ways of writing $F(X) = 0$ in the form $X = P(X)$. The question naturally arises: How do we choose a representation of $F(X) = 0$ so that the iteration (12.2.2) is stable? We will obtain a condition on $P(X)$. If $X = XX$ is the desired solution of (12.2.1), so that $XX = P(XX)$, then, adding equals to equals in (12.2.2), and applying the mean value theorem for differential calculus, we get

$$X(N + 1) - XX = P\big(X(N)\big) - P(XX) = \big(X(N) - XX\big) * P'\big(Z(1)\big),$$

where $Z(1)$ is between $X(N)$ and $XX$. But

$$X(N) - XX = P\big(X(N - 1)\big) - P(XX) = \big(X(N - 1) - XX\big) * P'\big(Z(2)\big),$$

where $Z(2)$ is between $X(N - 1)$ and $XX$, so that

$$X(N + 1) - XX = \big(X(N - 1) - XX\big) * P'\big(Z(2)\big) * P'\big(Z(1)\big).$$

Now, if $P'(X)$ is continuous near $X = XX$, and if the $X(K)$ stay close to $XX$, while $LIM\big(X(K)\big) = XX$, as $K$ App $\infty$, then we may expect

$$(12.2.3) \qquad X(N) - XX = \big(X(0) - XX\big) * PROD\big(P'\big(Z(K)\big)\big), K \in //1, N//,$$
$$\doteq \big(X(0) - XX\big) * P'(XX) ** N,$$

where $X(0)$ is the first guess at a solution of (12.2.1). From (12.2.3), a small error in the choice of $X(0)$ becomes a large error in $X(N)$ if $|P'(X)| > 1$ near $X = XX$, and the error in $X(N)$ becomes smaller if each $|P'\big(Z(K)\big)| < 1$. Thus,

$$(12.2.4) \qquad |P'(X)| < 1 \text{ near } X = XX$$

is the desired *condition* on $P(X)$ that (12.2.2) be *stable*.

*Note.* If $0 < P'(X) < 1$ near XX, the convergence to XX is monotone, while if $-1 < P'(X) < 0$ near XX, then elements of the convergent generated sequence oscillate about the solution $X = XX$. Here the only restriction on the first guess is that $X(0)$ be finite. The reader should construct examples corresponding to Figures 3.5.3a, b.

A condition for stability of Newton's Method (3.2.1) has the following form: (i) $F(X)$ has a single zero in an interval $[A, B]$; (ii) $F'(X)$ and $F''(X)$ are continuous, not zero, and do not change sign in $[A, B]$; (iii) The first guess $X(0)$ is in $[A, B]$.

In §3.8 we considered writing $F(X, Y) = 0$ and $G(X, Y) = 0$ as

$$(12.2.5) \qquad \begin{aligned} X &= FF(X, Y) \\ Y &= GG(X, Y). \end{aligned}$$

The condition for stability of the iteration process

$$(12.2.6) \qquad \begin{aligned} X(N + 1) &= FF(X(N), Y(N)) \\ Y(N + 1) &= GG(X(N), Y(N)) \end{aligned}$$

was that

$$|PAR ** (1,)FF(X, Y)| + |PAR ** (,1)FF(X, Y)| < 1$$

and

$$|PAR ** (1,)GG(X, Y)| + |PAR ** (,1)GG(X, Y)| < 1$$

near the desired solution of (12.2.5), and the first guess $(X(0), Y(0))$ is chosen "close" to this solution.

An iteration process like (12.1.6) may be useful in computing elements of a solution of certain difference equations. A combination of the methods used in the above example and in the example of §3.3 may be useful in establishing the stability (convergence) of such iteration processes.

The term stable is also applied to certain *solutions* of differential equations. One definition says in effect that $YY(X)$ is an *asymptotically stable* solution of

$$Y'(X) = F(X, Y), \quad Y(A) = Y0$$

if the solution $G(X)$ of $Y'(X) = F(X, Y)$ with side condition $Y(A + H) = Y0 + K$, for every choice $(A + H, Y0 + K)$ close to $(A, Y0)$, becomes and stays close to $YY(X)$ as $X$ increases indefinitely; i.e., $\text{LIM}|YY(X) - G(X)| = 0$, as $X$ App $+ \infty$. We now consider a type of *local* stability of solutions of this differential equation for *finite regions*.

Let $R$ be a region in the $X, Y$-plane where $R$ is simply covered by a family, (12.1.4), of solutions of $Y' = F(X, Y)$. The solution $YY(X)$ in $R$ of

$$Y'(X) = F(X, Y), \quad Y(A) = Y0$$

is *locally stable to-the-right in R* if whenever $(A + H, Y0 + K)$ is in $R$ and near $(A, Y0)$, then the solution $G(X)$ in $R$ of

$$Y'(X) = F(X, Y), \quad Y(A + H) = Y0 + K,$$

becomes close and stays close to $YY(X)$ in $R$. For example, $YY(X)$ is locally stable to-the-right if $E(X) = |YY(X) - G(X)|$ is such that $E(X2) < E(X1)$ whenever $X2 > X1$. In this case, we say an initial error is propagated "along" $YY(X)$ as a decreasing function of $X$. This property is illustrated in Figure 12.2.1 by a family of solutions of $Y'(X) = F(X, Y)$

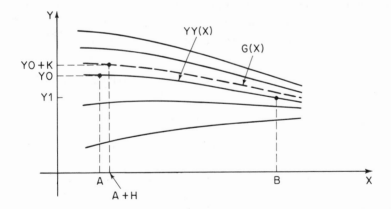

**Figure 12.2.1**

which are *converging to-the-right*. The reader should use the graphical method of §12.1 to sketch the solutions of $Y'(X) = Y(X)$. In Figure 12.2.1, the solution $YY(X)$ of

$$Y'(X) = F(X, Y), \quad Y(B) = Y1$$

is *locally unstable to-the-left in R*, since viewed from $X = B$ the family of solutions is *diverging to-the-left*.

A *differential equation* is locally stable to-the-right in R if each of its solutions in R is locally stable to-the-right in R. A *sketch* of the family of solutions (obtained, say, by the graphical method indicated in Figure 12.1.1) to estimate the stability of the differential equation may be helpful in choosing the order of a numerical method for solving the differential equation. If the family of solutions is converging in the direction of integration, then we can hope that truncation and/or round-off errors will not accumulate so rapidly that the numerical solution is rendered useless.

Some other types of stability are related to "which" numerical solution is produced by a particular *method* when an error is introduced in the initial data. The terminology used here is essentially that used by Henrici in [3].

Here we consider only numerical methods for computing estimates to the solution of

$$(12.2.7) \qquad Y'(X) = F(X, Y), \quad Y(A) = Y0,$$

where $F(X, Y)$ satisfies the hypotheses of the Theorem in §12.1. More specifically, we consider only numerical methods defined by difference equations obtained (as in Example 2 of §10.1 and in Example 5 of §11.1) using numerical integration formulas of the type listed in the tables of §10.2.

$$(12.2.8) \qquad Y(S) - Y(R) = \int Y'(X), \text{ over } X \in (X(R), X(S)),$$

$$= \int F(X, Y(X)), \text{ over } X \in (X(R), X(S)),$$

$$\doteq \sum F(X(K), Y(K)) * B(K, H), K \in //P, Q//.$$

This estimate suggests the difference equation, with index set $I = //0, \infty//$,

$$(12.2.9) \qquad \sum A(K) * Y(N + K), K \in //0, M//,$$

$$= \sum B(K) * F(X(N + K), Y(N + K)), K \in //0, M//,$$

where the $A(K)$ and $B(K)$ are real constants [not functions of N, and H appears only as a factor of the $B(K)$, recall (10.2.4)]. Compare (11.1.3, 4). Precisely two of the $A(K)$ are not zero, and one of these has the value $+1$ while the other has the value $-1$. A numerical solution of the differential equation is a table (compare the table in Example 4 of §11.1),

| K | 0 | 1 | 2 | $\cdots$ | M | $\cdots$ |
|---|---|---|---|---|---|---|
| X(K) | A | A + H | A+H*2 | $\cdots$ | A + H*M | $\cdots$ |
| Y(K) | Y0 | Y(1) | Y(2) | $\cdots$ | Y(M) | $\cdots$ |

where (12.2.9) is satisfied by each appropriately indexed subset of the Y(K). In practice, we can expect only $(X(0), Y(0))$ to be "on" the exact solution $Y = G(X)$ of (12.2.7). Even $(X(0), Y(0))$ may involve round-off errors when represented in a computer. For each choice of $H > 0$ the starting-values are usually in error, and this error is usually propagated to the other elements of the numerical solution.

A numerical method defined by the difference equation (12.2.9) is called a *one step method* if all elements of the corresponding numerical solu-tion of the initial-value problem (12.2.7) are defined when *one starting-value* is given. Since we may choose $(X(0), Y(0)) = (A, Y0)$, we say that one step methods are *self-starting*. If *two or more* starting-values are required for a numerical method to define a particular numerical solution of (12.2.7), then the numerical method is called a *multistep method*. One step methods are considered below in Example 2 of this section, and in §12.3. Multistep methods are considered below in Example 3 of this section, and in §12.4.

A *numerical method* defined by (12.2.9) is *convergent* if, for each choice of $F(X, Y)$ in (12.2.7) which satisfies the hypotheses of the Theorem in §12.1, all numerical solutions that start close to the exact solu-tion $G(X)$ of (12.2.7) remain close to $G(X)$ in the following sense. (Com-pare uniform convergence, and the sequence of numerical solutions in Ex-ample 3 of §11.2.) Consider *any* sequence of numerical solutions of (12.2.7) defined by (12.2.9), where successive elements of the sequence are defined by *reducing* H, and choosing starting-values so that as H ap-proaches 0 the starting-values approach $(A, Y0)$. The starting-values are not required to be elements of $Y = G(X)$. If for each $D > 0$ there exists an $HH > 0$ so that *every numerical solution* in the sequence that corre-sponds to $H < HH$ *lies inside* a strip of width $2 * D$ about $G(X)$ on $[A, B]$ (compare Figure 12.1.4), then the method is *convergent*, and we write [where $(X(N), Y(N))$ denotes a typical element of one of these numerical solutions corresponding to $H < HH$]

(12.2.10)    $LIM(Y(N)) = G(XX)$, as H App 0, for each $X(N) = XX \in [A, B]$.

It can be shown (see [3b]) that if a numerical method defined by (12.2.9) is convergent, then the roots of the polynomial equation

$$(12.2.11) \qquad \sum A(K) * Z ** K, \ K \in //0, M//, = 0,$$

denoted by Z1, Z2, ..., ZM, each satisfy $|ZK| \leq 1$, and any roots satisfying $|ZK| = 1$ are simple. This condition that the roots of (12.2.11) lie inside or (separated) on a unit circle is called the *condition of stability* for the numerical method. This type of stability does not depend on a particular choice for F(X, Y). Also, a convergent method is *consistent* (see [3c]), which implies that one root equals unity. Consistency (not defined here) *and* stability of a numerical method are sufficient to insure the convergence of the method (see [3d]).

The numerical methods defined by (12.2.9) obtained from estimates like (12.2.8) are *stable,* because (12.2.11) reduces to $Z ** P - 1 = 0$, and the roots are distinct and have modulus unity with one root equal unity. This type of stability has more meaning when (12.2.9) is more complicated.

Certain *special types of stability* for numerical methods are named in discussions of *discretization error*

$$E(N) = Y(N) - G(X(N)),$$

and depend on the particular differential equation being considered. Henrici considers discretization error the result of *genuine discretization error* (which corresponds to minus what we have called truncation error) and *starting error* [which includes errors in the Y(N) caused by errors in the starting-values]. In a discussion of discretization error, Henrici defines the terms *numerical stability*, *weak* or *conditional stability*, and *strong stability*. The stability referred to here is essentially different from the stability above, which only required the roots of (12.2.11) to be inside or on a unit circle. In Example 3 of this section, the numerical method is stable and also convergent; but, for the particular differential equation considered there, the method is sometimes numerically stable, sometimes numerically unstable and consequently weakly (or conditionally) stable.

We conclude our discussion of stability of numerical methods with two examples using the particular differential equation problem

$$(12.2.12) \qquad Y'(X) = A * Y, \quad Y(0) = Y0,$$

where A is any real constant, and the interval of interest is [0, 1].

**Example 2.** (A One Step Method). In Example 3 of §11.2 the numerical integration formula used in (12.2.8) is Euler's Formula, and the difference equation (12.2.9) with $F(X, Y) = A * Y$, from (12.2.12), becomes

$$(12.2.13) \qquad Y(N + 1) - Y(N) = A * H * Y(N).$$

The numerical method defined by (12.2.13) is *self-starting* with the starting-value $(X(0), Y(0)) = (0, Y0)$. The polynomial equation (12.2.11) is

$$Z - 1 = 0,$$

which has root $Z = 1$, so the numerical method defined by (12.2.13) is *stable*. From (11.2.15h) we see that when H is small, the numerical solution is close to the exact solution $Y(X) = Y0 * EXP(A * X)$ of (12.2.12) for any choice of constant A. Thus, the numerical method defined by (12.2.13) is *numerically stable* for the differential equation problem (12.2.12). Since the numerical method is not numerically unstable for any choice of A, the method is *strongly stable* for (12.2.12). Henrici's Proof of the sufficiency theorem of §12.1 [using (12.1.7d) to define numerical solutions of (12.1.3), which lie inside the strip in Figure 12.1.4] is essential in a proof that the numerical method defined by (12.1.7d) is *convergent*. Recall that convergence of a numerical method does not depend on the particular differential equation being considered. Since (12.1.7d) includes (12.2.13), the numerical method defined by (12.2.13) is convergent.

**Example 3** (A Multistep Method). In Example 4 of §11.2 the numerical integration formula used in (12.2.8) is Simpson's Rule, and the difference equation (12.2.9) with $F(X, Y) = A * Y$ from (12.2.12) becomes

$$(12.2.14a) \quad Y(N + 2) - Y(N) = A * H/3 * (Y(N) + 4 * Y(N + 1) + Y(N + 2)).$$

The numerical method defined by (12.2.14a) is a *multistep method* because *two* starting-values, say $(X(0), Y(0))$ and $(X(1), Y(1))$, are required to define a particular numerical solution of (12.2.12). The polynomial equation (12.2.11) is

$$Z ** 2 - 1 = 0,$$

which has roots $Z1 = 1$ and $Z2 = -1$ on the unit circle, so the numerical method defined by (12.2.14a) is *stable*. As in the preceding example, our discussion of the *discretization error* for the method involves the general solution of the corresponding difference equation, (12.2.14a), which involves the particular differential equation (12.2.12) [see (11.2.16d)].

$$(12.2.14b) \qquad Y(N) = C1 * (1 + A * H + ORDB(H ** 2)) ** N$$
$$+ C2 * (-1 + A * H/3 + ORDB(H ** 2)) ** N.$$

If H is fixed (H > 0) and *neither* C1 *nor* C2 is zero, and in practice this is almost certainly the case due to round-off errors after a few steps in the calculation, then one of the terms in (12.2.14b) will dominate the other. If A > 0, then the first term in (12.2.14b) dominates the sum, and the second term approaches zero exponentially as N approaches +∞. Then, with C1 = Y0 and C2 = 0, the numerical solution acts like the solution Y(X) = Y0 * EXP(A * X) of (12.2.12). Thus, for A > 0 the numerical method defined by (12.2.14a) is *numerically stable*. However, if A < 0, then the second term in (12.2.14b) eventually dominates (round-off errors insuring that C2 ≠ 0) and the *discretization error*

$$E(N) = Y(N) - G\big(X(N)\big)$$

increases in magnitude indefinitely and oscillates in sign. See the Example of §12.4, below. In this case the numerical solution is *not* close to the solution G(X) of (12.2. 12). However, for A < 0 the numerical method defined by (12.2.14a) is *numerically unstable*. Thus, the method is convergent. This is an example of a *weakly*, or *conditionally stable* numerical method [for the differential equation (12.2.12)]. Thus we have here an example of a numerical method that is *stable* (Z1 = 1 and Z2 = −1 are on the unit circle |Z| = 1) consistent (so convergent), *numerically stable* for A > 0, *numerically unstable* for A < 0, and *weakly stable* for A unspecified.

### 12.3. ONE STEP METHODS. THE EULER, TAYLOR SERIES, AND RUNGE-KUTTA METHODS. ORDER OF A METHOD

A numerical method is called a *one step method* if it defines all elements of a particular numerical solution

$$(12.3.1) \qquad (X(J), Y(J)), \ J \in //P, Q//,$$

of the differential equation problem

$$(12.3.2) \qquad Y'(X) = F(X, Y), \ \ Y(A) = Y0,$$

when the distinct grid points X(J), J ∈ //P, Q//, and *one element* (X(T), Y(T)) of (12.3.1) are specified. We assume each X(J) < X(J + 1). Because they require only one starting-value and we usually choose (X(T), Y(T)) = (A, Y0), one step methods are called *self-starting*. The one step methods considered here are defined by (generally nonlinear) difference equations of the form

$$(12.3.3a) \qquad Y(N + 1) = FF(X(N), Y(N), H(N)), \text{ with}$$
$$H(N) = X(N + 1) - X(N) > 0,$$

for N any $J \in //P, Q - 1//$, to execute *integration to-the-right*, or

(12.3.3b)    $Y(N - 1) = FF(X(N), Y(N), H(N))$, with

$$H(N) = X(N - 1) - X(N) < 0,$$

for N any $J \in //P + 1, Q//$, to execute *integration to-the-left*, where $FF(X(N),$ $Y(N), H(N))$ is a sometimes complicated function of $X(N), Y(X)$ and derivatives of $Y(X)$ at $X(N)$, and $H(N)$.

The form (12.3.3b) may be obtained from (12.3.3a) by changing the subscript on $Y(N + 1)$ and noting that $H(N)$ in $FF(X(N), Y(N),$ $H(N))$ is negative. Similarly, (12.3.3a) is obtainable from (12.3.3b). We usually define one step methods by specifying (12.3.3a) only. When no confusion is possible we delete the subscript on $H(N)$.

If the starting-value $(X(T), Y(T))$ is $(X(P), Y(P))$, then (12.3.3a) is used to generate (12.3.1). If $T = Q$, then (12.3.3b) is used to generate (12.3.1). And, if $P < T < Q$, then both formulas (12.3.3a) and (12.3.3b) are involved in the definition of (12.3.1). Recall Example 2 of §11.1.

Besides being self-starting, one step methods have another advantage over the multistep methods considered in §12.4. With one step methods, it is easy to vary the step length $H(N)$.

In this section we consider three related one step methods. The first (*Euler's Method*) is a special case of the second (the *Taylor Series Method*). The third (the *Runge-Kutta Method*) is a one step method that involves a linear combination of evaluations of $F(X, Y)$ at certain points $(X, Y) = (XX(K), YY(K))$ determined so that the discretization error

(12.3.4)    $E(N) = Y(N) - Y(X(N)), N \in //P, Q//,$

is approximately that which would result from application of a corresponding Taylor Series Method.

*Euler's Method* was used in Henrici's Proof of the sufficiency theorem in §12.1, and is defined by the difference equation (12.1.7d)

(12.3.5)    $Y(N + 1) = Y(N) + H(N) * F(X(N), Y(N))$, with

$$H(N) = X(N + 1) - X(N).$$

This is (12.2.9) with $M = 1, A(1) = 1, A(0) = -1, B(1) = 0$, and $B(0) = H(N)$. In Example 2 of §12.2 we applied Euler's Method to the particular differential equation problem (12.2.12) where $F(X, Y) =$

A $*$ Y. In these previous applications of Euler's Method we have assumed a uniform grid.

**Example 1.** Euler's Method applied to

$$Y'(X) = -Y, \quad Y(0) = 1$$

becomes

$$Y(N + 1) = Y(N) + H(N) * (-Y(N)), \text{ with } H(N) = X(N + 1) - X(N).$$

With $(X(0), Y(0)) = (0, 1)$ and $H(N)$ as indicated, elements of a numerical solution may be obtained by executing, one line at a time, the operations indicated in the following worksheet form. The reader should obtain additional lines in this and in subsequent worksheet forms.

| N | X(N) | H(N) | Y(N) | H(N) * Y(N) | Y(N + 1) | Y(X(N)) | E(N) |
|---|------|------|------|-------------|----------|---------|------|
| 0 | 0    | .05  | 1.0  | .05         | .9500    | 1.00000 | 0    |
| 1 | .05  | .05  | .9500| .0475       | .9025    | .95123  | −.00123 |
| 2 | .10  | .10  | .9025| .09025      | .81225   | .90484  | −.00234 |
| 3 | .20  | .10  | .81225| .08122     | .73102   | .81873  | −.00648 |
| 4 | .30  | .05  | .73102| .03655     | .69447   | .74082  | −.00980 |
| 5 | .35  | .05  | .69447| .03472     | .65975   | .70469  | −.01022 |
| 6 | .40  |      | .65975|            |          | .67032  | −.01057 |

On most desk calculators one would store $Y(0)$, subtract the product $H(0) * Y(0)$, and record only $Y(1)$. With $Y(1)$ still stored in the accumulator, subtract $H(1) * Y(1)$, and record $Y(2)$, etc. Notice that the discretization error $E(1) = Y(1) - Y(X(1))$ is approximately $.5 * H(0) ** 2$; compare the truncation error term in the corresponding Euler's Forward Formula in Table 10.2.3. However, the discretization error at subsequent steps is generally much greater than $.5 * H(N - 1) ** 2$—due, in part, to the accumulation of previous errors. The calculations for the examples of this section were executed, in convenient blocks, as a continuing sequence of operations using seven decimal fixed point numbers, and rounded for the tabulation.

The *Taylor Series Method* for computing numerical solutions (12.3.1) of the differential equation problem (12.3.2) is motivated by considerations of the type presented in Chapter 2, above. It can be shown that if $Y(X)$ is the solution of (12.3.2), and if $F(X, Y)$ is analytic (*represented* by its Taylor Series) in R, where

$$R: \{(X, Y)| \ |X - A| \le A1, |Y - Y0| \le B1\},$$

then $Y(X)$ *has* a Taylor Series Expansion about $X = A$

(12.3.6)    Y(A) + Y'(A) * (X − A) + Y''(A)/2! * (X − A) ** 2
               + Y'''(A)/3! * (X − A) ** 3 + ··· ,

and this power series in X − A *represents* Y(X) on some interval I containing X = A, say A − D ≤ X ≤ A + D where D < A1. For example, see
[1b]. If X is in I, then we may write Taylor's Formula with the Lagrange Form
of the remainder [see (2.2.2a) with (2.2.2b) substituted],

(12.3.7)    Y(X) = P(M; X, A) + R(M; X, A)
               = Y(A) + Y'(A) * (X − A) + Y''(A)/2 * (X − A) ** 2 + ···
               + DER ** (M)Y(A)/M! * (X − A) ** M
               + DER ** (M+1)Y(Z(X))/(M+1)! * (X−A) ** (M+1),

for some Z(X) between X and A. Since we are given Y(A) = Y0, and
Y'(A) = F(A, Y0), and since F(X, Y) has the continuity properties
mentioned above so that we may compute in order

             Y'(A) = F(A, Y0)
(12.3.8)    Y''(A) = PAR ** (1,)F(A, Y0) + Y'(A) * PAR ** (,1)F(A, Y0)
             Y'''(A) = PAR ** (2,)F(A, Y0)
                       + 2 * Y'(A) * PAR ** (1, 1)F(A, Y0)
                       + Y'(A) ** 2 * PAR ** (,2)F(A, Y0)
                       + Y''(A) * PAR ** (,1)F(A, Y0), etc.,

then P(M; X, A) may be evaluated as an estimate to Y(X). The *genuine
discretization error* at X is − R(M; X, A), and estimates to R(M; X, A)
may be obtained by the methods indicated in §2.2.

The *order* of the numerical method [motivated by the estimate
Y(X) ≐ P(M; X, A)]

             Y(N + 1) = P(M; X(N + 1), X(N))

is M. This is one less than the exponent of H [= X(N + 1) − X(N)] in
the first term omitted in the Taylor Series for Y(X(N + 1)) expanded
about X = X(N). The order of the method for a *particular* differential
equation is one less than the exponent of H in the first *nonzero* term omitted
in the Taylor Series for Y(X(N + 1)).

The *Taylor Series Method of order* M is defined by

$$(12.3.9) \quad Y(N + 1) = Y(N) + H(N) * Y'(N) \dotplus H(N) ** 2/2! * Y''(N)$$
$$+ \cdots + H(N) ** M/M! * DER ** (M)Y(N),$$

where $(X(N), Y(N))$ is the given (or just computed) starting-value, and $(X(N + 1), Y(N + 1))$ is the element of the numerical solution being computed. Here, $X(N + 1)$ is given, $H(N) = X(N + 1) - X(N)$ may be different for each N, and each $DER ** (K)Y(N)$ is computed using (12.3.8) where $(A, Y0)$ is replaced by $(X(N), Y(N))$, and $(X(N), Y(N))$ is used as if it were an element of $Y(X)$, i.e., as if $Y(N) = Y(X(N))$.

Euler's Method is the Taylor Series Method of order 1. Notice that the order defined for one step methods is different from the order defined for numerical integration formulas. Euler's One Step Method has order 1, while Euler's Forward Formula in Table 10.2.3 is of order 2.

**Example 2.** The Taylor Series Method of order $M = 2$ applied to

$$Y'(X) = Y ** 2 + X, \quad Y(0) = 1$$

becomes [using (12.3.8) to compute $Y''(N)$, and with $H(N) = X(N + 1) - X(N)$]

$$Y(N + 1) = Y(N) + H(N) * Y'(N) + H(N) ** 2/2 * Y''(N)$$
$$= Y(N) + H(N) * (Y(N) ** 2 + X(N))$$
$$+ H(N) ** 2/2 * (1 + (Y(N) ** 2 + X(N)) * (2 * Y(N)))$$
$$= Y(N) + H(N) ** 2/2$$
$$+ H(N) * (Y(N) ** 2 + X(N)) * (1 + H(N) * Y(N)).$$

With $(X(0), Y(0)) = (0, 1)$ and $H(N)$ as indicated, we may compute elements of a numerical solution by using the following worksheet form.

| N | X(N) | H(N) | Y(N) | H(N) ** 2/2 | H(N) * (Y(N) ** 2 + X(N)) | 1 + H(N) * Y(N) | Y(N + 1) |
|---|------|------|------|-------------|---------------------------|-----------------|----------|
| 0 | 0 | .1 | 1.0 | .005 | .1 | 1.1 | 1.1150 |
| 1 | .1 | .1 | 1.1150 | .005 | .13432 | 1.1115 | 1.2693 |
| 2 | .2 | .05 | 1.2693 | .00125 | .09056 | 1.06346 | 1.3669 |
| 3 | .25 | .1 | 1.3669 | .005 | .21183 | 1.13669 | 1.6126 |
| 4 | .35 | | 1.6126 | | | | |

One obvious *disadvantage* of Taylor Series Methods of higher order is the probable difficulty (high cost) of computing the derivatives in (12.3.8). We might evade the problem of evaluating the higher derivatives by defining new methods, related to (12.3.9), by replacing the second and higher derivatives by certain estimates. For example, with $Y'(X(K)) \doteq Y'(K) \equiv F(X(K), Y(K))$ where $Y(K) \doteq Y(X(K))$, we might use the following estimates.

$$Y'(X(N)) \doteq F(X(N), Y(N)) \equiv Y'(N)$$

(12.3.10a) $\quad Y''(X(N)) \doteq (Y'(N) - Y'(N - 1))/(X(N)-X(N-1)) \equiv Y''(N)$

$$= (F(X(N), Y(N)) - F(X(N - 1), Y(N - 1)))/$$

$$(X(N) - X(N - 1))$$

$$Y'''(X(N)) \doteq (Y''(X(N)) - Y''(X(N - 1)))/(X(N) - X(N-1))$$

$$\doteq (Y''(N) - Y''(N - 1))/(X(N) - X(N - 1))$$

$$\vdots$$

If the estimates (12.3.10a) are substituted into (12.3.9) with $M \geq 1$, then there would result a formula of the form

(12.3.10b) $\quad Y(N + 1) = Y(N) + H(N) * \sum C(K) * F(X(N - K),$

$$Y(N - K)), K \in //0, M - 1//,$$

where the $C(K)$ are functions of the $H(N) = X(N + 1) - X(N)$, $H(N-1) = X(N) - X(N - 1), \ldots, H(N - K) = X(N-K+1) - X(N-K)$. If $M > 1$, then (12.3.10b) defines a multistep method.

*Runge-Kutta Methods* are defined by formulas somewhat like (12.3.10b), but $(X(N), Y(N))$ is the only element of (12.3.1) required in the calculation. That is, Runge-Kutta Methods are self-starting and require several evaluations of $F(X, Y)$, but do not require evaluations of $Y''(X), Y'''(X)$, etc. in (12.3.8).

Many of the popular formulas defining Runge-Kutta Methods are written in the form[1]

(12.3.11a) $\quad Y(N + 1) = Y(N) + C(0) * K(0) + C(1) * K(1) + \cdots$

$$+ C(Q) * K(Q),$$

where

$$K(0) = H * F(X(N), Y(N))$$

$$K(1) = H * F(X(N) + A(1) * H, Y(N) + B(1) * K(0))$$

(12.3.11b) $\quad K(2) = H * F(X(N) + A(2) * H, Y(N) + B(2) * K(1))$

$$\vdots$$

$$K(Q) = H * F(X(N) + A(Q) * H, Y(N) + B(Q) * K(Q - 1)).$$

---

[1] For a more general form see [4a], and note (6.16.2) on page 236 there.

For each choice of Q, the $3 * Q + 1$ *parameters* C(0) and C(J), A(J), B(J), $J \in //1, Q//$, are determined so that when the right-hand member of (12.3.11a) is expanded in powers of $H = H(N) = X(N + 1) - X(N)$, then the resulting power series in H has leading terms identical with corresponding terms in (12.3.9) for as many terms as possible. That is, the parameters are varied to define points $(XX(J), YY(J)) = (X(N) + A(J) * H, Y(N) + B(J) * K(J - 1))$, $J \in //1, Q//$, at which F(X, Y) is to be evaluated, so that the linear combination (12.3.11a) of these derivatives *corresponds* to the Taylor Series Method (12.3.9) which is best in the sense that the right-hand member of (12.3.11a) equals the right-hand member of (12.3.9) plus a function ORDB(H ** (M + 1)) for M as large as possible with the parameters available. The term ORDB(H ** (M + 1)) is usually *not* R(M; X(N + 1), X(N)), since the right-hand member of (12.3.11a) usually does not define Y(X(N + 1)), even if Y(N) = Y(X(N)). If Y(N + 1) is the estimate to Y(X(N + 1)) defined by the Runge-Kutta Method (12.3.11a), and if P(M; X(N + 1), X(N)) is the estimate defined by the corresponding Taylor Series Method (12.3.9), then

$$Y(N + 1) = P(M; X(N + 1), X(N)) + ORDB(H ** (M + 1))$$
$$= Y(X(N + 1)) - R(M; X(N + 1), X(N))$$
$$+ ORDB(H ** (M + 1)).$$

Thus, it is natural that we define the *order* of a Runge-Kutta Method to be the order M of the corresponding Taylor Series Method. Since there is no reason to expect that $3 * Q + 1$ parameters are required to define a Runge-Kutta Method of any particular order, we are not surprised that one and/or two parameter families of Runge-Kutta Methods of the same order exist. We list a few formulas that define popular Runge-Kutta Methods.

**Table 12.3.1.** SOME FORMULAS DEFINING RUNGE-KUTTA METHODS
$$Y(N + 1) = Y(N) + \sum C(J) * K(J), J \in //0, M - 1//.$$

| | |
|---|---|
| Order M = 1. | Euler's Method.<br>$Y(N + 1) = Y(N) + C(0) * K(0),$<br>where C(0) = 1 and<br>$K(0) = H * F(X(N), Y(N)).$ |
| Order M = 2. | $Y(N + 1) = Y(N) + C(0) * K(0) + C(1) * K(1),$<br>where C(0) = C(1) = 1/2 and<br>$K(0) = H * F(X(N), Y(N))$<br>$K(1) = H * F(X(N) + H, Y(N) + K(0)),$<br>*or* C(0) = 0, C(1) = 1 and<br>$K(0) = H * F(X(N), Y(N))$<br>$K(1) = H * F(X(N) + .5 * H, Y(N) + .5 * K(0)).$ |

**Table 12.3.1 (cont.)**

| | |
|---|---|
| Order M = 3. | $Y(N + 1) = Y(N) + \sum C(J) * K(J), J \in //0, 2//,$ |
| | where $C(0) = 1/4, C(1) = 0, C(2) = 3/4$ and |
| | $K(0) = H * F(X(N), Y(N))$ |
| | $K(1) = H * F(X(N) + H/3, Y(N) + K(0)/3)$ |
| | $K(2) = H * F(X(N) + 2 * H/3, Y(N) + 2 * K(1)/3).$ |
| Order M = 4. | $Y(N + 1) = Y(N) + \sum C(J) * K(J), J \in //0, 3//,$ |
| | where $C(0) = C(3) = 1/6, C(1) = C(2) = 2/6$ and |
| | $K(0) = H * F(X(N), Y(N))$ |
| | $K(1) = H * F(X(N) + .5 * H, Y(N) + .5 * K(0))$ |
| | $K(2) = H * F(X(N) + .5 * H, Y(N) + .5 * K(1))$ |
| | $K(3) = H * F(X(N) + H, Y(N) + K(2)).$ |

**Example 3.** The second Runge-Kutta Method of order $M = 2$ in Table 12.3.1 applied to

$$Y'(X) = Y ** 2 + X, \quad Y(0) = 1$$

becomes

$$Y(N + 1) = Y(N) + 0 * K(0) + 1 * K(1)$$
$$= Y(N) + H(N) * F(X(N) + .5 * H(N), Y(N) + .5 * K(0))$$
$$= Y(N) + H(N) * ((Y(N) + .5 * K(0)) ** 2 + (X(N) + .5 * H(N))),$$

where

$$K(0) = H(N) * F(X(N), Y(N)) = H(N) * (Y(N) ** 2 + X(N)).$$

With $(X(0), Y(0)) = (0, 1)$ and $H(N)$ as indicated, elements of a numerical solution may be obtained using the following worksheet form.

| N | X(N) | H(N) | Y(N) | .5 * H(N) | K(0) | K(1) | Y(N + 1) |
|---|------|------|------|-----------|------|------|----------|
| 0 | 0    | .1   | 1.0  | .05       | .1   | .11525 | 1.1152 |
| 1 | .1   | .1   | 1.1152 | .05     | .13438 | .15482 | 1.2701 |
| 2 | .2   | .05  | 1.2701 | .025    | .09065 | .09776 | 1.3678 |
| 3 | .25  | .1   | 1.3678 | .05     | .21210 | .24723 | 1.6151 |
| 4 | .35  |      | 1.6151 |         |      |      |          |

Compare the numerical solution obtained in Example 2. Both methods have order $M = 2$, but the numerical solutions are not the same. Indeed, two Runge-Kutta Methods of the same order usually define different numerical solutions.

### 12.4. MULTISTEP METHODS. PREDICTOR-CORRECTOR METHODS

In this section we briefly consider a small class of multistep methods to define numerical solutions

$$(12.4.1) \qquad (X(J), Y(J)), J \in //0, Q//,$$

of the differential equation problem

$$(12.4.2) \qquad Y'(X) = F(X, Y), \quad Y(A) = Y0.$$

Specifically, we consider only a few examples of multistep methods defined by difference equations of the form (12.2.9), with index set $I = \{N|N \in //0, \infty//\}$,

$$(12.4.3) \qquad \sum A(K) * Y(N + K), K \in //0, M//,$$
$$= \sum B(K) * F(X(N + K), Y(N + K)), K \in //0, M//,$$

obtained as in (12.2.8) using numerical integration formulas of the type listed in the tables of §10.2. Thus, one $A(K)$ is $+1$, another is $-1$, and all other $A(K)$ in (12.4.3) are zero. Since (12.4.3) defines a multistep method, at least two starting-values are required to define (12.4.1). We assume that the consecutive starting-values

$$(12.4.4) \qquad (X(0), Y(0)) = (A, Y0), (X(1), Y(1)), \ldots, (X(M - 1), Y(M - 1))$$

are given—obtained, say, by one of the one step methods in §12.3. Interpretations of (12.4.3) for *integration to-the-right,* or *to-the-left,* corresponding to (12.3.3a, b), are clear.

The stability and convergence of these multistep methods depend on the defining equation (12.4.3), as indicated in §12.2. One measure of the quality of a one step method was provided by the *order* of the one step method. We do *not* define order of a multistep method. [A natural definition would be order obtained by expanding the right-hand member of (12.4.3) in powers of H, etc. But, since the grid and coefficients are specified, this order probably would not be useful.] A corresponding estimate of the quality of a multistep method is complicated—involving the order of the difference equation defining the multistep method, the order of a corresponding difference operator, and an error constant. See [3e]. The accumulation and propagation of round-off errors are also important, but not considered in this introductory treatment.

For the multistep methods considered here, our estimate of the quality of a method involves the truncation error term for the numerical integration formula used to define the method *and* the cost of applying the method. We will refer to a multistep method as a method defined by a numerical integration formula of order M, etc.

Each of these multistep methods is one of two general types.

1. A multistep method is a *predictor method* if it is defined by a difference equation (12.4.3) obtained using a *half-open* (or an *open*) numerical integration formula, e.g., one of those listed in Table 10.2.3. Elements of one class of predictor methods are defined by *predictor formulas* of the form (corresponding to elements of Table 10.2.3)

$$(12.4.5) \quad Y(N + M) = Y(N) + \sum B(K) * F(X(N + K),$$
$$Y(N + K)), K \in //0, M - 1//,$$

so that with $N = 0$ and the starting-values (12.4.4), we may *without iteration* compute Y(M), a predicted value for Y(X(M)). Then, with Y(K), $K \in //1, M//$, as starting-values, we may compute Y(M + 1), etc. We do not present a list of predictor formulas because they correspond to elements of the Tables 10.2.2, 3, 4 with the integral replaced by a difference, like $Y(N + M) - Y(N)$, with the F(K) replaced by F(X(N + K), Y(N + K)), and with T(F, H) deleted.

2. A *predictor-corrector method* is a multistep method that defines a numerical solution (12.4.1) of (12.4.2) satisfying a difference equation (12.4.3) obtained using a *closed* numerical integration formula. For example, one class of predictor-corrector methods define numerical solutions (12.4.1) which satisfy *corrector formulas* of the form (corresponding to elements of Table 10.2.1)

$$(12.4.6) \quad Y(N + M) = Y(N) + \sum B(K) * F(X(N + K),$$
$$Y(N + K)), K \in //0, M//,$$

where for $N = 0$ the starting-values Y(J), $J \in //0, M - 1//$, are known, but Y(M) is unknown, so generally F(X(M), Y(M)) is unknown. In this case an iteration process is employed to define Y(M). For example, the successive substitutions iteration in (12.1.6) for Simpson's Rule (12.4.8a) is written as

(12.4.8b). To start the iteration, a *first guess* Y(0, M) at Y(M) is required. This first guess is often provided by a predictor formula like (12.4.5), where (12.4.5) is defined by a numerical integration formula of order less than or equal to that used to define (12.4.6). It is (12.4.6) that is used to define an iteration process designed to *correct* the predicted value Y(0, M), hopefully generating estimates Y(K, M) such that LIM(Y(K, M)) = Y(M), as K App ∞. Hence, (12.4.6) is called the *corrector formula*. A predictor-corrector method is not defined until *both* the predictor formula and the corrector formula are specified. Both formulas are involved in a qualitative analysis of a predictor-corrector method. The predictor formula is involved in an analysis to determine (often empirically) the number of iterations with the corrector formula required to obtain an acceptable numerical solution (recall the *criterion* in §12.1). Since the numerical solution must satisfy the corrector formula, then a study of the discretization error, E(N) = Y(N) − Y(X(N)), involves the corrector formula.

Sometimes we find it convenient to define methods that are neither of type 1 nor of type 2, but a combination of the two. For example, Milne and Reynolds [5] modified a numerically unstable predictor-corrector method to define a new method which is numerically stable by applying periodically in the iteration another corrector formula.

These predictor methods, and predictor-corrector methods, are multi-step methods. For repeated application, they require a uniform grid X(J + 1) = X(J) + H, J ∈ //0, Q − 1//; or the grid may be piecewise uniform. After a few elements of the numerical solution have been computed, the mesh length H can usually be increased by an integral multiple of the old mesh length without much trouble; but a reduction of the mesh length requires calculating some new starting-values. For a predictor-corrector method to be practical it is important that the predictor formula define a predicted value adequate to insure that very few (one or two) iterations with the corrector formula are sufficient to define an acceptable numerical solution.

Only one new evaluation of F(X, Y) is required in each iteration with a corrector formula. The old values of F(X(N + K), Y(N + K)) are presumed stored. Because storage and reference to this storage pose no special problems in desk calculator operations, the predictor methods and predictor-corrector methods are often used when only a desk computer is available. However, since the Runge-Kutta Methods are particularly easy to code [the *several* evaluations of F(X, Y) pose no special problems], and since the step length is easily varied, then Runge-Kutta Methods are preferred for programs to be used on most modern computers.

We conclude this section with an example of Milne's Predictor-Corrector Method. We are already familiar with examples using Euler's Method, which may be considered a one step predictor method (and a Runge-Kutta Method of order $M = 1$).

*Milne's Method* is a predictor-corrector method which may be used to define a numerical solution

$$(X(0), Y(0)) = (A, Y0), (X(1), Y(1)), \ldots, (X(Q), Y(Q))$$

of the differential equation problem

$$Y'(X) = F(X, Y), \quad Y(A) = Y0.$$

The *predictor formula* for Milne's Method is

(12.4.7a)    $Y(N + 4) = Y(N) + 4 * H/3 * (2 * F(X(N + 3), Y(N + 3))$
$$- F(X(N + 2), Y(N + 2))$$
$$+ 2 * F(X(N + 1), Y(N + 1))),$$

which corresponds to the (fifth order) third formula in Table 10.2.2, and the *corrector formula* is

(12.4.8a)    $Y(N + 4) = Y(N + 2) + H/3 * (F(X(N + 4)), Y(N + 4))$
$$+ 4 * F(X(N + 3), Y(N + 3))$$
$$+ F(X(N + 2), Y(N + 2))),$$

which corresponds to (fifth order) Simpson's Rule in Table 10.2.1. The corrector formula is considered the "better" of the two formulas because the magnitude of the constant coefficient in the truncation error term for Simpson's Rule is $1/28$ of that in the truncation error term for the integration formula defining (12.4.7a). This difference is graphically illustrated by the amount of correction required for each predicted value in the particular example tabulated below.

A set of starting-values so that we may use (12.4.7a) with $N = 0$ to predict $Y(4)$ is

$$(X(0), Y(0)) = (A, Y0), (X(1), Y(1)), (X(2), Y(2)), (X(3), Y(3)).$$

Given all four starting-values, we may compute (with $N = 0$)

(12.4.7b)    $Y(0, N + 4) = Y(N) + 4 * H/3 * (2 * F(X(N + 3), Y(N + 3))$
$$- F(X(N + 2), Y(N + 2))$$
$$+ 2 * F(X(N + 1), Y(N + 1))),$$

where the *first* argument in $Y(0, N + 4)$ denotes the 0*th* estimate to $Y(N + 4)$. Recall that $(X(4), Y(4))$ is an element of the numerical solution whose elements are required to satisfy the corrector formula (12.4.8a). Now, with $N = 0$, the iteration process [which defines a sequence of estimates to $Y(4)$] corresponding to the corrector formula is, for $K \in //0, \infty//$,

$$Y(K + 1, 4) = Y(2) + H/3 * (F(X(4), Y(K, 4)) + 4 * F(X(3), Y(3))$$
$$+ F(X(2), Y(2))),$$

where the first argument in $Y(K + 1, 4)$ involves the *iteration index* K.

In general, the iteration process is, for $K \in //0, \infty//$,

┤(12.4.8b)     $Y(K + 1, N + 4) = Y(N + 2)$
$$+ H/3 * (F(X(N + 4), Y(K, N + 4))$$
$$+ 4 * F(X(N + 3), Y(N + 3))$$
$$+ F(X(N + 2), Y(N + 2))).$$

Notice that only *one term* in the right-hand member varies with the iteration index K. In particular, if $K \geq 1$, then

(12.4.8c)     $Y(K + 1, N + 4) = Y(K, N + 4)$
$$+ H/3 * (F(X(N + 4), Y(K, N + 4))$$
$$- F(X(N + 4), Y(K - 1, N + 4))),$$

where $Y(K, N + 4)$ and $F(X(N + 4), Y(K - 1, N + 4))$ have already been computed. When $Y(K + 1, N + 4)$ agrees with $Y(K, N + 4)$ to the desired number of significant digits, then we define $Y(N + 4) \equiv Y(K + 1, N + 4)$, and proceed to predict the next element. We increase N by unity, predict $Y(N + 4)$ using (12.4.7b), and correct the predicted value using (12.4.8b) for $K = 0$, and use (12.4.8c) for $K \geq 1$.

**Example.** Milne's Method applied to

$$Y'(X) = - Y, \quad Y(0) = 1$$

becomes (12.4.7b)

$$Y(0, N + 4) = Y(N) + 4 * H/3 * (-2 * Y(N + 3) + Y(N + 2) - 2 * Y(N + 1))$$

as predictor for $Y(N + 4)$, and (12.4.8b)

$$Y(K + 1, N + 4) = Y(N + 2) + H/3 * \big(-Y(K, N + 4)$$
$$- 4 * Y(N + 3) - Y(N + 2)\big)$$

as corrector to define a sequence $Y(K, N + 4)$, $K \in //1, \infty //$, of corrections for $Y(0, N + 4)$ to obtain $Y(N + 4)$. In the following worksheet form we indicate an application of Milne's Method with *five* corrections at each step. We assume that a uniform grid with mesh length H = .5, and the starting-values $Y(J)$, $J \in //0, 3//$, are given. For $J \geq 4$, we define $Y(J) \equiv Y(5, J)$; and for $K \in //2, 5//$, we use (12.4.8c)

$$Y(K, J) = Y(K - 1, J) + .5/3 * \big(-Y(K - 1, J) + Y(K - 2, J)\big).$$

Notice that even though the predictor formula is obtained using a numerical integration formula of the same order as Simpson's Rule, the corrected value $Y(5, J)$ is significantly better than the predicted value $X(0, J)$. The reader should supply the data omitted for the cases N = 3, 4, and 5.

| N | J | X(J) | Y(J) | K | Y(K, J) | Remarks |
|---|---|---|---|---|---|---|
|   | 0 | 0 | 1.0 |   |   | Given |
|   | 1 | .5 | .60653 |   |   | Given |
|   | 2 | 1.0 | .36788 |   |   | Given |
|   | 3 | 1.5 | .22313 |   |   | Given |
| 0 | 4 | 2.0 |   | 0 | .1390400 | $= Y(0) + 2/3 * (-2 * Y(3) + Y(2) - 2 * Y(1))$ |
|   | 4 | 2.0 |   | 1 | .1346400 | $= Y(2) + .5/3 * (-Y(0, 4) - 4 * Y(3) - Y(2))$ |
|   | 4 | 2.0 |   | 2 | .1353733 | $= Y(1, 4) + .5/3 * (-Y(1, 4) + Y(0, 4))$ |
|   | 4 | 2.0 |   | 3 | .1352511 | etc. |
|   | 4 | 2.0 |   | 4 | .1352714 |   |
|   | 4 | 2.0 | .13527 | 5 | .1352681 |   |
| 1 | 5 | 2.5 |   | 0 | .0844167 | $= Y(1) + 2/3 * (-2 * Y(4) + Y(3) - 2 * Y(2))$ |
|   | 5 | 2.5 |   | 1 | .0816923 | $= Y(3) + .5/3 * (-Y(0, 5) - 4 * Y(4) - Y(3))$ |
|   | 5 | 2.5 |   | 2 | .0821463 | $= Y(1, 5) + .5/3 * (-Y(1, 5) + Y(0, 5))$ |
|   | 5 | 2.5 |   | 3 | .0820707 | etc. |
|   | 5 | 2.5 |   | 4 | .0820833 |   |
|   | 5 | 2.5 | .08208 | 5 | .0820812 |   |
| 2 | 6 | 3.0 |   | 0 | .0511134 | $= Y(2) + 2/3 * (-2 * Y(5) + Y(4) - 2 * Y(3))$ |
|   | 6 | 3.0 |   | 1 | .0494861 | $= Y(4) + .5/3 * (-Y(0, 6) - 4 * Y(5) - Y(4))$ |
|   | 6 | 3.0 |   | 2 | .0497573 | $= Y(1, 6) + .5/3 * (-Y(1, 6) + Y(0, 6))$ |
|   | 6 | 3.0 |   | 3 | .0497121 | etc. |
|   | 6 | 3.0 |   | 4 | .0497196 |   |
|   | 6 | 3.0 | .04972 | 5 | .0497184 |   |
| 3 | 7 | 3.5 |   | 0 | .0311967 |   |
|   | 7 | 3.5 | .03022 | 5 | .0302170 |   |
| 4 | 8 | 4.0 |   | 0 | .0186834 |   |
|   | 8 | 4.0 | .01825 | 5 | .0182458 |   |
| 5 | 9 | 4.5 |   | 0 | .0116000 |   |
|   | 9 | 4.5 | .01116 | 5 | .0111572 |   |

Calculations were performed with seven decimal fixed point numbers using the $Y(J)$ as tabulated (five decimals). We saw in Example 3 of §12.2 that a method defined by (12.2.14a), or (12.4.8a), is numerically unstable when $F(X, Y) = C * Y$ and $C < 0$.

In the present example $C = -1$, and the characteristic oscillation about the exact solution is present.

| J | X(J) | Y(J) | Y(X(J)) | E(J) = Y(J) − Y(X(J)) |
|---|------|--------|---------|------------------------|
| 0 | 0    | 1.0    | 1.0     | 0                      |
| 1 | .5   | .60653 | .60653  | 0                      |
| 2 | 1.0  | .36788 | .36788  | 0                      |
| 3 | 1.5  | .22313 | .22313  | 0                      |
| 4 | 2.0  | .13527 | .135335 | −.000065               |
| 5 | 2.5  | .08208 | .082085 | −.000005               |
| 6 | 3.0  | .04972 | .049787 | −.000067               |
| 7 | 3.5  | .03022 | .030197 | .000023                |
| 8 | 4.0  | .01825 | .018316 | −.000066               |
| 9 | 4.5  | .01116 | .011109 | .000051                |

This instability is due to the numerical method used. The reader should use the graphical method of §12.1 to show, for $X \geq 0$, that the family of solutions of the differential equation $Y'(X) = -Y$ is converging to-the-right.

## SUGGESTED READING

1. Milne, W. E. (1953): *Numerical Solution of Differential Equations.* John Wiley & Sons, Inc. New York.

1a. _____ (Page 39.)

1b. _____ (Page 31.)

2. Hartman, P. (1964): *Ordinary Differential Equations.* John Wiley & Sons, Inc. New York. (Chapter II.)

3. Henrici, P. (1962): *Discrete Variable Methods in Ordinary Differential Equations.* John Wiley & Sons, Inc. New York.

3a. _____ (Page 15.)

3b. _____ (Page 218.)

3c. _____ (Page 224.)

3d. _____ (Page 244.)

3e. _____ (Section 5.2.)

4. Hildebrand, F. B. (1956): *Introduction to Numerical Analysis.* McGraw-Hill Book Company. New York.

4a. _____ (Page 233.)

5. Milne, W. E. and R. R. Reynolds (1959): "Stability of a numerical solution of differential equations." *J. Assoc. Comp. Mach.*, 6. (196–203). Also, see the same *Journal* (1960), (46–56).

# APPENDIX:
# SUMMARY OF NOTATION

| WE USE | FOR |
|---|---|
| $//0, N//$ | $\{k \mid k = 0, 1, 2, \ldots, n\}$ |
| $//P, Q, R//$, allow Q negative. | $\{p, p + q, p + 2q, \ldots,$ $p + mq = R\}$ |
| A ∗ B | $ab$, or $a \cdot b$ |
| A/B ∗ C | $\dfrac{a}{b} \cdot c = \dfrac{ac}{b}$ |
| A/B ∗∗ C ∗ D | $\dfrac{a}{b^c} \cdot d = \dfrac{ad}{b^c}$ |
| A ∗ B ∗∗ C/D + E | $\dfrac{ab^c}{d} + e$ |
| A ∗ B ∗∗ (C/D) | $ab^{c/d}$ |
| $\Delta$Y(K) = Y(K + 1) − Y(K) sometimes: $\Delta$Y $\equiv$ Y − YY | $\Delta y_k = y_{k+1} - y_k$ |
| \|F(X)\|, or ABS(F(X)) | $\|f(x)\|$ |
| MAX(F(X)), over X $\in$ [A, B], | $\max\limits_{[a,b]} f(x)$ |
| MAX\|F(X)\|, over X $\in$ [A, B], | $\max\limits_{[a,b]} \|f(x)\|$ |
| $\sum$ A(K) ∗ X ∗∗ K, K $\in //0, N//$, | $\sum\limits_{k=0}^{n} a_k x^k$ |
| LIM(F(N, X)) = G(X), as N App $\infty$, or LIM(F(N, X)), as N App $\infty$, = G(X) | $\lim\limits_{n \to \infty} f_n(x) = g(x)$ |

WE USE                                                    FOR

$$\int F(T, X), \text{ over } T \in (A, B), = G(X) \qquad \int_a^b f(t, x)dt = g(x)$$

*Note.* $\int F(T)$, over $T \in (A, B), = - \int F(T)$, over $T \in (B, A)$.

We write $T \in (A, B)$, whether the interval is proper or improper.

$F'(A) = DER(F(A))$                                 $f'(a)$

$F''(A) = DER ** (2)F(A)$                           $f''(a)$

$DER ** (K)F(A)$                                    $f^{(k)}(a)$

$PAR ** (1,)F(X, Y)$                                $\dfrac{\partial f}{\partial x}(x, y)$

$PAR ** (,1)F(X, Y)$                                $\dfrac{\partial f}{\partial y}(x, y)$

$PAR ** (J, K)F(A, B)$                              $\dfrac{\partial^{j+k} f}{\partial x^j \partial y^k}(a, b)$

$PROD(X - X(J)), J \in //0, N//,$                   $(x - x_0)(x - x_1)\cdots(x - x_n)$

$PROD(X - X(J)), J \in //0, N//,$ and $J \neq K,$   $(x - x_0)\cdots(x - x_{k-1})$
                                                   $\cdot(x - x_{k+1})\cdots(x - x_n)$

$SIN(X), COS(X)$, etc.                              $\sin x, \cos x$, etc.

$ARCTAN(X),$                                        $\tan^{-1}x$, or arctan $x$

$EXP(X)$                                            $e^x$

$LOGN(X), LOGC(X), LOGBA(X)$                        $\ln x, \log_{10}x, \log_a x$

$SQRT(X) \equiv X ** (1/2)$                         $\sqrt{x}$

$X ** (1/K)$                                        $\sqrt[k]{x}$

$BINCO(N, K)$, See page 203                         $\dbinom{n}{k}$

$POLP(X)$, used in (7.4.12)                         $(x - x_0)(x - x_1)\cdots(x - x_n)$

$ORDB(H ** 2)$, See page 23                         $0(h^2)$. Read: "Big oh" of $h^2$.

$DET(A)$                                            determinant: $|A|$

See [1]                                            See item 1 listed in Suggested Reading for the chapter containing the citation.

§12.1                                              Section 1 of Chapter 12.

(7.4.12)                                           The name for a display in Section 4 of Chapter 7.

| WE USE | FOR |
|---|---|
| Figure 3.5.3a, b. | Figure 3.5.3a *and* Figure 3.5.3b in Section 5 of Chapter 3. |
| $\Delta F(K)$ | $\Delta f_k = f_{k+1} - f_k$ |
| $\nabla F(K)$ | $\nabla f_k = f_k - f_{k-1}$ |
| $\delta F(K)$ | $\delta f_k = f_{k+\frac{1}{2}} - f_{k-\frac{1}{2}}$ |
| $[X(P), X(Q)]F$ | $f[x_p, x_q] = \dfrac{f_q - f_p}{x_q - x_p}$ |
| $\mu F(K)$ | $\mu f_k = (f_{k+\frac{1}{2}} + f_{k-\frac{1}{2}})/2$ |
| $EF(K)$ | $Ef_k = f_{k+1}$ |

# INDEX

**383**